The UFO Mystery Solved

by the same author:
The Loch Ness Monster:
The Evidence

The UFO Mystery Solved

An examination of UFO reports and their explanation

Steuart Campbell Explicit Books 1994

First published in 1994
by Explicit Books,
4 Dovecot Loan,
Edinburgh EH14 2LT
Scotland, UK

British Library Cataloguing-in-Publication Data
A catalogue record for this book is available from the British Library.

ISBN 0–9521512–0–0

Production by Indelible Ink, Edinburgh.
Main text set in 10/12 pt Linotype Palatino.

Printed in the United Kingdom
by Bell & Bain Ltd, Glasgow

In memory of Donald Menzel,
who had the solution,
but did not seem to realize it.

CONTENTS

1 **Introduction** 9
The UFO mystery 9
The UFO myth 12
The origin and development of the UFO myth 17
Statistical studies of UFO reports 20
Definitions 21

2 **The UFO report** 23
The psychology of perception 23
Problems of human visual perception 25
Problems of memory 33
The reliability of UFO reports 34
A test of reliability 35
'Ghost rocket' tailpiece 37

3 **Sources of deception** 40
Psychological sources 40
False association 41
Reports of vehicle engine/light failures 42
Reports of physiological effects 44
Hoaxes 45
Swamp gas, street lights and 'Earth lights' 47
Aircraft and 'Foo-fighters' 48
Ball lightning and unusual sources of deception 49
Astronomical objects 50
Mirages. 54
Criticism of the Astronomical Mirage Hypothesis 59
Observation of an astronomical mirage 61
Reaction to explanations 64

4 **The major sources of astronomical mirages** 65
Reports caused by the Moon 65
Reports caused by planets 66
Reports caused by stars 81

5 **The first flying saucers** (the Arnold report) 98

6 **The Trindade UFO pictures** 109

7 **The star over Socorro** (the Zamora report) 118

8 **Venus down under** (the New Zealand film) 132

9 **Venus down in the forest** (the Livingston incident) 143

10 **The Air Force hunts a UFO** (Rendlesham) 159

11 **The case of the flying airfield** (the JAL 1628 report) 168

12 **Conclusions** 177
Science and ufology 179
The lessons of investigation 182
The lessons of the Astronomical Mirage Hypothesis 185

Appendices:
1 The Halt Memorandum 188
2 Transcript of Halt's tape recording 189
3 Testing the Astronomical Mirage Hypothesis 194
4 The Conclusions of the USAF on UFOs 198

References 200
Index 205

Acknowledgements

This book could not have been written without the services provided by The National Library of Scotland, the City of Edinburgh Central Library, the British Library Document Supply Centre (Boston Spa), the National Museum of Photography and Television (Bradford) and the National Meteorological Library (Bracknell). I thank them all for their help. I also acknowledge the assistance of the European Commission, the Canadian High Commission, the Australian High Commission, the New Zealand High Commission, the (US) Federal Aviation Administration, the (US) National Technical Information Service, the British Airports Authority, Trinity House, DSIR New Zealand, Center for UFO Studies, Aerial Phenomena Research Organization Inc. (APRO), Societe Belge D'Etude Des Phenomenes Spatiaux (SOBEPS), Citizens Against UFO Secrecy (CAUS), Prof. R V Jones, Prof. Waldemar Lehn, Dr Neil Charman, Dr John Mason, Dr Helen Ross, Dr Willy Smith, Dr Ernest H Taves, Dr Keith Weston, Dr Richard White, Steve Burnett, Barry J Greenwood, Philip J Klass, Bernard Pobiner, and Ian Ridpath.

The following reproduction permissions are gratefully acknowledged: Nelson-Hall Inc. for figure 2:5; Cambridge UP for figure 3:1; Harvard University Press for figure 3:7; Van Nostrand Reinhold for figure 5:5; Director, British Geological Survey for figure A3:1; Scotsman Publications for plate 3:1; George Coyne SJ of the Vatican Observatory and Cambridge UP for plate 3:2; SOBEPS for the pictures used in plate 6:1 and British Airport Services Ltd for plate 11:1.

1 Introduction

A civilian pilot reports seeing a formation of strange-looking craft flying towards him just above the mountain tops. Another pilot disappears after reporting that a large strange craft was hovering above him. An air force pilot dies after failing to catch a huge craft above him and the crew of an electronic intelligence plane believe they were buzzed by a UFO (Unidentified Flying Object). An airliner crew take evasive action when what looks like a mysterious craft seems to be shadowing them.

Air force personnel hunt a UFO which they believe landed near their base. A forester reports that a UFO attempted to abduct him and two women report being irradiated by a huge UFO on a lonely road. A police patrolman reports seeing a spacecraft land and take off again, and another reports a spacecraft blocking the road ahead of him. A UFO is photographed buzzing an island in the South Atlantic and a film is taken of a UFO following an aircraft off New Zealand. Other films show groups of UFOs milling about in the sky.

Very many ordinary people report seeing and even being threatened by large glowing objects hovering just above the ground. Some subsequently report being taken aboard spacecraft (which they believe these objects to be) and being examined by the occupants, aliens from other planets. Even ex-US-president Jimmy Carter reported seeing a UFO.

Surely all these people cannot be mistaken. Surely they are not all deluded or liars. Surely all this is compelling evidence that the Earth is being visited by aliens and that perhaps even now they control the world. Yet what other explanation can there be?

This book shows that there is a simple explanation for all these reports and a solution to the UFO mystery.

The UFO mystery

UFOs are a mystery. According to Arthur C Clarke they are a 'Mystery of the Second Kind', that is to say, a mystery today which is expected to be solved tomorrow. Indeed, he chose UFOs as 'spectacular modern example' of such a mystery (Welfare and Fairley 1980:9). Some may consider that UFOs are a mystery of Clarke's Zeroeth (*sic*) Kind, that is a mystery which is not a mystery at all. They would argue that it is self-evident that UFOs, as alien craft, do not exist and hence that the only mystery is why people believe in them. This argument is circular. If alien craft are not visiting Earth, then UFOs cannot be alien craft. But UFOs may be the only evidence that alien craft are visiting Earth! Assumptions should not be made without good reason (see Campbell 1981b), and while there are good reasons for not believing that aliens are visiting Earth, not all UFO-sceptics will have considered these reasons. It is also a mistake to assume that, if UFOs are not alien craft, they are nothing else. UFOs may not exist, but UFO reports certainly do exist. The mystery that requires solving is why people believe in UFOs and report seeing them. In short, if UFO reports are generated by external stimuli, what are those stimuli? As Clarke pointed out in relation to the UFO problem ('a can of worms into which I refuse to probe'), where there are so many answers there is something wrong with the questions. Indeed there is. On all sides, ufologists (and some scientists) seek the answer to the UFO mystery without asking themselves the nature of the questions that need to be asked. They ask whether or not they have the right answers instead of asking whether or not they have the right questions.

The Condon Report (Gillmor 1969) demonstrated this erroneous approach. It should have stated clearly what questions it set out to answer. Instead it implied that the questions are obvious. Perhaps the project was misled by the United States Air Force (USAF) which, in its letter inviting Colorado University to establish a group to investigate UFOs (*sic*), referred to 'the varied physical and psychological questions raised in conjunction with this phenomenon'. There was no mention of what these questions were. It appears that the project team then proceeded, on their own initiative, to examine the UFO mystery as a whole without stating exactly what questions they were attempting to answer. However, from one of their conclusions ('that there is no evidence to justify a belief that extraterrestrial visitors have penetrated our skies') it can be concluded that they addressed the question 'Are UFOs extraterrestrial craft?'. Their other conclusions imply that they were answering the questions: 'Do UFO reports reveal anything that could be considered as adding to scientific knowledge?' and 'Would further extensive study of UFOs be justified in the expectation that science will be advanced thereby?'. These were the wrong questions, at least initially, and it is interesting to note that, in the Report's introduction, Walter Sullivan, who was not a member of the project team, asked a more relevant question. He asked 'What, in fact, have they [UFO reporters] seen?'. Insofar as the Report gave any answer to this question, it was that all UFOs are misperceptions of natural or man-made objects. This despite the fact that, in one quarter of their own cases, the object could not be identified. Most of the identifications made by the project are not convincing; this may have resulted from the prejudice of the project team, especially the director Edward Condon, that UFOs do not exist and their inadequate understanding of some of the phenomena that can cause UFO reports. It is ironic that some of these phenomena were well understood by some of the experts commissioned to write sections of the Report.

I intend to solve the UFO mystery. That is to say I intend to find the objective causes (if there are any) of UFO reports. In particular I seek an archetypal cause, a special type of cause which gives UFO reports their peculiar character. I shall show that there is one particular phenomenon that can be described as being the cause of the core reports. The core, or 'high profile', reports are those which stubbornly resist easy explanation, even after decades, and which are both strange and reliable. Chapters 5 to 11 deal with the major core reports. The explanation for the core reports, especially if it applies to most of them, may be taken as the solution to the UFO mystery.

I shall not define a 'UFO' (much time has been wasted on this problem); it is not possible to define an unknown and it is known that very many different stimuli are responsible for UFO reports. In any case we are not dealing with UFOs; we are dealing with UFO reports. There have been attempts to define a 'UFO Report', but they are thinly disguised definitions of a UFO. There is no mystery about a UFO report and so no need to define it. A UFO report is made by someone who saw something in the sky that they could not explain or thought was an alien craft.

I have no interest in debating the plausibility of the idea that UFOs are spacecraft from other planets (The Extraterrestrial Hypothesis, or ETH). There is no reason to believe that any of the stimuli for UFO reports are such craft and there are very many reasons for being sceptical of the ETH. I shall not waste time trying to show how unlikely (or how ridiculous) it is to believe that alien spaceships are responsible. Nor will I labour the point that the defence forces of the world would have detected alien spaceships if they existed. The credibility of various hypotheses has already been discussed (Campbell 1981b).

For over twenty years, the USAF was charged with investigating and evaluating UFO reports brought to its attention in the USA and at US bases, stations or property in other countries. This task was assigned to the Air Technical Intelligence Center (ATIC) at Wright-Patterson Air Force Base in Dayton (Ohio). For most of that period the project was code-named 'Blue Book'. Occasional reference will be made to Blue Book.

The UFO myth

A myth is a legend, often involving supernatural beings, which offers an explanation for some puzzling fact or phenomenon; for example, an echo was thought to be the voice of a mischievous nymph who pined for love of Narcissus. Ancient myths exist to explain nearly every natural phenomenon, but there is another class of myth or legend which is not related to observed phenomena. This is the group of myths regarding the existence of entities such as fairies, ghosts, the Yeti, or the Loch Ness monster. Evidence for the existence of such entities is scant or vanishingly small, and sceptics are convinced that they do not exist.

It is to this latter class of myth that the UFO myth belongs. Interest in UFOs centres on the possibility that they are evidence, not only for the existence of aliens, but that some aliens are visiting Earth, albeit covertly. This is the UFO myth, a belief system that may be called ufoism. Ufoism is based on the ETH, the belief that UFOs originate from space.

Ufoism is a network of beliefs centred on the idea that one or more alien civilizations is monitoring human progress by discreet observation, and may have been doing so for a long time. Once thought to come from Mars, or another planet in the solar system, they are now believed to originate on planets which may orbit distant stars. Such a belief necessitates acceptance that the aliens are more advanced than humans, have superhuman powers, great longevity, and great wisdom. It is assumed that they have very advanced technology, or even impossible technology such as faster-than-light space travel (using nuclear power), anti-gravity, death-rays, etc. In a House of Lords debate on UFOs in 1979, Lord Rankeillor claimed that UFOs give off blinding lights, crippling rays, beams that immobilize humans, start forest fires, eradicate crops and cause great distress to animals (Michell 1979:73). It is also believed that UFOs can perform manoeuvres, such as instantaneous stops or starts or changes of direction which defy the laws of inertia. UFOs also appear to travel faster than the speed of sound in the atmosphere without creating sonic booms, and vanish without creating the giant thunderclap that should result. Nor do they appear to be hampered by the fact that a discoid is aerodynamically unstable. There are many reports of UFOs 'falling like a leaf', that is, swinging from side to side as they descend. Claims that UFOs are real spacecraft have been supported by reports that some visual sightings have been confirmed by simultaneous detection by radar.

Many believe that UFOs are powered by some magnetic force (or that their power system generates a powerful magnetic field). A French scientist claimed to have found a time correlation between UFO reports and geomagnetic disturbances (Poher 1974, but see Campbell 1985a).

Some believe that magnetic fields accompanying UFOs induce current surges in electricity power lines, so causing widespread power failures when the protecting relays open (McCampbell 1973:64). There is also a widespread belief that these supposed magnetic fields cause temporary failure of vehicle electrical systems and/or engines.

Ufoists may believe that aliens created humanity in the distant past, that what appear to be human achievements were actually the work of aliens, that the whole of modern science is a crude lie, that alien science is materially and spiritually superior to ours (involving 'fundamental forces' such as ESP, 'etheric waves', etc.) and that the aliens would give us the 'truth' but for wicked scientists and politicians who conceal the facts from the public. Ufoists may believe that aliens abduct humans and/or their vehicles and that they have been responsible for the death of at least one pilot. It is also generally believed by ufoists that the governments of the world (at least those of the West) know the 'truth' about UFOs, indeed that they possess the remains of a crashed UFO and (perhaps) its dead occupants. Some believe that major world governments are co-operating with aliens. Christian ufoists believe that UFOs are manifestations of the devil (perhaps carrying his angels) and that their appearance heralds the end of the world (Weldon and Levitt 1976; Inglesby 1978).

As the result of two books on the subject, belief in abductions has recently spread, in the USA if not elsewhere. Hypnosis is used to elicit fanciful tales of examination (or worse) by aliens. There is a belief that aliens have conducted bizarre genetic experiments by invading the bedrooms of teenage girls to impregnate them, later returning to remove the unborn babies. It is also believed that aliens have kidnapped young children and removed flesh samples as part of an effort to cross-breed with the human race. It is believed that many people have had conscious memories of the incidents erased by the aliens (Klass 1988). The effect of these superstitions is of great concern in the USA. Fortunately the British do not seem to be so credulous (yet). A television series called 'UFO' exploited these sinister aspects. In fact many films and television series have been based on the myth.

The first UFO film was *The Flying Saucer* (1949), in which a US government agent was sent to Alaska to discover the origin of the saucers. This was followed by a low-budget serial in twelve episodes called *Flying Disc Man From Mars* (1951); aliens were always 'Martians' in those days. In this series a Martian was intent on making Earth subordinate to the Martian dictator (for 'Martian' read 'Russian'). The same year saw the appearance of two more UFO films, *The Thing* and *The Day the Earth Stood Still*. The latter has become a classic, but not because the alien arrived in a flying saucer. The most celebrated film of recent years has been *Close Encounters of the Third Kind* (in which

Allen Hynek made an appearance). The latest, based on Travis Walton's alleged abduction in 1975 (but claiming that the story is true), is *Fire in the Sky* by Paramount Pictures.

Some films (for example *Hanger 18*) have exploited the belief that the US government possesses a crashed UFO and/or its dead occupants. It is believed that the US government (to speak of no other) can keep this colossal secret when it could not even keep the secret of the Stealth aircraft. Every official denial regarding UFOs is interpreted by ufoists as a 'cover-up' and they are busy obtaining official documents under the US Freedom of Information Act. A sinister interpretation is then placed on the many deletions in these documents.

In 1953 the director of the International Flying Saucer Bureau reported being visited by three men dressed in black (it was alleged that they were government agents) who told him what he described as the frightening answer to the UFO mystery. He claimed, however, that he was warned that he could be jailed if he revealed the answer (it is easy to invent incontrovertible stories like this). Since then there have been spasmodic reports of visits by 'men-in-black' (MIBs) and they have been linked to government secrecy (or even to an alien organization on Earth).

Despite the silence (or near silence) of officialdom, the statements of politicians are interesting. In 1955 Winston Churchill (then British Prime Minister) asked the Air Ministry 'What does all this stuff about Flying Saucers amount to? What can it mean? What is the truth? Let me know at your earliest convenience.' He was probably told the conclusions of the Ministry's study of the subject four years before. This concluded that reports could be explained as: 'known astronomical or meteorological phenomena, mistaken identifications of conventional aircraft, balloons or birds, optical illusions or psychological delusions, or even deliberate hoaxes'. One wonders if Churchill was convinced by this. The Ministry's conclusions echoed those of the USAF, although in the early 1950s the latter actually decided that UFOs were alien craft. This wild conclusion was quickly reversed and the official investigations have since always concluded that no threat to security has been discovered. The USAF did consider the possibility that reports of UFOs might have been made by communist sympathizers in order to cause mass hysteria in the USA over the fear of a secret Russian weapon. However the FBI found no evidence of subversive activity. One can easily see how the internal security services might fear that UFO groups could form a cover for subversion; investigations and sky watches could cover spying. A group of workers in St Louis (USA) once complained to the FBI that a UFO journal called *The APRO Bulletin* was 'communistic' because it 'slurred and criticized the USAF and its officials'. Indeed I believe that the British UFO movement may have been under observation by MI5; when I was a member of a UFO group, some distinctly military types would join temporarily. They surely reported that such groups are composed of harmless eccentrics. On the other hand it is reported that some people have impersonated Air Force or Defence officials, contacting citizens who have reported seeing UFOs. I suspect that they wore dark suits and so reinforced the belief in MIBs.

On a more serious level it has been noted that UFO reports have the potential to clog intelligence channels, or (during the Cold War) to start World War III. In the days before ICBMs a US writer alleged that enemy bombers could be reported as UFOs and so be ignored 'for precious minutes'. He also alleged that reports could hide enemy reconnaissance missions. In 1971 the USA and the USSR agreed on measures to reduce the risk of nuclear war by accident. Among the dangers mentioned was the detection of 'unidentified objects' on early warning systems. It is reported that an unidentified luminous object, which was assumed to be a helicopter, caused great concern to the USAF when the 'craft' appeared to have penetrated the defences of a base where nuclear weapons were stored. Ten other Air Force bases were told to go on alert during the hours of darkness (see p. 81).

To return to politicians. The House of Lords debate on 18 January 1979 lasted for 3 hours and was instigated by Lord Clancarty, an Irish peer formerly known as Brinsley LePoer Trench, one-time editor of *Flying Saucer Review*. He formed an organization called Contact International. When, in 1978, the number of reports reached 1000 per month, he feared that an alien landing or take-over was imminent and that it would result in panic. His purpose, in the debate, was to get the British Government to open its UFO files (if it had any) and to prepare the public for the great day. Fourteen other lords spoke on the motion that called for 'an intra-governmental study of UFOs' (Lord Kings Norton noted that 'intra' means within, not what Lord Clancarty intended).

The Bishop of Norwich feared that the mystery of UFOs was in danger of producing a twentieth century superstition. He also saw a danger of linking religion with UFOs, producing a gnostic subculture (this has already happened). But he wanted the study of UFOs kept well away from Christianity. Five lords were unsympathetic to belief in UFOs, but others endorsed the myth (or other myths). The Earl of Kimberley claimed that the Ministry of Defence would not deal with messages from space because that was the function of the BBC and the Post Office. Lord Oxfuird confused stars with galaxies and claimed that the universe was only as old as the Sun (it is much older). Lord Hewlett, who actually referred to belief in UFOs as a myth, had a heated debate with Lord Davies of Leek as to whether or not there was anything to investigate. Lord Gladwyn reminded the House that the subject had caused the usually solemn Andrei Gromyko, then Soviet Foreign Minister, to make his one and only known joke. When asked what he thought about flying saucers, he replied:

> Some people say that these objects are due to the excessive consumption in the United States of Scotch whisky. I say that this is not so. They are due to the activities of a Soviet athlete, a discus thrower in Eastern Siberia, practising for the Olympic Games and quite unconscious of his strength.

The UFO myth comes in many varieties. Apart from the ETH and the HEH (Hollow Earth Hypothesis), there is the Ultra-terrestrial Hypothesis (they come from another dimension or universe) and the Time Travel Hypothesis (they come from the future). Then there are hypotheses which propose that UFOs are secret weapons, if not from a terrestrial government then from some secret group, perhaps Nazis. A variation on the UTH is the belief that UFOs are piloted by angels (either God's or the Devil's) and this is linked by some to belief in the Second Coming of Jesus. Some believe that UFOs have bases under the oceans. Others that there are space animals. There is strong support for various projection theories, either psychic projection in the mind (as Jung thought) or in real space. A variant myth claims that UFOs are holographic projections from another planet, or perhaps from a future time. There is a hypothesis which claims that UFOs interfere with our brains, so producing hallucinations (or induced dreams). Other hypotheses hold that UFOs are connected with secret societies, fairies, elementals, etherians, or an unknown organization similar to Wings Over The World or the survivors of Atlantis.

These are the superstitious hypotheses. There are also some pseudo-scientific hypotheses to account for UFO reports. An example is the Tectonic-Strain Theory. This holds that UFOs are luminous plasmas created by the electrical activity associated with Earth faults (cracks in the Earth's crust). Further it is alleged that reports of aliens or abductions are hallucinations caused by these plasmas interfering with brain activity. Proponents of this hypothesis go to great lengths to associate the site of a UFO report with fault lines, a kind of modern ley hunting. Indeed the arch-proponent of this theory (Paul Devereux) is also the editor of *The Ley Hunter*.

Those who believe that aliens have been visiting Earth throughout history must necessarily find evidence in the historical record. All kinds of mysterious reports are adduced as examples, from Ezekiel's vision to the Star of Bethlehem. A particularly interesting set of reports came from the USA in 1897. These were reports of mysterious 'airships', generally described as cigar-shaped, apparently metallic, with wings, propellers, fins and other appendages. At night they appeared to be brilliant lights, with dark superstructures sometimes visible behind the lights.

Some believe that UFOs appear on great circle lines around the Earth, forming a web or network suggesting systematic aerial exploration; this idea is called 'orthoteny' and was coined by a French ufoist, Aimé Michel.

Plato wondered if a 'magnificent myth' could be constructed that would in itself carry conviction to the whole community (*Republic* 3:414). It seems likely that the UFO myth is such a myth. Jung described it as one of the great myths of the twentieth century.

The origin and development of the UFO myth

The UFO myth is essentially American, for several reasons. It began with the Arnold report from the USA (see chapter 5). By 10 July 1947 the London *Times* was able to report that 'during the past fortnight reports that disc-like objects nicknamed flying saucers have been seen travelling through the air at great speed singly or in groups, have come from various parts of the United States and Canada'. The report added that no hypothesis yet put forward by scientists satisfactorily accounted for all the phenomena reported, unless it is that 'in weather as hot as this the imagination tends to become fevered'. As a result of Arnold's report, the press was inundated by similar reports, at least by reports of unusual objects seen in the skies. All over the world, people reported seeing flying objects, not just saucers.

However, despite the publicity given to these reports, the flying saucer scare would probably have died (and with it the UFO myth) but for the efforts of a talented writer, editor and publisher of science fiction, Raymond A Palmer. It is even claimed that Palmer created the UFO myth.

Shrunken in stature and partially crippled, Palmer was editor in the 1930s and '40s of *Amazing Stories* and *Fantastic Adventures*, two of America's best-selling SF magazines. In July 1946 (before Arnold's report) Palmer suggested (in *Amazing Stories*) that space ships were regularly visiting Earth, and he suggested that he had evidence for this in his files. This was typical Palmer hype. When Palmer heard about Arnold's report of 'flying saucers', he wrote to Arnold. This was one of the few letters that Arnold actually answered. As a result, the two men collaborated on articles and, ultimately, on a book.

Palmer wrote about Arnold's report in 1947, but soon afterwards he fell out with his publishers. The next year he and Curtis Fuller started *Fate* magazine, a publication devoted to exploration of strange phenomena. The first issue carried an article by Arnold defending his saucer sightings (in fact the article owed much to Palmer's imagination). The next two issues carried articles under Arnold's name such as 'Are Space Visitors Here?'; Palmer encouraged the belief that the answer was 'Yes' and that Arnold had seen some of the aliens' craft. This idea flourished, partly because no one could properly explain Arnold's report. Suggestions were made, but no definitive explanation emerged, not even from the USAF, which was beginning to take an interest in the subject.

In the early 1950s, Palmer started several other magazines, including *Search*, *Mystic Universe* and *Other Worlds Science Stories*. *Fate* moved into the realm of mysticism and occultism, and Palmer sold it. *Other Worlds* began to concentrate on flying saucers and appeared under several different titles, including *Flying Saucers from Other Worlds* and *Flying Saucers: the Magazine of Space Conquest*. In 1961 the latter was issued as *Flying Saucers* and Palmer also published books on UFOs, a term coined by the USAF in 1952.

In 1959, when UFOs had become, largely through his own efforts, a well-known phenomenon, Palmer dropped the ETH. Instead he adopted the HEH. However Palmer was nothing if not ambiguous, and often presented his theories about UFOs in the form of rhetorical questions. He once replied to a question about UFOs by asking 'What would you say if I told you the whole thing was a joke?'. This might have been the truth.

It was not a joke to thousands, perhaps tens of thousands, who believed in the myth and founded UFO clubs and societies all over the world. A branch of the International Flying Saucer Bureau was formed in Bristol (England) as early as 1952. This was incorporated, with other societies, into The British UFO Research Association (BUFORA) in 1962. BUFORA still exists, and is very active. Palmer died in 1977.

If Palmer invented the myth, it was given form and substance by a Polish-American guru and part-time bartender. George Adamski was a mystic, already fairly well known in California for his lectures and radio broadcasts. He had begun teaching and writing on so-called philosophical subjects in 1928; in 1937 he published a work called *Satan, Man and the Hour*. He also had a following of devotees who addressed him as 'Professor'. He was described as a man of meagre scholastic achievements who had an excellent imagination, a pleasing personality and an apparently endless supply of gall (Edwards 1967). He was certainly very plausible when I met him on tour in England in April 1959. Adamski saw the stories of spacecraft (or flying saucers) as an ideal way to promote his own beliefs. All he needed to do was to put the beliefs into the mouths of aliens. Necessarily he would have to claim to have met and to have spoken with aliens. He came to world-wide attention in 1950 when *Fate* published one of his photographs. He was adept at faking pictures of flying saucers, the most famous of which is thought to show some common object (although there is no agreement on the identity of the object). Subsequently *Fate* published Adamski's own account of his (alleged) experiences, before he claimed to have met aliens. But this publicity, for Adamski and the myth, was dwarfed by the publicity for his story of meeting a Venusian near Desert Center in Southern California. This account was published as a sort of appendix (only 60 pages including 14 of photographs) in what was otherwise a tedious survey of many thousands of peculiar objects which have been seen in the skies over thousands of years (Leslie and Adamski 1953). With this book the myth was well and truly launched. The book achieved phenomenal world-wide sales and its title (*Flying Saucers Have Landed*) seems to have been taken as a statement of fact. As a result of this and other books (in Adamski's name but thought to be mostly ghosted) Adamski was in demand everywhere. He toured the USA on the lecture circuit and later toured the world, even gaining an audience with Queen Juliana of the Netherlands. A subsequent claim to have met the Pope appears to have been a hoax. As Edwards put it, 'this genial con man sold a jillion books to those eager to believe that somebody from space was crossing millions of miles of trackless void for the dubious privilege of conversing telepathically with former hamburger cooks' (see Campbell 1983a).

Arnold was a genuine UFO-reporter, someone who sees something unusual and who makes an honest report of it. Adamski was an out-and-out fraud. Nor was he the only one. Several other people claimed to have met aliens in remote places. In this way ufoists were at the mercy of both genuine and fraudulent reports. Unfortunately they had no way of telling the difference. The myth grew and prospered, fed by all sorts of reports, some genuine, some not.

There is an interesting postscript to Adamski's hoax. The following year saw the publication of a book which claimed that the author had met and talked with a man from Mars (Allingham 1954). The author claimed to have had this experience while on a caravan holiday near Lossiemouth in Scotland in February that same year. The idea of caravanning in Scotland in February should have alerted everyone to the possibility that this was another hoax. Attempts to find the author were fruitless and eventually the publisher declared that he had died abroad. Some years ago it was alleged that the author was in fact broadcaster and writer (and UFO debunker) Patrick Moore (Allan and Campbell 1986). Moore has never commented on this allegation.

In recent years, the myth of government secrecy, and even co-operation with aliens, has been propagated by London violinist Timothy Good.

In the development of the UFO myth, the shape of the classical 'flying saucer' (two soup plates stuck together) has remained surprisingly constant. Reporters frequently describe such a shape; even hoaxers make discoid models. The origin and persistence of this form needs explanation. It owes nothing to the form of man-made spacecraft, or indeed to rocket technology. Why should it be imagined that aliens travel in discoid craft?

Psychologist Carl Jung believed that mankind has a mental sub stream which is the source of all mythological and cosmogonic notions. He called this myth-creating level, which, he believed, has a positive function in giving meaning and significance to our existence, the 'collective unconscious'. He asked 'If they [flying saucers] are fantasy, why should such a rumour exist?' (Jung 1959:ix). Rather unwillingly, he attempted to find a psychological answer. He suggested that mankind's collective unconscious had constructed a new myth, one in which superhuman beings were visiting Earth in craft far superior to any man-made vehicle. Further, he suggested that this fantasy was the result of mankind's concern for its fate at a time of increasing world tension. Mankind, he thought, sought a saviour from the sky (ibid.:10). Jung himself was not convinced that this psychological explanation was adequate; he had heard that some UFOs produced radar echoes, and he concluded that either psychic projections throw back radar pulses or else the appearance of real objects afforded an opportunity for mythological projections (ibid.:147). Jung did not believe that flying saucers are real, objective 'projections' from the racial, unconscious mind.

The UFO myth is a bandwagon, onto which many want to jump. It provides a vehicle for personal idiosyncratic theories which otherwise would have to fend for themselves. It is seized on as an explanation for everything from the weather to the Second Coming of Christ. It is slipped unexamined into pre-existing philosophies, incorporated into all sorts of religions, cults, histories and prophecies, even to the extent of becoming the dominant feature of the philosophy.

Statistical studies of UFO reports

The Condon Report regarded statistical studies as 'fruitless'. However they did note that the geographical distribution of reports correlated roughly with the population density of rural areas. However there was no evidence that UFOs were reported more often near military installations (Gillmor 1969:22), and the idea that waves of reports correlated with the opposition of Mars was unfounded (ibid.:32). Many studies of UFO reports indicate that most reports are of objects seen at night, peaking about 2100L (9:0 pm).

One of the Condon team (Gordon D Thayer) noted that, in nineteen cases considered by the team, the weather was stated to be either clear or nearly clear. In fifteen cases, the weather was CAVU (Clear Air Visibility Unlimited), and in many cases there was 'exceptional visibility'. In four cases, the weather was 'generally clear', with some scattered clouds, or high thin broken conditions. He noted that such weather is indicative of stable atmospheric conditions that are favourable for the formation of layered, stratified, refractive index profiles, that is, they are conducive to anomalous propagation effects. The a priori probability of such a result, from a truly random sample of dates and times, is roughly in the order or one chance in 200 000 (assuming that the probability of clear weather is roughly 0·5 in any single case) (Gillmor 1969:172). In other words, there is an unexplained relationship between UFO reports and the weather, especially anticyclonic conditions.

Definitions

'Altitude' is used in the astronomical sense, meaning the vertical plane angle between an object and the unobstructed horizon. Altitude in the aeronautical sense will be described as height above mean sea level. Both terms are used in aeronautics.

'Azimuth' is the horizontal plane angle between the direction of an object and true north, but only in a direction to the observer's right. Zero (and 360°) azimuth is true north and 90° azimuth is due east, etc.

A distinction is drawn between the 'form' an object really possesses and the 'shape' of that object as perceived by an observer (Haines 1980:151).

'Stationary' means perceived to be stationary; it does not necessarily mean that the source was in fact stationary.

An 'observer' is a person who observes an object in the sky, there being no question about the fact. A 'reporter' is a person who reports seeing an object (UFO), there being an implicit question about the facts.

An occulting light is one that is on longer that it is off, while a flashing light is one that is off longer than it is on.

Mensuration is SI metric.

Times are given in 24-hour style, designated either 'L' for local time or 'Z' for Universal Time (UT).

The apparent brightness (as distinct from the absolute brightness) of an astronomical body is expressed in terms of its 'apparent magnitude' (or simply 'magnitude'). The mean of the twenty brightest stars is defined to be magnitude 1 (or first magnitude). Fainter objects have a higher magnitude number and brighter objects have a lower magnitude number (expressed as a negative number if necessary). Thus the brighter the star or planet the lower its magnitude. Sixth-magnitude stars are defined to be 100 times fainter than first-magnitude stars, thus a difference of 5 magnitudes corresponds to a difference in brightness of a factor of 100. The scale is logarithmic; a difference of 1 magnitude corresponds to a difference in brightness of $\sqrt[5]{100} = 2{\cdot}512$. If two objects have respective magnitudes of m_1 and m_2 (where m_1 is the brighter), the ratio between their apparent brightnesses (b_1/b_2) is found as follows:

$$\frac{b_1}{b_2} = 10^{0 \cdot 4(m_2 - m_1)}$$

Textual references are by means of the name/date system, sometimes with the addition of the relevant page number.

Full details of the works quoted will be found in the References at the end of the book (from p. 200).

2 The UFO report

UFO reports come to us via an unreliable instrument; where there was an objective stimulus, this instrument can severely distort the appearance and/or behaviour of the stimulus. The instrument I refer to is the human observer!

Most students of UFO reports make insufficient allowance for the problems of human perception and memory; it is therefore necessary to note these problems, especially the visual ones.

The psychology of perception

Philosophers of science believe that 'perception is theory-laden', that is to say, perception is a complex interaction between what we actually see and what we expect to see. Cosmologist Stephen Hawking (1993:43) explained that 'what we regard as reality is conditioned by the theory to which we subscribe'. Interpretation is the result of imposing theories on sensory input. In our everyday experience this imposition is slight, or justified. In the case of the unfamiliar it becomes of immense importance and may not be justified. UFO reports are usually reports of unfamiliar objects behaving in an unfamiliar way. Necessarily therefore, a UFO report must be regarded with suspicion; it must be suspected that reporters can become the victim of their mind's attempt to make sense of what they saw.

Perception takes place not, as many believe, in the sense organs, but in the brain. The brain receives nerve impulses and the mind interprets these as a perception of the environment (I use 'mind' to describe the brain's operating system, or software). However, the mind is liable to adjust the impulses so as to make more sense of them. The study of illusions has demonstrated that the mind can be fooled into misinterpreting these impulses. Gestalt psychology has shown that the mind tends to modify or rearrange what we see (or hear) so as to structure it. For instance, shapes which do not possess simplicity, regularity, symmetry or continuity, tend to become modified and be perceived with more simplicity, regularity, symmetry or continuity than they actually possess. As a rule we are concerned to perceive only as much as will enable us to identify what we see, that is to say, to allocate it to a particular class of objects or forms with which we are familiar. UFOs are a class of objects with which we are familiar only through the UFO myth. We all have a pretty good theory about them, and this theory will inevitable interfere with perception of a stimulus that is obscure enough to be interpreted by the mind as an object in this class. Distinguishing between seeing-belief failures and hallucinations (the latter lack an objective stimulus), one psychologist noted that the former occur when observers mistake what they see for something else. It is not necessary for them to know anything about the actual stimulus; all they need to know is the nature of the object they believe it to be, and under no conditions would they be able to correct their failure in seeing the stimulus unless they acquired appropriate knowledge about it. Perceptual beliefs about an object can be erroneous in respect of its existence, the category to which it belongs, its characteristics or knowledge concerning it (Soltis 1966).

Experience during the Second World War showed that observers were usually correct then they said that something had happened at a particular place. However they could be wildly incorrect about what had happened. In one case, the observers were disposed to see enemy paratroops at a time when they were told to look for them. What they looked for, they saw (Jones 1968).

Because the optic nerves cannot carry all the information available in the eyes, the neurons from the eyes to the brain have to transmit complex pulses of a 'broken-up' picture for reconstruction by the mind. The human mind has been likened to a probability computer program in which a decision is based on the best bet in a given situation. The mind takes the meagre evidence of the senses and builds and tests hypotheses to explain these inputs. If the mind were unable to fill in gaps and deduce 'truth', activity as a whole would come to a halt. But the (small) price we pay for this process is the possibility of making mistakes, manifested as illusions.

The human perceptual system does not perform well when suddenly placed in an unfamiliar environment. It is like asking a computer to produce the right answer to a problem it has not been programmed to solve (Gregory 1972:225-6). John Napier noted that 'although we do not always know what we see, we tend to see what we know'. This is the same as saying that we have to choose what we have seen or know about before. Since we tend to perceive the conceivable it is very difficult for us to perceive the inconceivable (Murray 1975).

Evidently human perception can be faulty; it can play tricks with us. Seeing is not necessarily believing. Observers can believe that they see something that is non-existent (hallucination), or they can believe that they sees something which in fact is something else altogether (illusion). They can misidentify an object and lend it characteristics which it ought to have (if it is the object they thinks it is); they can also perceive movement that does not exist and miscalculate an object's distance and/or linear size. Given that we are considering the perception of unfamiliar objects (indeed, *unidentified* objects), it seems certain that most of the perceptual errors which are possible will occur in the observation of the stimuli which are reported as UFOs.

Problems of human visual perception

When the Imperial College UFO Research Group used the London Science Museum's 'Stardome' to test the ability of the average person to describe visual observations, the scale of the inaccuracies surprised them. Eighteen people were asked to describe the nature of various phenomena and estimate size, speed, angular separation, etc. The tests cast grave doubts on the usefulness of any numerical data derived from sighting reports (Wickham 1968). Studies have been made of the illusions which pilots experience (Vinacke 1947), especially those experienced at night (Imus et al. 1951). Most of the problems have been dealt with elsewhere (Haines 1980), but emphasis needs to be placed on some relevant ones.

(1) *Visual acuity*: The minimum angle of resolution is usually accepted to be one arcminute (1') and people who can make this resolution at a distance of 6 m are said to have '6:6 vision' (or an acuity of 1). The greater the acuity the greater the distance at which the observer can make the resolution. For particularly appropriate objects the mind manages to improve on this acuity to about 10 arcseconds (Durham and Watkins 1967) and it is believed that normal resolution ranges from 60-120 arcseconds (Emsley 1952:49). The British Ministry of Transport's driving test requires a visual acuity of 0·4 (Weale 1968:13). Acuity improves as the difference in luminance between the target and background (see (9) below) increases. Resolution also depends on the colour of the light and the size of the pupil in the eye. Consequently acuity is worse at night (when the pupil is enlarged) and worse in blue light. It should be easier to see red lights than blue ones of the same size (Emsley 1952:I:47-48). The pupil's enlargement in the dark can cause 'night myopia', although people vary greatly in their ability to focus on distant objects in the dark. Bright stars and planets (and the Moon) will be out-of-focus to varying degrees (Leibowitz and Owens 1975).

(2) *Estimates of movement*: The visual system cannot detect motion if it is below the visual motion threshold for a particular part of the retina.

Objects seen in a totally homogenous (plain) field must move at about 15 arcminutes/s or more for the movement to be detected. Stellar movement is not detected because it is not greater than 0·25'/s. An object which is tracked visually seems to move at only half the speed it would appear to have when it is viewed with the line of sight fixed. Objects viewed against a heterogeneous (varied) background appear to travel faster than when viewed against a homogenous background. Vertical movement appears faster than horizontal movement, even if both are the same. An increase in angular size (over a certain rate) will be perceived as movement towards the observer (with a decrease perceived as movement away); this is known as 'gamma' movement. Visual acuity falls in proportion to the speed of movement of an object and at a certain angular velocity (depending on object size, range, contrast, etc.) an object's image will blur.

Given the same distance and speed, larger lights appear to move more slowly than smaller ones (Ross 1974:132).

Since all motion is relative, observers have to determine what is moving and what is not, or whether or not they themselves are moving. For movement of part of the retinal image the mind usually bets that the smaller objects are moving. 'Induced movement' is the phenomenon seen when an object which is in fact stationary appears to move against a large homogenous field which is in fact moving. This effect is seen when clouds scud past the Moon, making it seem that the Moon is moving in the opposite direction (see figure 2:1).

Apparent movement of a truly stationary source can be caused by linear or angular acceleration of the observer (the 'oculogyral illusion') and rotating observers who do not know that they are rotating will perceive angular movement of a truly stationary source. Perception of induced movement by one observer can be communicated to others.

Other movement illusions include 'beta' movement (also call 'the phi phenomenon'), which is caused by proper timing of individual light sources in a series. The perceived direction and velocity of a visual stimulus may be significantly influenced by changing the shape of the stimulus.

A stationary light can appear to move as a result of the *autokinetic effect*. This is the phenomenon whereby a stationary point of light, when steadily regarded in darkness, will appear to move. The angular velocity of the apparent motion is from 2-3°/s and total movement may amount to at least 30°. The effect is influenced by a number of factors, some of them attitudinal. The movement may seem like that of a 'shooting star'. If the point of light is first seen off-centre, when it is centred the movement will, at first, be in the opposite direction to that of the direction of rotation of the eye. Then the movement will reverse direction (Gregory 1974). The cause of autokinesis is still disputed, but it is not due to unconscious eye movements. It may be caused by conflicting messages from the eye muscles to the brain. Pilots have been known to mistake stars or ground lights for the lights of moving planes (Ross 1974:127).

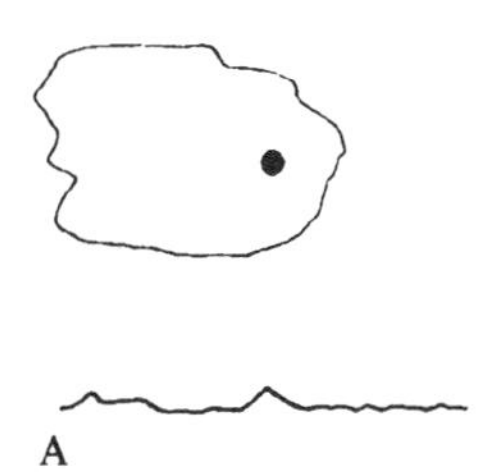

Fig. 2:1 An illustration of 'induced movement'. The celestial body remains stationary (from picture A to picture B) while the translucent cloud has moved to the right. The result is that the body appears to have moved to the left. In real time the movement is continuous, giving the impression that the body is moving to the left.

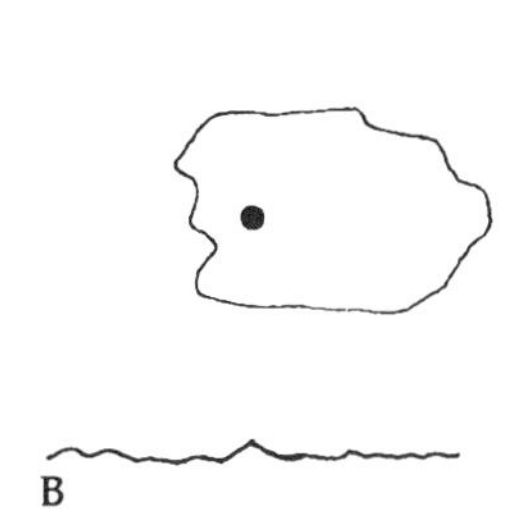

An induced movement illusion can occur when the observers are moving but the perceived object is not. A low-altitude Moon (or other bright celestial body) is assigned a distance of only a few hundred metres (see below) but moving observers note that it neither gets left behind nor changes its angle relative to them. Since the Moon is perceived to be small in relation to the landscape the mind assigns movement to the Moon, not to the landscape. For two reasons therefore, moving observers assume that the Moon must be moving in the direction in which they are travelling (figure 2:2). It is curious that the perceived speed of the Moon is less than that of the observers, and is seen to be so, even though the moon is not left behind (Durham and Watkins 1967b). At a speed of (say) 50 km/h, the Moon will seem to move at only 10-20 km/h (Gregory 1972:114).

Necessarily the perceived speed of a low-altitude celestial (or very distant) object must decrease as the angle between the object and the course of the observers decreases (forwards or backwards). But it is only the perceived speed in a direction parallel to that of the observers which reduces. As the angle reduces, and the object is seen more to the fore or aft of the vehicle, then it must appear to move towards the heading (or reciprocal direction) of the vehicle. This is because the horizon is now 'moving' in a direction across the direction of travel,

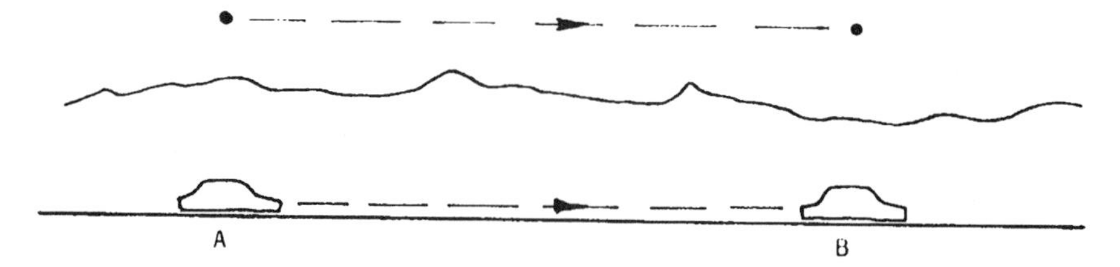

Fig. 2:2 If the occupants of a vehicle travelling from A to B observe a celestial (or very distant) object abeam on the horizon the object will appear to travel with them at their own speed or less (see figure 2:3). The mind 'forgets' that the horizon must be moving to the left and insists that it is the object that is moving.

causing the object to appear to move in the opposite direction (see figure 2:3). When the angle is zero, the object must appear to lie dead ahead (or astern), but not necessarily stationary (see below). Complications set in if the observers change course; the object will appear to move rapidly from one area of the sky to another and will appear to have changed velocity. An object seen dead ahead may be perceived as stationary or hovering in the path of the observers. Similarly an object seen dead astern may be perceived as following or catching up with the observers.

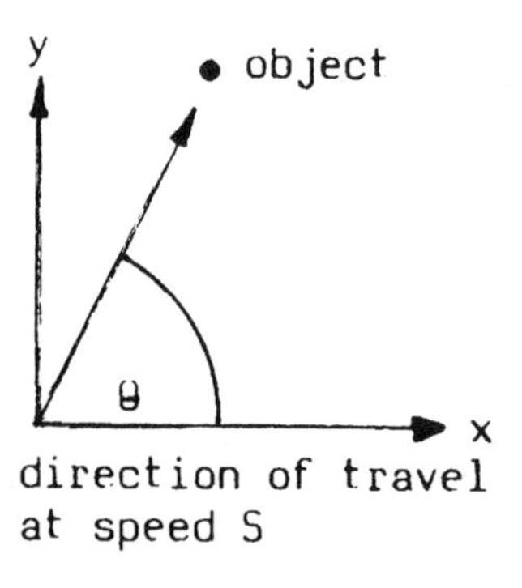

Fig. 2:3 The perceived velocity of the object in the x-direction (S') will depend on the angle between the object and the direction of travel (θ), as follows:

$$S' = S \sin \theta$$

However, the smaller θ is, the more the object will appear to move across towards the heading of the vehicle, and loss of perceived velocity in the x-direction may be compen-sated by gain of perceived velocity in the (-y)-direction.

If the object is seen ahead but a little above a slightly elevated horizon (or through trees), and the observers are travelling horizontally, it will be perceived as descending. This is because the altitude of the horizon increases as the distance decreases. Because of induced movement and because the observers know that the horizon cannot rise, the small object will seem to be falling (see figure 2:4). Similarly an object observed astern in the same conditions will appear to be rising.

For observers in an aircraft, illusions and errors are frequent and dramatic. Because of the lack of any sensation of movement, pilots have to learn to dispense with normal perception and to rely on their instruments (Gregory 1972:115). However, they can forget to do this during times of stress or excitement.

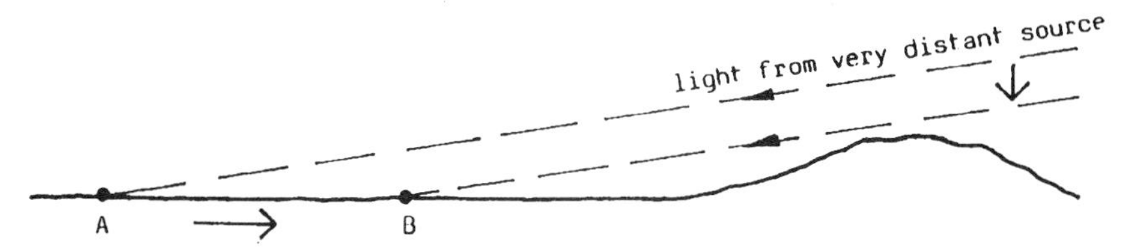

Fig. 2:4 A diagram showing how a very distant source (although it is stationary) appears to fall towards the horizon as the observer approaches it (from A to B). In fact it is the horizon which rises.

Drake noted that observers always overestimate velocity (Sagan and Page 1972:255); when a small hot-air balloon was launched at Northport (Washington) in January 1974, it was reported to have zoomed across the sky at speeds up to 100 km/h (Klass 1974:292).

(3) *Estimates of size and distance*: Although all angular sizes tend to be overestimated (Gilinsky 1955), there are some particular causes of such error.

The *moon illusion* occurs when the full Moon is at low altitude; it appears larger than when high in the sky. This is probably due to a combination of several different factors, including the reduction in area of sky around the Moon and the size of objects on the horizon. Other bright objects near the horizon can suffer the same distortion, appearing larger than they really are.

Bright objects appear larger than dim objects and bright stars seem larger than dim stars. Hazy objects are perceived as further away than clear sharp objects. The brighter an object is, the larger it appears to be; a small (1°) bright source can appear to be 75 per cent larger, probably due to scatter within the eye (Haines 1980:240). The Sun and Moon both subtend an angle of about 0·5° (and each can be covered by a pea held at arm's length). However they both appear larger than this, estimates range from 1·5° to 3·5°. Indeed, the Sun appears larger than the Moon because of its greater brightness, even though most people know that, for total eclipses of the Sun to be possible, the two bodies must subtend approximately the same angle. Because of the error noted above, comparison between the angular size of an unknown with the angular size of the full Moon should be treated with caution.

It is believed that estimates of linear size and distance are inextricably linked and both can be wrong. A more accurate estimate of angular size may be obtained by asking the reporters to give both their estimate of linear size *and* their estimate of distance. An angular size can be calculated from the two estimates (Durham and Watkins 1967b). Observers may deduce an object's linear size from an assumption about its distance, or vice versa.

An object later discovered to be a hot-air balloon (about 1 m across) was reported as a 'UFO' 6 m or more in diameter (Klass 1974:292). An experienced observer, formerly a combat pilot, reported an object which was only 76 m up as being at a height of 1500 m. Some soap bubbles were perceived as 'immense' spheres travelling at 'fantastic speed' towards distant mountains (Menzel and Boyd 1963:56-58).

A phenomenon sometimes called *size constancy* appears to operate in the mind to maintain the perceived linear size of a known object despite variation in the angular size of the retinal image. Naturally we do not know the linear size of unknown objects and could only guess at their real size

Given the same distance and speed, slower lights appear larger than faster lights (Ross 1974:132).

(4) *Estimates of altitude*: Estimates are usually incorrect when the object is near 0° or 90° altitude (Steiger 1976:330) and differences from 0° or from 90° of angles near the horizon or near the zenith tend to be substantially overestimated. Anything that is more than 45°, or even 30°, above the horizon is often reported as 'overhead' (Gillmor 1969:565). Reporters may state that an object zoomed up into the sky because it appeared to recede (perhaps caused by a reduction in brightness and/or size). However this does not mean that there was any change in the object's altitude, let alone its height. The nose-up attitude of an aircraft taking off causes a light ahead to appear lower (and the aircraft higher) than it actually is. On descent, with the nose down, the reverse applies (Beaty 1991:71).

(5) *Estimates of form*: Because of an effect called *shape constancy*, objects viewed at an angle (or thought to be at an angle) are perceived as seen more nearly straight on. For example, an elliptical image, which the mind interprets as a circle viewed at an angle, is perceived as less elliptical than it really is. It may even be reported as a circle or disc (Durham and Watkins 1967b). Various form illusions may occur if the object is irregular in shape; the visual system can be fooled into making unfounded assumptions about the nature of the object (Haines 1980:152). Nevertheless the mind makes fairly accurate estimates of the ratio between an object's maximum and minimum dimension.

The reported shape of a bright object may not correspond to its true form. If square, rectangular or triangular, diffusely reflecting forms are made bright enough ($C = 10^7$, see (9) below) and viewed against a dark background, each form appears almost completely round. Consequently, round bright objects seen against a dark background may be very bright luminous objects which are not round at all (Haines 1980:243).

At night, most people see points around small bright lights such as stars or planets (see figure 2:5). This is caused primarily by scattering from the fibres of the lens in the eye, but it is modified by aberrations of the particular eye, notably by astigmatism. The enlarged pupil allows light to pass through parts of the lens that are not used in good light. However, heightened interest can cause the pupil to enlarge in daylight, producing similar points. The defocusing of small images, such as in myopia or hypermetropia, may produce break-up of the image into several blobs due to refractive irregularities across the pupil.

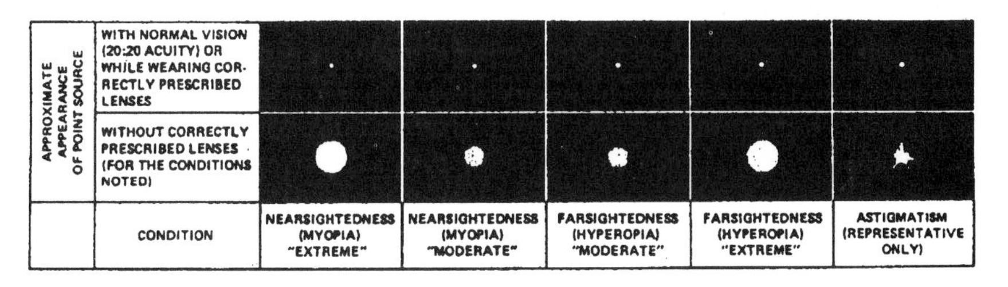

Fig. 2:5 An illustration showing the approximate appearance of an optical point source such as a star to people who possess different degrees of 'spherical refractive error' and 'astigmatism' (Haines 1980).

(6) *Estimates of colour*: Drake concluded that colours are not accurately recorded (Sagan and Page 1972:255). The colours of familiar objects recalled from memory tend to shift toward the predominant hue of the object. For example, grass is recalled as being greener than it really was (Haines 1980:52). The perceived colour of a very bright object, and perceived changes in its colour, do not necessarily represent the actual colour of the object, or the actual changes in its colour. A bright green (wavelength 560 nm) object will appear desaturated, increasingly white with time. A yellow-green (560-580 nm) object will go from green, through a deeper green, yellow, and orange, to a yellow or greenish yellow. An orange-red (580-655 nm) goes from orange, through yellow and green, to orange-yellow, and a dark red (655 nm) appears greenish. In general, small coloured sources become more pastel with increase in their luminance (Haines 1980:245).

Allowance should be made for some observers having defective colour vision; about 10 per cent of men (including me) cannot discriminate between red and green under certain conditions.

The eye is relatively insensitive to the colour of small sources (small field tritanopia), with sensitivity proportional to size. Defocusing of an image (for example, in a telescope) will make colours more apparent. Colour vision is poor at night.

Coloured spectacles or sun glasses will alter colour perception, but only if worn for a short time. Long term use adapts the visual system to the colour shift and causes it to see colours through the spectacles as if the latter were not coloured (Gregory 1972:212-213).

(7) *Estimates of direction*: The perceived direction of an object is determined by the direction in which the light from it enters the eye. Because the light rays may have been diverted in their course (for example, by refraction in the atmosphere), the object may not necessarily have been in the observed direction (Haines 1980:105-106).
Many UFO reporters do not give the direction (azimuth) of the object they claim to have seen (believing that it was very close to them). This makes the elimination of astronomical explanations very difficult. Where azimuth is given it can be very inaccurate; few reporters know the direction of true north and few carry a compass to give a magnetic bearing.

(8) *Estimates of time span*: Time span is overestimated by observers who are bored and underestimated by those who are busy (Haines 1980:163). A reporter who filmed what he thought was a 'UFO' for 23 s, estimated the time as only 12 s (Campbell 1991). However, Drake thought that estimates are 'reasonably accurate' (Sagan and Page 1972:254). Two stimuli can be discriminated if they are at least 0·16 s apart (vision), 0·001 s apart (sound) or 0·002 s apart (tone). Conversely events as much as 12 s apart may be perceived as simultaneous (Haines 1980:163). Collecting reports of the fireball of 25 April 1969, BUFORA's then Director of Research concluded, from analysis of the reports of the duration (which ranged from 1 s to 3 min.), that casual observers are incapable of making accurate estimates of the passage of short periods of time (*BUFORA Research Bulletin*, 2 (2), 13 September 1969).

(9) *Estimates of brightness*: 'Brightness' is not an objective term. Our assessment of intrinsic brightness is a product of the perceived contrast. The mind can be deceived into thinking that a brightly-illuminated black object against a dim background is actually white (Durham and Watkins 1967b)!

Contrast (C) is calculated as follows:

$$C = (L_s - L_b)/L_b$$

where L_s is the luminance of the source and L_b is the luminance of the background. C falls off exponentially, and an object will be invisible when the contrast is reduced to about 2 per cent (Ross 1975). Luminance is measured in candelas (cd) per m^2.

The visual system is poor at estimating absolute brightness, but good at estimating relative brightness (Haines 1980:171). Two lights must differ in brightness by more than 8 per cent before the difference in brightness between them can be detected by observers (Myers 1986:143).

The human optical system can detect a candle 48 km away (Myers 1986:149), or stars down to magnitude 8·5, equivalent to a standard candle at a distance of 34·5 km (Emsley 1952 II:307). A candle 1 km away yields an apparent magnitude of 0·8, and the small, battery-operated lights, long used on meteorological balloons in the USA, have a known luminosity of about 1·5 cd (Sagan and Page 1972:94). In the UK, free balloons must display a steady red light of at least 5 cd while flying at night. A Tilley lamp produces about 300 cd of white light (Klass 1974:235), while a modern car headlamp has an output of about 80 kcd.

Problems of memory

Whatever they have seen, reporters must make use of memory to make a report. All people include an inventive, imaginative (and therefore spurious) element in their remembering, and all remembering depends heavily on reconstruction rather than on mere reproduction alone. It has been shown how unreliable eyewitness testimony can be, and how witnesses may have trouble separating fact from fiction. They may not have been paying much attention, the event may have been too short, or the viewing conditions may have been poorer than they allowed (Buckhout 1974).

Tests show that reliability decreases with time, and it is strongly suspected that witnesses attempt to make facts fit theory. In the case of UFO reports, the UFO myth provides a powerful theory on which to draw if memory fails.

The USAF regarded the value of information as being 'greatly decreased' if not obtained within seven days. They thought that, if investigation is undertaken after weeks or months, the original reporters cease to provide new information. They claimed that late interrogation merely produces repetition of 'facts' originally reported, plus an inability on the part of the reporters to be objective (Steiger 1976:261). However, McDonald claimed that there is evidence that time does not seriously distort either major features or many finer details of the original incidents if they were extremely unusual. He concluded that the more unusual the basic experience, the more reliable the recollection account tends to be (Sagan and Page 1972:58). Conversely, Drake claimed that, after five days, people report more imagination than truth and that memory of exotic events fades very quickly (ibid.:254).

Phillis Fox noted that loaded questions (such as 'Did you see a flying saucer?') from friends and acquaintances may alter witnesses' memory of their observations. Consequently the memory may be reconstructed with the appropriate details (Haines 1979:32).

The reliability of UFO reports

It is possible for UFO reporters to 'see' things that were not actually present. Many preliminary interpretations of what the perceived object may be may return to awareness periodically to become an integral part of the final perception. Reporters may also add certain types of percepts (a percept is a sub-unit of perception) from memory and/or delete other types. The result may be to make the objects described appear more like objects reported by others (Haines 1980:41). Reporters may also impute to an aerial object motion characteristics which it did not actually display, but which correspond to the type of object they believe it to be (ibid.:191). A pre-existing schema for UFOs (the UFO myth) is available to help us interpret ambiguous sensations; confronted with an ambiguous moving object in the sky, different people may apply different schemas (Myers 1986:180). If outnumbered by fraudulent witnesses, observers may be persuaded that they had seen something that did not in fact exist.

A Reliability Index (P_r) has been devised, as follows:

$$P_r = [1 - (p)^m].P_i.2^{1-n}$$

where p is the average witness reliability factor (three categories from 0·5 to 0·75), m is the number of witnesses, P_i is the investigation reliability factor (three grades from 0·999 to 0·5), and n is the nth handedness of the report. P_r has a maximum of 1·0 (although this could only be approached where there were very many witnesses, a very reliable investigation and a firsthand report) and a minimum of zero (Olsen 1966).

An observer credibility rating has also been devised. It consists of a very detailed medical, neuro-ophthalmic, neurological and psychiatric examination (Walker 1968). In all cases it is important to investigate witnesses as much as what they report.

The above ratings are practically useless if the reporter has seen some genuinely strange phenomenon; the assessors are likely to draw conclusions that agree with their own prejudices. A worked example of Walker's method concluded that the witness could not have seen what he reported and that he had therefore suffered a hallucination (Roush 1968:152). However, from the data given, I was able to find an astronomical explanation, indicating that the report was both reliable and credible.

The USAF assessed the 'short-term reliability' of a report from the logic and coherency of the original report and from the age and occupancy of the reporter. They paid particular attention to whether or not the occupancy involved observation reporting or technical knowledge (Steiger 1976:261). In fact technically trained reporters are as likely as the average person to suffer misperceptions if the phenomenon they see is not one with which they are familiar.

More relevant is the knowledge and suggestibility of the reporter; a simple-minded reporter can be more reliable than one who knows the UFO myth and has the imagination to use it. In the end, investigators have to judge for themselves whether or not a reporter is either reliable or credible.

UFO reports can be distorted by repetition and distance. Over 200 years ago, the philosopher David Hume observed that a story, which is 'universally exploded' in the place where it first started, 'passes for certain at a thousand miles [1600 km] distance'. He also observed that, while fools propagate 'the imposture', 'the wise and learned are content in general to deride its absurdity, without informing themselves of the particular facts, by which it may be distinctly refuted' (Hume 1927:120). The 'facts' may be easier to obtain today than they were 200 years ago, but even so UFO reports from remote areas are hard to check and one is at the mercy of local investigators. The strangest accounts seem to come from the furthest corners of the world. It is tempting to conclude that, the greater the distance between the writer of a UFO account and the site of the alleged incident, the more distorted and exaggerated the report will be (the distortion will be in the direction of the UFO myth). However, it may be that strange reports get more publicity and travel further than mundane reports.

No reliance should be placed on reports obtained from hypnotized subjects (Campbell 1982b). Hypnosis is a temporary state of heightened suggestibility in which some people narrow their focus of attention and experience imaginary happenings as if they were real (Myers 1986:653). In addition, the hypnotist's beliefs frequently work their way into the subject's memories (ibid.:213). Hypnotized people do no more than play out an elaborate acting role to satisfy the hypnotist. The extent to which subjects can develop their fantasies under hypnosis can be seen in Frank Johnson's book *The Janos People* (Campbell 1981a).

A test of reliability

An attempt to determine the reliability and objectivity of UFO reports was made by the Society for the Investigation of UFO Phenomena (SIUFOP) in 1970. This was done, somewhat unethically, by means of a carefully arranged hoax on ufoists who were in the habit of congregating on Cradle Hill at Warminster (Wiltshire, England). The area had the reputation for UFO 'activity'.

At 2300L on 28 March that year, SIUFOP shone a powerful lamp at Cradle Hill from Sack Hill, just over 1 km away. The light was purple in colour and lasted for two periods, one of 5 s and one of 25 s, separated by a period of 5 s (35 s overall). The lamp remained stationary. At the site of the lamp, some simulated landing marks were dug, and an appropriate area of grass was singed. Some members of SIUFOP were on Cradle Hill among the innocent enthusiasts, and they had with them a 'UFO detector' and a camera on a tripod. The detector was rigged to sound 15 s after the purple light. While the ufoists watched the light and heard the detector buzzing, one of the SIUFOP group pretended to photograph the light. In fact his film had already been double exposed to show a spurious UFO in a different position and bearing no resemblance to the purple light. However the film had been exposed looking in the same direction at a similar time. This film was handed to a ufoist who had contacts with *Flying Saucer Review* (FSR), and who arranged for the film to be processed.

A photographic consultant and Dr Pierre Guérin (Director of Research at the Astrophysical Institute of the French National Centre for Scientific Research) concluded that the film was absolutely genuine. It was accepted that it did show three-dimensional objects. Despite a search, the ground marks were not found. Subsequent publication of the case in FSR was accompanied by an artist's impression of the purple light; however it exaggerated the size by an order of magnitude (about ten times). The account raised the object's altitude from 0° to 20°, changed its shape from circular to ovoid, added a white periphery and a crimson centre, moved it across the sky and extended the period of observation to 1-1·5 minutes. The photographic consultant went so far as to deduce which side of the UFO carried 'propulsive jets'. Calculations were later made that the UFO was 17 m long and that it was 45 m from some car headlamps (visible in the photograph). Despite prompting by SIUFOP, the investigators failed to apply techniques which could have revealed inconsistencies between the photograph and the light. They could even have found evidence that the UFO photographs were not taken the same night as the light (Simpson 1976).

It was unfortunate that a more objective observer was not available to give a more accurate account of the incident and that the case was not investigated more skilfully. A repeat of the incident did result in a fairly accurate account from another observer. Nevertheless the test demonstrated some of the principal distortions made by reporters and the prejudices of ufoists.

'Ghost rocket' tailpiece

Several lessons concerning both the interpretation of UFO reports and the identification of evidence can be learned from the experience of the British intelligence service. 'Ghost rocket' was the term given to strange phenomena reported (principally) over Sweden during the summer and autumn of 1946. The term 'flying saucer' had not then been coined. The objects were described as rocket-like, usually glowing and travelling at heights between 300 and 900 m. They were variously reported as travelling slower than airplanes or crossing the sky in seconds at fantastic speeds.

The spate of reports led the Swedish General Staff to issue a press release on 11 August 1946; it stated that 'ghost-rockets, mysterious spool-shaped objects with fiery tails, have become a common sight in Sweden' and reported that the authorities were certain that their country was in the path of experimental electronically-directed missiles. Some of the unknowns were depicted as fairly small, squarish and, at least partly, coloured red (Flammonde 1976).

At the time it was commonly assumed, especially by Washington, that the 'rocket bombs' or 'flying bombs', as they were also known, originated in the USSR, and even that they were launched from Peenemunde. Flammonde stated that, although there was testimony that some 'bombs' had crashed, nothing was found. However, he also noted that, on 15 August 1946, a newspaper reported that Swedish Army investigators had come upon a fragment of metal. 'It was less than three inches [75 cm] long and letters were found on it. The implication was that this physical "evidence" might help solve the mystery'. Nothing more was heard of the fragment.

Light has since been shed upon these events by Britain's wartime Air Force Intelligence scientist R V Jones (later to become Professor of Natural Philosophy at the University of Aberdeen). He has revealed that the idea that Russia was intimidating Sweden by flying some sort of new weapon was accepted by officers in his own department. They even worked out the performance of the 'bombs' from the reported sightings in one of the incidents, where the object appeared to have dashed about at random over the whole of southern Sweden at speeds up to 3200 km/h. Even Field Marshall Smuts believed in the Russian 'flying bombs', to the extent that he broadcast a warning to the British people. However Jones was sceptical. He was sure that the bombs were not real and that the more dramatic reports were caused by meteors. On one spectacular occasion, he noted that every observer reported the object as well to the east, and that it could have been as far east as Finland. He concluded that the fantastic speeds reported were merely due to the fact that all observers had seen the object more or less simultaneously, but that they had varying errors in their watches. Consequently any attempt to draw a track by linking up observations in a time sequence was unsound. He also asked two sensible questions: (1) What conceivable purpose could it serve the Russians, if they indeed had such a controllable flying bomb, to fly it in great numbers over Sweden without doing any more harm than to alert the West to the fact that they had such an impressive weapon?; (2) How had the Russians succeeded in making a flying bomb of such fantastic reliability? The Germans had achieved no better than 90 per cent reliability in their flying bomb trials of 1944, at very much shorter range. Surely, at least one bomb must have crashed somewhere. Jones challenged his staff to bring him a piece of one of the bombs.

It was with considerable surprise that he received the news that the Swedes had several pieces which were reported to have fallen off one of the 'bombs', and he awaited their arrival in London with curiosity. They turned out to be an odd assortment of four or five irregularly solid lumps, none of which looked as if it had ever been associated with a mechanical device. Among the specimens was a lump 5 to 8 cm across that was hard, shiny, grey and porous. He and a colleague immediately identified it, but in order to satisfy the curiosity of his staff he sent it, together with the other specimens, for chemical analysis at Farnborough.

The Farnborough report came back, not to Jones, but to another Director of Intelligence, Air Commodore Vintras, who excitedly telephoned Jones as soon as he had read it. Apparently, the report declared that 98 per cent of one of the lumps consisted of an unknown element! Vintras was sure that this justified his view that the flying 'bombs' did exist. Excitement on the Air Staff rose; not only did the Russians have a flying bomb of fantastic performance, they were driving it with a fuel made from an element that was new to the world of chemistry.

Jones telephoned the head of chemistry at Farnborough and asked if he was joking. Was he perhaps giving a silly answer to a silly question? Apparently not; the chemist was perfectly serious and declared that his section was baffled. Jones then asked if it had occurred to the chemist that the lump looked remarkably like a piece of coke! The gasp at the other end of the telephone told Jones that he was right and that the Farnborough chemists had tested for nearly every element except carbon. There was nothing mysterious or even significant about the Swedish specimens.

Although Jones's staff were 'somewhat dampened' by this experience, they did not abandon their belief in the 'bombs'. Consequently, when they received a telephone report that one of the 'bombs' had fallen onto a farm in Kent, they jumped at the opportunity to show their Director the error of his beliefs. Travelling at a weekend, in order that Jones should not know of the investigation until they could bring back the 'bomb', they followed instructions given to them by a farmer. But the instructions were false (or inaccurate) and all they succeeded in doing was frightening the life out of a farmer whose name sounded like that of the caller. Dejected, they returned to London convinced that Jones himself was responsible for the hoax (he had a reputation as a practical joker). Jones only uncovered the incident when a senior British officer on General MacArthur's staff in Tokyo asked for the latest intelligence concerning Russian 'flying bombs' and for confirmation of a story that such a 'bomb' had fallen in England in the last few days (Jones 1978:510-513).

We may imagine that from that date British Air Intelligence ceased to believe in the existence of Russian 'flying bombs' and that this may have not a little to do with subsequent scepticism regarding the existence of UFOs. With hindsight it is clear that the 'ghost-rocket' reports were the result of misperceptions, possibly arising from Swedish concern regarding Russian intentions in the immediate post-war years. It is significant that similar reports came from other countries bordering the USSR. The predominance of reports from Sweden may be explained by the fact that the Swedish General Staff took the reports seriously, made public pronouncements, and asked the public to send in reports. Their reaction may be understood in the light of the fact that, during 1944, a test V-2 rocket accidentally fell in Sweden. Naturally the Swedish public reported all sorts of aerial phenomena as 'flying bombs', but the volume of these reports then convinced the authorities, not only in Sweden but elsewhere, that the 'bombs' were real.

No doubt there was some real stimulus for each report, and natural phenomena are the most obvious cause; but the stimuli were misinterpreted. The reports were interpreted as evidence of the power and hostility of the USSR. Today many interpret UFO reports as evidence of the power (and often the hostility) of alien races, but this conclusion is no more logical than that concerning the 'ghost-rockets'. Jones's questions apply with equal force to the belief that UFOs are alien craft, and the lack of a UFO fragment is as significant as the lack of a genuine fragment of a 'ghost-rocket'.

3 Sources of deception

Given that UFO reports are not stimulated by sight of alien spaceships, they must be stimulated by what I call 'sources of deception'. These sources deceive observers into believing that they are looking at a UFO, or are experiencing its effects. There are also some 'sources of deception' which deceive investigators. There are very many such sources (Hendry 1979). In 1970 the (UK) Ministry of Defence (MoD) listed the following explanations for UFO reports:

- satellites and debris (re-entries?)
- balloons
- celestial objects
- meteorological and natural phenomena
- aircraft
- miscellaneous (hoaxes, reflections of lights on cloud, flares, fireworks, kites, lights on tall structures and photographic aberrations).

About 10 per cent of all reports could not be explained because of insufficient data.

To this list should be added a category called:

- psychological.

Psychological sources

Many would argue that anyone who reports seeing a UFO must be suffering from some abnormal psychology (that is, they are not sane). One of the Gallup Poll's standard questions on UFOs asks whether they are 'something real' or 'just people's imagination', and in the USA in 1966 48 per cent of those interviewed thought that UFOs are imaginary. These latter interviewees must have meant that UFO reporters are suffering from delusions (that is, they report as real, objects or sights which are not real). In fact this amounts to a conclusion that the reporters have suffered hallucinations (perception without external stimulus). It is easy to make this accusation, but less easy to justify it. Only a small proportion of the world population suffers from abnormal psychology and it certainly cannot account for more than a few UFO reports. On the whole, UFO reporters are no more psychopathological, fantasy prone and hypnotizable or less intelligent than normal (Spanos et al 1993). Any accusation of 'imagination' must be justified by medical reports or at least reasonable cause.

I have encountered only one report which seemed to have this cause; a Swedish UFO buff reported a landed spacecraft and aliens at Loch Ness. I concluded that he suffered a hallucination brought about by his preoccupation with the UFO myth (Campbell 1981c).

A wave of UFO reports in the USA during October 1973 was explained by amateur psychologists as being due to reaction to the stress that the country was then undergoing as a result of the Watergate inquiry, the Agnew scandal and the Middle East war. 'During a period of turbulence', said an astronomer (*sic*), 'people think of and turn to other things, that lead to a sort of near psychosis, which I think this all is' (*New Scientist*, 1 November 1973, p. 357). It only goes to show that astronomers should stick to astronomy.

An experimental psychologist thought that belief in UFOs must be explained as a psychological aberration, an attempt to satisfy our need to reach simple, understandable answers to the confusion around us. He claimed that 'if UFOs did not exist it would have been necessary to invent them' (Evans 1973:175). This may explain the UFO myth, but it does not explain UFO reports. The myth is invented, but most of the reports are not.

False association

Closely related to the psychological category are reports generated by false association or wrong interpretation. The latter may be described as a syndrome in which observers approach a situation with a mental set which leads them to misinterpret stimuli and/or associate two or more events or items of information which have no connection (other than via their mental set).

After it is believed that a UFO has landed in a certain area, investigators and others are likely to search the ground for evidence of the landing. Frequently they will find what they regard as evidence: imprints, marks, tracks, footprints, flattened grass, broken fences or trees, burned patches, etc. Usually this 'evidence' existed before the event and is entirely unconnected with it. Since the investigator may not be the first on the scene, some 'evidence' may have been produced by previous visitors, equally curious to see what can be found. Thus one investigator may regard as evidence a trace left by another investigator!

At least one major US report appears to have arisen because of a widespread failure of the public electricity supply at night. It appears that the reporter was then frightened by some natural light (probably astronomical), which could only be seen because of the unaccustomed darkness.

The incident which started the sequence of events reported in *The Janos People* (Johnson 1980) occurred as a family were returning from a funeral late at night in darkened countryside. The parents had previously seen the film *Close Encounters of the Third Kind*, and they appear to have made an association (mostly under subsequent hypnosis) between the film and sight of a bright astronomical object. Both Jupiter and Venus were setting at the time.

On hearing an unusual noise, or sensing an earthquake, most people will rush outside. If it is dark and the sky is clear they are most likely to see some astronomical objects, perhaps under unusual atmospheric conditions. It would be natural for them to assume that the objects (if they did not recognize them) were responsible for the noise, or that they had been produced by the earthquake. The images may have been seen on other occasions, but they were only reported (as UFOs) because the observers were forced out into the open by another unconnected incident. In the modern era, the initial stimulus can come from a radar screen or electronic surveillance equipment.

Reports of vehicle engine/light failures

An example of false association is the belief that UFOs can interfere with vehicle electrical circuits, causing engines and/or lights to fail. In order to test this idea the Condon Report team went so far as to subject a car to an intense DC magnetic field (as thought to be emitted by UFOs) to see if it would cause the car's engine to fail. They found that a field of 2 teslas (T) at the coil was needed to stop the engine, and that such a strong field permanently altered the state of magnetization of the car's body-shell. Since the body-shell magnetization pattern is standardized for each type of car, it is easy to test for changes to this pattern in cars alleged to have suffered interference by a UFO. They found no such change in the examples examined (Gillmor 1969:38).

It was later alleged that the Condon team should have examined the effect of an oscillating (AC) field and that such a field could have effects upon engines, radios and headlamps without altering the magnetic signature of the car body (McCampbell 1976:58). A decade earlier, a British experiment had shown that an oscillating current through a solenoid surrounding a car's HT coil (inducing a field of 0·04 T) did reduce engine power. However it was calculated that to produce this effect at the coil, the field intensity at a UFO 6 m away would need to be

0·25 T (Watts 1964). In fact (because a bipolar field falls off as the cube, not the square, of the distance) the field at the UFO would need to be 5 T. Watts's conclusion was criticized in the next issue of the *BUFORA Journal & Bulletin* and it was claimed that the field at the UFO would need to be 50 T. It was not determined whether or not oscillating fields would alter the car body's magnetic signature.

A scientist who believed in *inverted* magnetic fields, and that UFOs were powered by them, claimed that such fields were responsible for engine and/or lights failures (Burt 1970:69). NICAP (National Investigations Committee on Aerial Phenomena, USA) compared the engine failures with the effect of the electromagnetic pulse produced by a nuclear bomb (Hall 1964:76), and BUFORA published a special study of the phenomenon (Falla 1979).

Although some have been at a loss to explain these alleged failures of car electrical systems (Klass 1968:96-97), the simplest explanation is that the drivers involved unwittingly caused the engines to stall as they concentrated on some mysterious light. They then wrongly associated the failure with the light. In some cases the innocent failure of an engine or electrical system may have led the car's occupants to assume that it was caused by a UFO. Then, looking for the UFO they may have seen a mysterious light.

Such a conclusion is supported by what British Scientific Intelligence (BSI) discovered just before the Second World War. They heard rumours that something emitted by a new television tower erected on the summit of the Brocken mountain (near Feldberg in Germany) was able to paralyse internal combustion engines. It was alleged that tourists, driving their cars on the roads in the vicinity, found that their engines had ceased to operate. It was reported that a German Air Force sentry would then appear from the side of the road and tell the drivers that it was no use trying to get the car going again for the time being. The engines started later when the sentry told the drivers to try it. Not to be outdone and to puzzle the Germans, BSI started a similar rumour in Britain. The story spread rapidly, and they very soon received reports, with ever-increasing detail. The last they heard, a Quaker family was crossing Salisbury Plain when the engine of their car stopped. In due course a soldier appeared and told them that it would now start again, and it did.

Later the intelligence officers discovered that, when the site for the Brocken transmitter was being surveyed, trials were done by placing a transmitter at a promising spot, and then measuring the field strength that it would provide for radio signals in the area around it. Since the signals concerned were of high frequency, the receivers could easily be jammed by the unscreened ignition systems of the average motor car. Any car travelling through the area at the time of the trial would cause so much interference as to ruin the test. In Germany at that time, with its authoritarian regime, it was a simple matter to decide that no cars should run in the area at the relevant time, and so sentries were posted on all roads to stop the cars. After the 20 minutes or so of the test, the sentries would tell the drivers that they could proceed. Evidently the story of an engine-stopping ray arose from the drivers transposing the first appearance of the sentry and the stopping of the engine (Jones 1978:50, 84). Such transposition may account for stories of UFOs emitting similar rays or fields.

It has been suggested that engines can fail when the vehicle runs into a zone where a lightning leader stroke is preparing its upward climb and that the highly-charged state of the atmosphere can earth a vehicle's electrical system (Meaden 1993).

Reports of physiological effects

UFO reporters often claim that the UFO caused a physiological effect. These effects include a feeling of tension (as before a thunderstorm), popping ears (or earache), prickly skin, hairs standing on end, teeth vibrating, headaches, sore or watering eyes, sore throats, a burning or tingling sensation and paralysis. Some claim that the effects persist long after the incident. In one case the after-effects are alleged to include blisters, hair loss, dizziness, photosensitivity, and even cancer (see pp. 82-83).

Reporters often allege that these symptoms are caused by 'radiation'. One writer believes that microwaves emitted by UFOs are responsible (McCampbell 1976:76-88). Few seem to realize that these symptoms are typical human fear responses.

In one incident a witness felt a tingling sensation which began from his feet and ran upwards through his body until he was completely immobilized. He recovered when the object 'departed' (Fowler 1979:13). I have myself suffered this symptom and know it to be a sign of hyperventilation, a normal fear response; at the time I thought I was having a heart attack (Campbell 1990b).

Intense fear will be generated in observers who believe the UFO myth and that a UFO is close to them, or worse, approaching. They will then display various normal fear responses, attributing the responses to an influence from the UFO. Any persistent effects will likewise be attributed to such an influence. Various psychosomatic symptoms may appear as a result of their concern that they have been affected. Shock can sometimes result in partial or total hair loss (alopecia). There will be a tendency to attribute a subsequent illness (such as cancer) to the incident. In fact solid cancers take 10 years to appear.

Hoaxes

The source of deception *par excellence* is the hoax, a hazard for all investigators. Hoaxes are probably more prevalent where it is generally known that some group of people are looking for a particular phenomenon. This gives hoaxers an incentive and stimulus to produce what is sought, or at least what appears to be evidence for it. Many people probably believe that all or most UFO reports are hoaxes, but this is not true. Ufoists would claim that hoaxes prove the existence of genuine UFOs. On the other hand sceptics would claim that hoaxes can be modelled on the UFO myth (although that begs the question of the origin of the myth).

Extremely good UFO hoaxes can be perpetrated very easily, and by quite young people. In the USA, some youths wrapped themselves in aluminium foil and fashioned antennae out of old coat hangers. In this disguise, and with a flashing red light, they stopped motorists on a main highway. The hoax was repeated by others a few days later, and a police officer photographed such a 'creature', which ran away when he pursued it (Klass 1974:286). In another incident (actually a 'psychology experiment'), petrol was burned in circular patches to support a false story of a UFO landing (ibid.:72). Many hoaxes (mainly in the USA) have been accomplished by making a small hot-air balloon out of the light plastic covers used to protect newly dry-cleaned clothes. Juveniles have often rigged these with a candle at the base to provide both hot air and illumination. In 1981 I exposed a photographic hoax by a young resident of a children's home in Scotland. He had photographed a small, shiny, helium-filled balloon (Campbell 1985c).

A particularly audacious hoax was perpetrated in the 1970s by Eduard Meier, a one-armed Swiss mystic. Not only did he claim to have spoken to aliens from the Pleiades, and to have travelled to their planet, but he faked photographs of their ship (using small-scale models), flattened grass in circles to fake landings, produced odd scraps of metal as samples of the ship's hull and played weird noises on a tape recorder in woods near his home. He even fooled some American 'investigators' and the author of a book about the incident (Kinder 1987).

Several hoaxes have involved the production of material alleged to have fallen off UFOs, just as the coke sent to R V Jones was alleged to have fallen off a ghost-rocket.

The commonest type of UFO hoax is the fake photograph of a UFO. Many would argue that, because UFOs do not exist, all UFO photographs are fakes. This would be a mistake; some of the photographs may show unusual or genuinely new phenomena.

Hoax photographs are usually easy to recognize. The 'UFO' will appear all too solid, and it will be placed in a setting where its size cannot be determined. Usually hoaxers produce only one picture (because of the difficulty involved) and they usually keep it to themselves for some time (probably plucking up courage to release it), or they do not have the film developed immediately. He (I know of no female hoaxers) may also be vague about the date and time of the event. Several of these characteristics were displayed by Alex Birch from Mosborough near Sheffield (England).

In 1962, Birch (only 14 at the time) produced a rather out-of-focus picture of a group of saucer-shaped objects, which he claimed to have seen hovering motionless near his home in either February or March that year (later he decided on 4 March). He claimed that they were 400 m away and 150 m up, and that they emitted dazzling balls or blobs of light. They made no sound and zoomed away after a few seconds. Before they left he managed to take a picture with an old box camera. He left the film undeveloped for some weeks, and it was not until 20 June that the story (and the picture) appeared in the local press. Several accounts appeared in FSR, and Alex addressed a packed inaugural meeting of BUFORA in Sheffield on 22 September. Leonard Cramp, a hovercraft expert and author of a book on flying saucers, declared that the photographs (it seems there was more than one) were authentic and that it was inconceivable that either the boy or his father could have perpetrated a hoax. In August, Alex and his father visited the Air Ministry in London, where Alex was subjected to a sceptical interrogation lasting nearly three hours. Later the Ministry told his father that what Alex had photographed were probably cloud formations seen in unusual conditions (there was a temperature inversion) and aggravated by the smoke and haze over Sheffield (an industrial area). In October Alex appeared on BBC-TV. Ten years later (6 October 1972) Alex Birch admitted the hoax (on TV). He had painted the 'saucers' on a sheet of glass and photographed a background of trees through the glass (Bowen 1972).

A hoax photograph was produced by a Royal Canadian Air Force pilot (Childerhose) by doctoring a picture of storm clouds he took while on a record-breaking run across Canada in August 1956. The altered picture accompanied an article on flying saucers which the pilot wrote for a Montreal newspaper in 1966. For many years the picture was accepted as genuine, even by Philip J Klass, who used it in one of his books (Campbell 1988b).

A hoax can sometimes be too ready an explanation; it is not an explanation in itself and needs to be explained. An investigator needs to explain how and why a hoax was perpetrated. In order to assess the reliability and objectivity of ufoists, a controlled UFO hoax was conducted in the South of England in March 1970 (Simpson 1976). The hoax was more successful than the organizers anticipated (see p. 35).

Swamp gas

Many sceptics have claimed that some UFO reports are caused by sight of ignited swamp gas (methane). This phenomenon is usually called will-o'-the-wisp or ignis fatuus (foolish fire).

The most famous incident involved J Allen Hynek, who initially suggested it as a possible explanation for several reports near Ann Arbor (Michigan) in March 1966. He did this because the lights were reported above swamps (Story 1980:354).

However the existence of will-o'-the-wisp is doubtful. Although marshes and swamps certainly do emit gas, a mixture of methane and carbon dioxide, it is not self-igniting. In addition, the accounts of ignis fatuus are mostly inconsistent with a dull glowing gas in a bog. It is very likely that several other phenomena have been mistaken for will-o'-the-wisp (Mills 1980), although several of those listed by Mills are themselves doubtful and he omitted to mention astronomical objects. Because marshes and swamps tend to be flat and treeless, they often provide good views of the horizon; this makes it possible to see some distant light (even an astronomical body) above the swamp and believe that it is actually over the swamp.

Street lights

Puzzled by a 'large and yellowish' object in the sky, a Staffordshire couple reported the matter to the police. The object was still visible when the police officers arrived, and they took photographs. These photographs showed a large and variously shaped blob which was presumed to be the object reported. However investigation showed that the blob was a street lamp. The object reported had been the planet Mars, but it did not show up in the photographs (Hynek and Hennessey 1972).

'Earth lights'

Some believe that UFOs are illuminated plasmas generated by strain in (but not movement of) geological faults (Devereux 1982). This is a development of the belief by some scientists that earthquakes can produce lights. Experiments have shown that fracturing rocks produce sparks, and this might justify the belief that an earthquake can produce illumination (although the evidence is sparse and inconclusive). Some rocks, such as quartz, will produce electric polarization when subjected to strain (the piezoelectric effect), but there is no evidence that this can produce illumination, and certainly none that it can explain UFO reports. In particular, the advocates of this hypothesis have not been able to show a direct correlation between UFO reports and geological faults, nor have they been able to show that the faults they believe responsible were subjected to strain at the time (Campbell 1983b).

Aircraft

It is understandable that some reports of UFOs will be caused by sight of aircraft, especially at night when only the aircraft's lights can be seen. However it is often not realized that a light that appears to be stationary can be that of an aircraft flying directly towards the observer. This is particularly true if the aircraft is approaching an airfield and has its landing lights on. It has been suggested that not even pilots fully realize this fact (Haines 1980:192). Below a certain height, aircraft must show some landing lights, even in daylight. In daylight, short vapour trails (contrails) of jet aircraft can be sources of deception. Usually the aircraft responsible can be neither seen (without optical magnification) nor heard. I investigated two unusual cases involving aircraft in daylight. One was caused by a mirage of an air liner (Campbell 1987c), and one by burning fuel released from a damaged military jet (Campbell 1991). Plane surfaces on aircraft (for example, the tail fin) can sometimes reflect sunlight to produce a very bright light which makes the aircraft responsible invisible.

'Foo-fighters'

This is a term coined by Allied aircrews towards the end of the Second World War in Europe (the origin of the term was explained by Story 1981:42). They reported seeing, or being followed by, strange lights which they thought might be a new type of enemy weapon. Indeed, a major who reported that his B-17 was followed by a 'small amber disc' in December 1944 from Klagenfurt in Austria to the Adriatic Sea, was told by an intelligence officer that it was a 'new German fighter' (Hall 1964:19). Strangely the German aircrews reported similar sights and were equally suspicious.

Bomber crews in particular reported single-engined fighters with yellow lights in the nose, but over a long period when the Germans had no single-engined night fighters in the area. BSI could only suggest aberrations under the stress of operations, or misinterpretations of genuine phenomena.

The same objects were reported from the Japanese war theatre and (later) from Korea. A special US mission to Korea saw no such 'fighters', although they did identify one such object as the Moon (Menzel and Taves 1977:55).

Almost certainly these 'foo fighters' were astronomical objects, usually bright planets at low altitude. During the Japanese war in 1945, US bomber crews often mistook Venus for a 'ball of fire' which followed them. Some even opened fire on it (Klass 1974:90). After seeing an astronomical mirage over Alaska (see below) Donald Menzel was able to identify Venus as the most frequent cause of the famous sightings from the Korean War theatre in the early 1950s (Menzel and Taves 1977:135). My own analysis of the few reports which give details confirms that bright stars or constellations were responsible.

Ball lightning

It is sometimes alleged that UFO reports are caused by sight of ball lightning, usually thought to be a ball of ionized air (plasma). This idea begs the question of the existence of ball lightning and merely substitutes one unknown phenomenon for another.

There is no authenticated photograph, film or video of ball lightning, no theory exists to explain all its reported behaviour and characteristics, and it has not been created in the laboratory for longer than about 1 s. It is possible that some reports of ball lightning are caused by sight of astronomical objects (see below). I have shown that at least one report of ball lightning was caused by sight of the rising Venus, or a mirage of it (Campbell 1988a). It has been noted that a small percentage of UFO reports are so similar to a certain class of ball lighting reports that they must both refer to the same 'imperfectly understood physical phenomena [*sic*]' (Uman 1971:133).

Lately it has been suggested that giant plasmas, associated with the vortices thought to be responsible for some corn circles, might be responsible for some UFO reports. At present there is insufficient evidence to justify belief in such plasmas.

Unusual sources of deception

These have included owls illuminated by city lights, headlamps reflecting off overhead power cables, fireflies, rocket launches, chemical releases in the upper atmosphere (see plate 3:1), powered model aircraft and parachute flares. One persistent set of reports was explained (not very convincingly) as insects emitting light after being stimulated by an electric field (Callahan and Mankin 1978). The latest source is the use of lasers projected upwards to form patterns on low-lying clouds as entertainment.

Plate 3:1 A barium cloud release over the Western Isles of Scotland at about 2150L (2050Z) on 7 September 1971. The cloud was about 112 km high and dull yellow in colour (*The Scotsman*).

Astronomical objects

Most bright astronomical objects are sources of deception, especially planets and bright stars. However the Sun and Moon are sometimes such sources. On 13 October 1917, at Fatima in Portugal, the Sun appeared to change colour, rotate, and hurl itself towards the Earth (Campbell 1989b). Some ufoists claim that these manoeuvres were undertaken by a UFO (not the Sun).

A resident of Kilrenny in Fife (Scotland) was puzzled by a 'large orange object just above the sea' which, he said, was 'too large to be the moon and [was] the wrong colour'. Because he gave the date and time I was able to show that he had indeed seen the Moon.

The naked-eye planets (Mercury, Venus, Mars, Jupiter and Saturn) are all sources of deception, although rarely Mercury because of its proximity to the Sun. Venus is known to be the cause of very many, if not most UFO reports.

But why should observers be deceived by such common sights? The explanation lies in the altitude at which these objects are seen and an optical illusion. Stars and planets high in the sky are accepted as such;

that is where they are expected to be. But the lower in the sky the object is (or the smaller its altitude), the more likely it is to be reported as a UFO. A bright astronomical object seen near the horizon can easily be mistaken for some craft in the atmosphere. If the observer does not consider, or rejects, an astronomical hypothesis, then his mind will be forced to consider the alternative (that it is a nearby object in the atmosphere). The lack of distance clues helps in this respect. There is also the effect of an illusion created by the mind and most commonly described as the 'moon illusion' (see p. 29); the object appears to be larger than it really is

Conventional astronomy believes that viewing (the ease with which an object can be seen) decreases with altitude and that, near the horizon, atmospheric extinction makes it almost impossible to see stars. Extinction can be caused by dust in the atmosphere; at low altitude this dust will obstruct much of the light. Extinction can also be caused by the reddening produced by Rayleigh scattering; the molecules of the air scatter shorter wavelengths preferentially (that is why the sky is blue) and cause astronomical objects to look redder (and so dimmer) than they really are. This explains the reddening of the Sun and Moon when they are near the horizon. However the amount of dust in the atmosphere varies greatly. Sometimes there may be very little and extinction may be small. Consequently it should not be assumed that it is always impossible to see bright stars at low altitude, and the belief that it is should not be allowed to stand in the way of an astronomical explanation for a UFO report.

From the surface of the Earth astronomical objects are seen through a thick and turbulent atmosphere. This interferes with their appearance via two mechanisms, refraction and scintillation.

The light from all astronomical sources is refracted to some extent on entering the atmosphere if its path is not perfectly vertical. The effect is to make such objects appear rather higher in the sky than they really are. Displacement is at a maximum near the horizon; at 0° altitude it is normally +35 arcminutes (0·6°).

Elevated observers (for example thoseee a celestial object displaced even more than 0·6° when they see it bel in aircraft) can sow the horizontal plane. This is because the light not only has to travel down through the atmosphere to the horizon between itself and the observers, but it has to travel back up again to the aircraft (see figure 3:1). The rays are refracted in the same direction whether they go up or down through the atmosphere. Because the density of the atmosphere decreases with height, refraction of extended sources, such as the Sun or Moon, is differential, causing a flattening of the disc at the base. Different wavelengths also suffer differential refraction; shorter wavelengths are refracted more than longer wavelengths. In this way the light of a point source, such as a star, can be spread out vertically in a spectrum. But this does not place the blue light below the red; figure 3:2 shows how the red light appears below the blue. Even planets can display this colour separation (see colour plate 3:2).

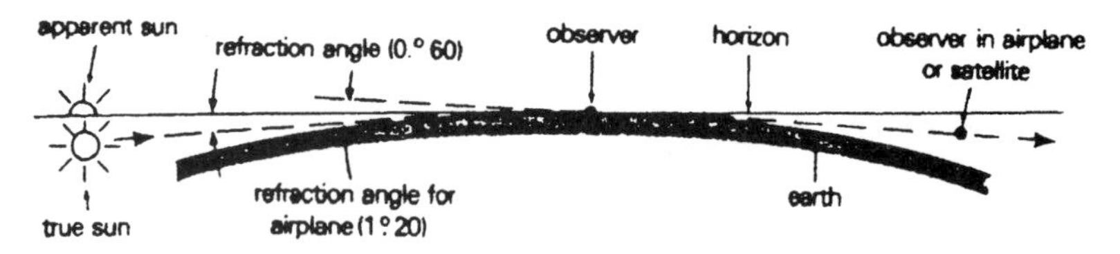

Fig. 3:1 The normal effect of the Earth's atmosphere on the position of an astronomical body (here the Sun) seen near the horizon, or even below it. For an observer on the surface of the Earth (at sea level) refraction lifts the image about 0·6°. For an observer at high altitude in an aircraft or in a satellite refraction is doubled (to 1·2°) (Meinel and Meinel 1983:13).

Because astronomical bodies are such a great distance away, their light arrives as a series of almost parallel rays (or plane wave-fronts) over the whole Earth. Naturally rays which are obstructed by the Earth do not reach observers. However, other rays, which would not have been seen by the observers in other circumstances, can reach them. In particular those rays which strike the atmosphere tangentially can, if conditions are suitable, be refracted or ducted around the Earth to the observers. In this way they can see an image of an astronomical body which is actually below their horizon. Because this is not a direct image, it may be described as a mirage (see below). The temperature gradient necessary for a ray to follow the Earth's curvature is +11·6 °C/100 m (see figure 3:3). Such a rise in temperature with height only occurs in a temperature inversion.

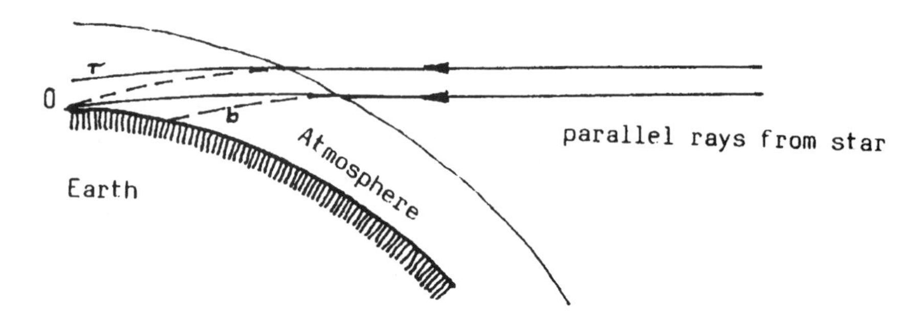

Fig. 3:2 A diagram showing how refraction will spread the image of a star when seen at low altitude; the red (r) part of its spectrum appears below the blue (b) part. The red and blue images come from separate but parallel rays which converge at the observer (O).

The distance which the light must travel around the surface of the Earth (d) is related to the angle of the object below the horizon (ϕ) by the equation:

$$d = \phi r$$

(where r is the radius of the Earth and ϕ is in radians).

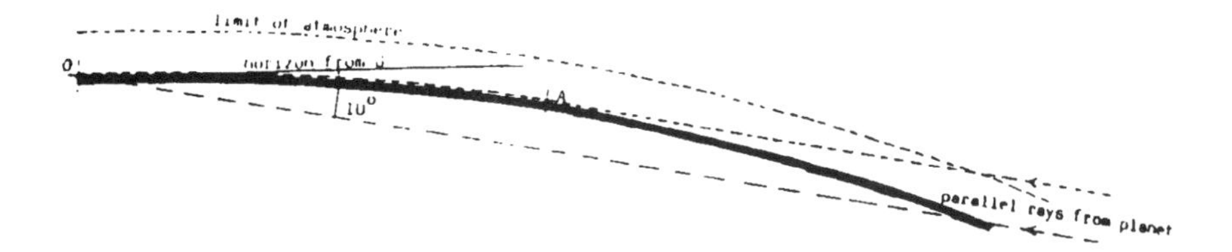

Fig. 3:3 A diagram showing how light from a planet which is 10° below the horizon from O can reach the observer at O by continual refraction (or ducting) around the Earth's surface (from A to O).

Scintillation is what astronomers call twinkling. It is caused by turbulence in the atmosphere, where minor refraction takes place between air pockets at different densities. Because of the greater depth of atmosphere involved, it too is at a maximum near the horizon. As a result, a bright star can appear to jump about, flashing different colours and/or flashing on and off, as if signalling. Only with great difficulty did an American scientist convince a UFO reporter that what the latter thought was a spaceship signalling to him was a star close to the horizon scintillating through red, green and white (Salisbury 1967). Hynek identified a brilliant multicoloured object, 'chased' by a pilot over Northern Michigan on 29 July 1952, as the star Capella scintillating as it reached lower culmination on the northern horizon (Hynek 1953). Viezee claimed that the average frequency of scintillation is about 10 Hz, a frequency to which the human eye (mind?) is most sensitive (Gillmor 1969:645).

Because the scattering effect of the air molecules is a maximum in the direction of the incident light (from the Sun) and in the opposite direction, and a minimum in the plane at right angles to the direction of the incident light, a clean atmosphere will show a band of deeper blue from horizon to horizon at right angles to the direction of the Sun. Stars are seen more easily in daylight or dusk in this 'line of darkness' (Minnaert 1940:104).

Elevated observers (for example, those in an aircraft), whose horizon is depressed, can see astronomical objects which would be invisible to a surface observer. The angle (in degrees) by which the horizon is depressed (α) is related to the height of the observer above the Earth's surface (h) by the equation:

$$\alpha = \arccos 1/[1 + (h/r)]$$

(where r is the radius of the Earth).

Only the brightest stars are likely to cause UFO reports; the first magnitude stars are listed in Table 3:1. The Air Almanac lists 57 bright stars, including nearly all the named stars and those with which the constellations are identified.

Table 3:1 The First Magnitude Stars
(in brightness order)

common name	Bayer designation	apparent magnitude	colour §
Sirius	α CMa	-1·47	A1
Canopus	α Car	-0·71	F0
Alpha Centauri*	α Cen	-0·1	G2
Arcturus	α Boo	-0·06	K2
Vega	α Lyr	0·03	A0
Rigel	β Ori	0·08	B8
Capella	α Aur	0·09	G8
Procyon	α CMi	0·34	F5
Achernar	α Eri	0·49	B5
Beta Centauri*	β Cen	0·61	B1
Altair	α Aql	0·75	A7
Aldebaran	α Tau	0·78	K5
Alpha Crucis*	α Cru	0·80	B2
Betelgeuse	α Ori	0·85	M2
Antares	α Sco	0·92	M2
Spica	α Vir	0·98	B1
Pollux	β Gem	1·15	K0
Fomalhaut	α PsA	1·16	A3
Deneb	α Cyg	1·26	A2
Beta Crucis*	β Cru	1·28	B0

* Alternative name as follows:
(α Cen = Rigel Kent; β Cen = Hadar; α Cru = Acrux; β Cru = Mimosa).
§ According to the Harvard classification of spectral class, stars are colour coded as follows: B = blue; A = white; F = green; G = yellow; K= orange; M= red.

Mirages

I have shown that the atmosphere can distort the appearance and shift the position of astronomical objects. However there is a particularly extreme form of distortion which lies at the heart of the hypothesis expounded in this book. It is a distortion and/or displacement which applies to any bright source near the horizon, whether or not it is extraterrestrial, and so it qualifies as a major source of deception. I refer to mirages.

A mirage is usually defined as an effect caused by total reflection of light at the upper surface of shallow layers of hot air in contact with the ground, the appearance being that of pools of water in which inverted images of more distant objects are seen. This is the *inferior mi-*

rage, which occurs where a very hot plane surface, such as a desert or a roadway, heats a layer of air very close to it.

The temperature gradient in the thermocline (the region of rapidly changing temperature) between this hot layer and cooler air above it can be so steep as to constitute a discontinuity. This discontinuity acts as a mirror (or caustic) for light striking it above a critical (large) angle to the normal. In this way one can see distant objects such as the sky or vehicles reflected in the surface (see figure 3:4).

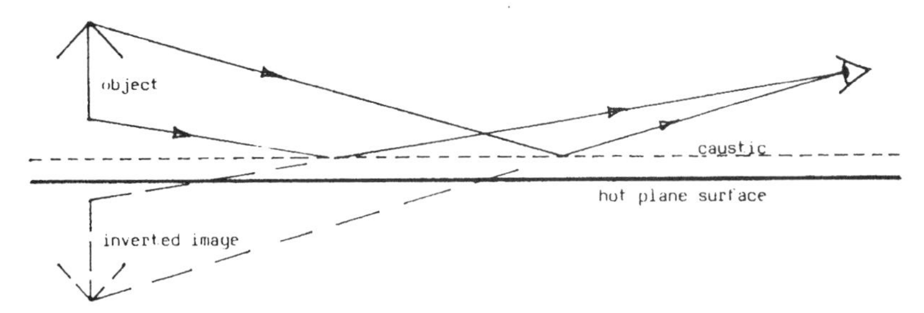

Fig. 3:4 How an inferior mirage is formed. Light travelling at a very small angle to the hot surface is reflected from the discontinuity (caustic) in the thermocline, so producing inverted images of distant objects. Vertical scale exaggerated for clarity.

However we are concerned only with the *superior mirage*, that is, a mirage seen above the source or object being reflected. A superior mirage is caused by light being reflected off the underside of a discontinuity in a temperature inversion (where a layer of warm air overlies cold air) (see figure 3:5). In this way an inverted image of some bright but distant ground source may be seen in the sky. Naturally this must be considered a major source of deception. Where the source is already in the sky (for example, an astronomical object) the image may be elevated, considerably so where the thermocline is curved. Non-horizontal thermoclines may displace the image laterally, and moving thermoclines may produce a moving image. Because an inversion forms in a fluid (air), the image can take various shapes and alter its shape with time. Consequently superior mirages can be unusual and protean.

Not all mirages are reflections; some are caused by abnormal refraction (as discussed above). If a temperature inversion forms over a very wide area (say over a cold ocean or ice field), and the temperature gradient is strong enough, light can be ducted around the curvature of the Earth, so allowing one to see an image of an astronomical object that is below the horizon. A Novaya Zemlya mirage is one where an astronomical body (at Novaya Zemlya, where it was first observed, it was the Sun) is seen to set or rise when it is well below the horizon. The light in such a mirage can be ducted for hundreds of kilometres and the image may be distorted. It may also change shape and/or colour. However it can be very bright; the light is ducted as if through a window in the atmosphere (Lehn and German 1981).

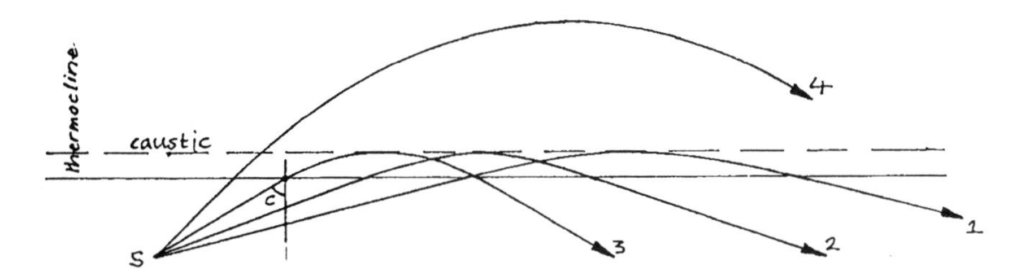

Fig. 3:5 How rays from a source (S) are reflected by the caustic in the thermocline of a temperature inversion if they strike it at or above the critical angle (c). Ray 4 enters at below the critical angle and so penetrates the caustic and undergoes normal gradual refraction.

Light striking the discontinuity below a critical (large) angle to the normal, will not be reflected, but will pass through it and be refracted (see figure 3:5). An observer above the thermocline may then see a bright source elevated above its normal position.

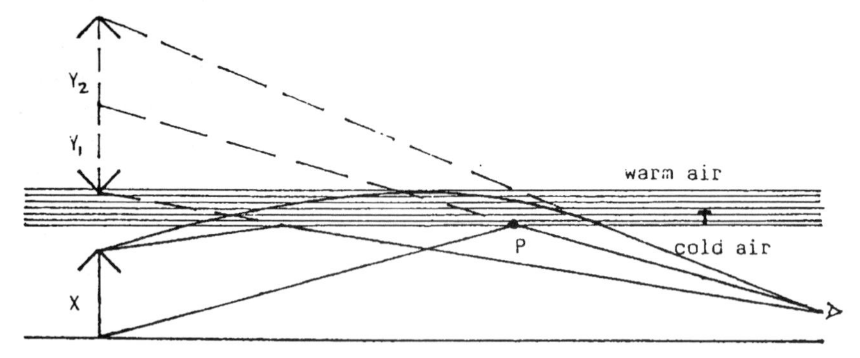

Fig. 3:6 One means by which the twin images of a mirage can be formed. Image Y_1 is formed by reflection from the discontinuity in the thermocline (T) of the inversion. At P reflection ceases because the critical angle is not exceeded and the observer sees a refracted (upright) image (Y_2). It can be seen that as the height between the object (X) and the inversion increases, the two images will merge, eventually disappearing. Conversely, as the height decrease, Y_1 and Y_2 separate. If T is very shallow, Y_2 will not appear. Drawn with exaggerated vertical scale for clarity.

Mirage images can consist of double images, with an upright image above the inverted one. The cause of the upright image is not known for certain, but one explanation is that it results from light penetrating the thermocline and being bent back down towards the observer (as shown in figure 3:5). Where the thermocline is low over the source, the separation of the two images will be large. However, as the height of the thermocline increases, the two images can merge, making it difficult to recognize the image (see figure 3:6). There is some reason to believe that each mirage image can split in the plane of the inversion, creating two separate images; if this occurs when there are already two images, the result will be four images of the same object!

Mirage images can be greatly enlarged and/or distorted by atmospheric lens effects. Menzel exhibited a diagram showing how both magnification and double images could be formed, but only for observers located at the inversion layer (see figure 3:7). Plate 3:3 shows a photograph of a superior mirage exhibiting both enlargement and distortion.

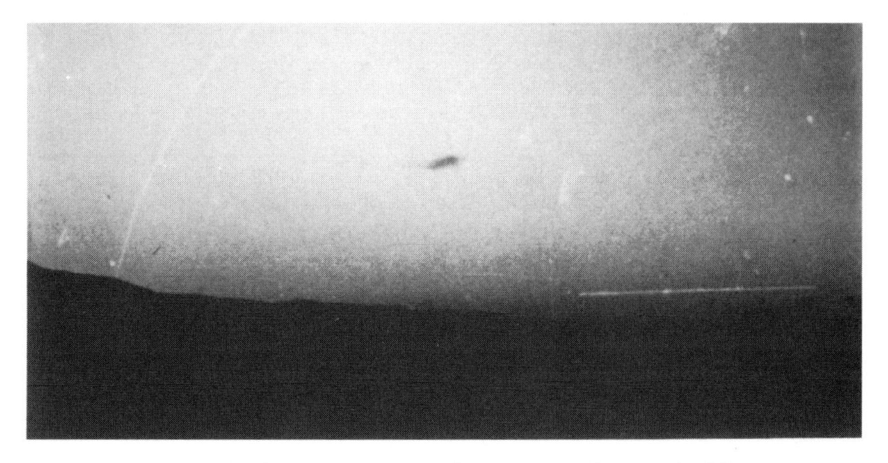

Plate 3:3 A photograph of a superior mirage of a snow-capped mountain 95 km away. Photo by Bransby Clarke (Campbell 1987b)

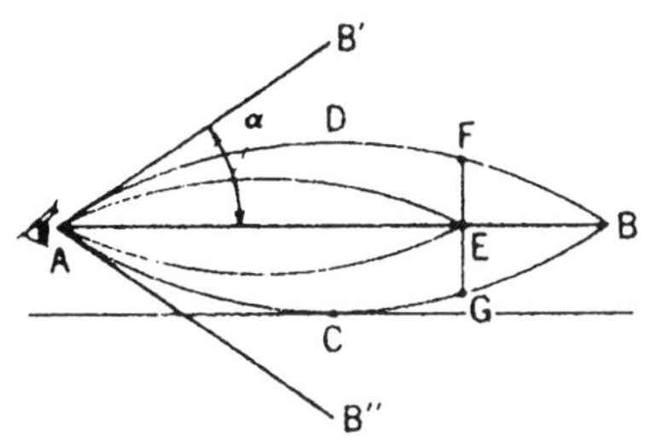

Fig. 3:7 Menzel's diagram of mirage formation. A is the observer's eye, 10 m above the ground, and B is some object 26 km away, also 10 m above the ground. The distribution of atmospheric density* acts like a convex cylindrical lens. B is seen twice, once from above and once from below, along the respective paths BDA and BCA, appearing in the directions B' and B", separated by the angle B'AB" (about 10' in this case). A point intermediate between A and B, such as E, will also show twice, but at slightly smaller angles of separation. Between B' and B", therefore, will appear images of all the objects along the line AEB. The more distant the object, the greater the magnification. Thus the line FEG will appear to subtend the angle B'AB" (Reprinted by permission of the publishers from *Flying Saucers* by Donald H Menzel, Cambridge, Mass.: Harvard University Press, Copyright © 1953 by the President and Fellows of Harvard College). See Menzel 1953:309.

*In this case it is assumed that the temperature decreases upwards to 10 m where a temperature inversion occurs. It is assumed that from 10-20 m the temperature increases at the rate of 2×10^{-5} deg. C/m.

As Menzel observed, the more distant the object, the greater the magnification (because of the greater size of the atmospheric lens). Sources outside the atmosphere may be subject to the greatest magnification; among these, the commonest are astronomical sources. It may be expected therefore that the largest and most common mirages will be those of astronomical objects at low altitude. Magnification also increases as the source aligns with the thermocline (for the reasons Menzel explained). This means that, as the disc of an astronomical object approaches the thermocline, the two images enlarge and merge until they form a classic 'flying saucer' shape (see figure 3:8). The two images may not always be the same size.

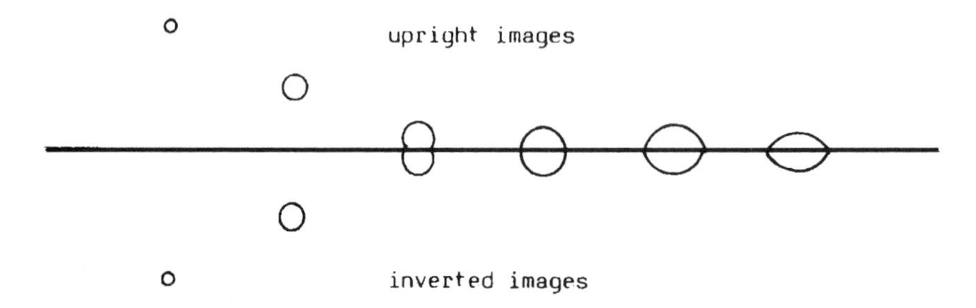

Fig. 3:8 Diagram showing how the two images of an astronomical body in a mirage can appear with different separation. As the images merge and enlarge they form a classic 'flying saucer'.

Assuming no transmission losses, the brightness of the magnified image of an extended object (such as a planet) is equal to that of the naked eye image (Sidgwick 1979:6). In fact, atmospheric absorption may greatly reduce the brightness of objects near the horizon. However, short wavelengths (for example, blue light) are absorbed more than long wavelengths (red light), and a dusty atmosphere will absorb more light that a clean one. Consequently the degree of absorption is highly variable. For any given magnification, the larger the lens (aperture) the brighter the image. Point sources (such as stars) can appear brighter when magnified, allowing them to be seen in daylight. In all cases, magnification darkens the sky background, making it easier to see astronomical images (ibid.:8).

It follows that, in a mirage, the magnified image of a star in daylight should be bright, and that the corresponding image of a planet should be dull (although seeming bright at night). If the intensity falls below that of the sky then a dark object will be seen. If the intensity is higher than that of the sky then a bright object will be seen. The 'brightness' of the image will depend on the contrast (see chapter 2). Darkening of the image does not preclude the occasional bright patch or flash as a result of fluctuations in brightness as a result of scintillation.

Some mirage images of astronomical objects may display clusters of lights, perhaps multiple images of the object. It is common for mirage images to shimmer. The enlargement of an astronomical object in a mirage will make its intrinsic colour more apparent, although differential refraction may produce several different colours at once, spatially separated.

In a statement submitted to a Symposium on UFOs organized by a committee of the US House of Representatives (to which he was not invited), Menzel explained how strange an astronomical mirage could appear:

> Sometimes a layer of warm air, sandwiched between two layers of cold air, can act as a lens, projecting a pulsating, spinning, vividly colored, saucer-like image of a planet. Pilots, thinking they were dealing with a nearby flying object, have often tried to intercept the image, which evades all attempts to cut it off. The distances may seem to change rapidly, as the star fades or increases in brightness. Actual 'dog fights' have been recorded between confused military pilots and a planet. I myself have observed this phenomenon of star mirage. It is both realistic and frightening [Roush 1968:200].

The various forms that an astronomical mirage can take are well illustrated by figure 3:9, although the typical double saucer is predominant. The idea that UFO reports are caused by sight of mirages may be described as the Mirage Hypothesis (MH), or, in the case of astronomical mirages, the Astronomical Mirage Hypothesis (AMH). Testing the AMH requires some special data and poses some particular problems which are discussed in Appendix 3.

Unfortunately there is no definitive work on the subject of mirages and it is a rather neglected area of study. Indeed, textbook explanations are often incorrect. Theorists are divided on the mechanisms involved and there have not been enough observations (including photographs) to allow a clear and comprehensive theory to evolve. Not all optical physicists would agree with my account above.

Criticism of the Astronomical Mirage Hypothesis

Smith (undated) pedantically and mischievously claimed that stars are point sources and that their images cannot be expanded. He claimed that all powerful telescopes do is to produce a diffraction pattern (the Airy disc surrounded by concentric rings of light). In fact, for all practical purposes, astronomers regard this pattern as the image. If the images of astronomical objects could not be magnified, telescopes would be useless. In any case, the diffraction pattern is an artefact of telescopes and would not appear in the atmosphere. While the images of stars are small to the naked eye, they are not without angular size. Measurement of Vega showed that it subtends an angle of 0·00370 arcseconds (Brown 1964). Smith allowed that planets have angular size and that this size could be increased by atmospheric refraction near the horizon. However he would not allow the size to increase to that reported for UFOs, and noted that the intensity of the image must decrease and that haze near the horizon would obscure the image. These objections have been dealt with above.

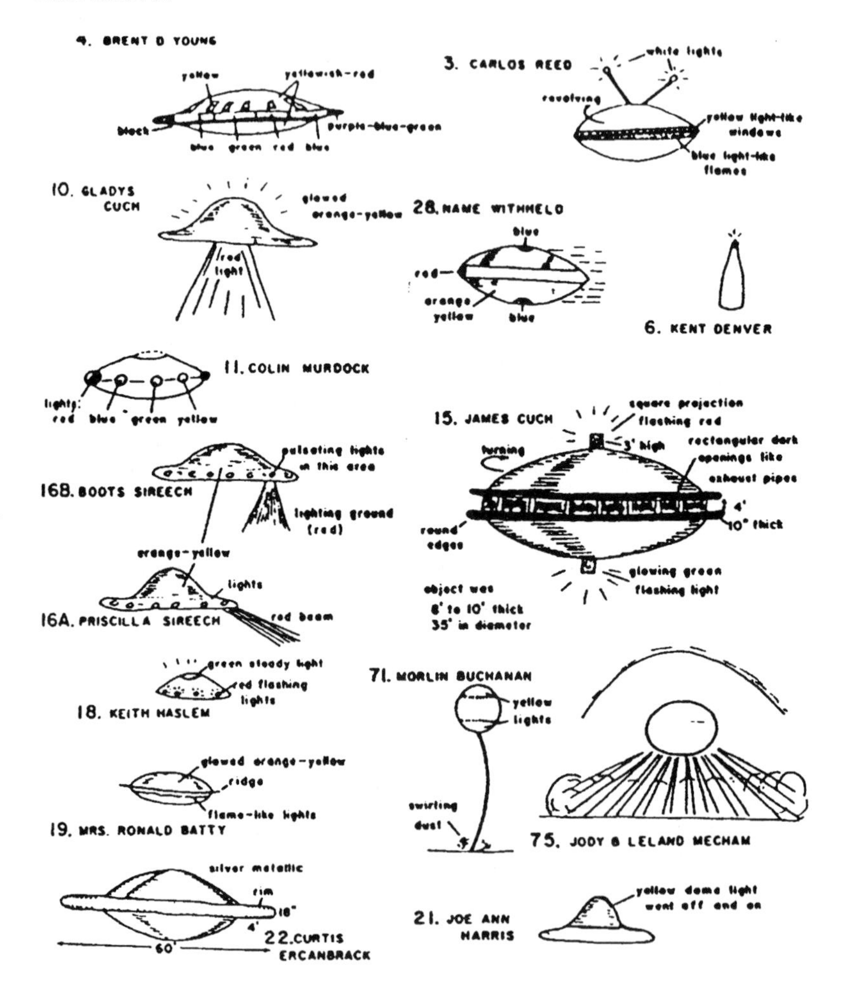

Fig. 3:9 Fifteen drawings of objects reported by people living in the Uintah Basin in Utah (1965-70), as collected by Joseph Junior Hicks and published by Frank B Salisbury. Because of lack of azimuth, most cannot be identified, although they are most probably mirages of astronomical objects. No. 75 can be identified as Jupiter (Salisbury 1974:Fig. 2).

Smith also claimed that astronomical images are fixed (at least for the few minutes of a sighting) and cannot move about the sky. Of course this is true, provided the image is not a reflection off a mobile and/or curved inversion layer (see above).

Observation of an astronomical mirage

Professor Donald Menzel was a world-famous astronomer and director of the Harvard College Observatory. He was also a great debunker of the UFO myth. It is ironic therefore that he was one of the few scientists to see what others would have described as a UFO. In fact his account is unique.

In 1955, when Menzel was a civilian scientist with the rank of Commander in the US Navy, the USAF asked him to go to Alaska to study the aurora borealis, and in particular to evaluate problems they were having with radio communications on polar flights. The investigation (code-named 'Ptarmigan') required daily flights from Fairbanks over the North Pole to study weather conditions within the Arctic Circle. These flights were undertaken in a battered relic of the Second World War, a Boeing B-29 Superfortress, manned by a crew of ten, plus two airmen trained to make radiosonde studies and other observations of atmospheric conditions. Menzel made the thirteenth member of the crew.

Shortly before dawn on 3 March 1955, this aircraft, carrying Menzel, was returning on a roughly south-east course somewhere between Point Barrow and Bering Strait. According to Menzel, most of the flight was at a height of 6000 m, but if his calculation of the distance to the horizon (320 km) is correct the aircraft must have been at about 8000 m. Menzel and the meteorologists were in the aft pressurized compartment with Menzel seated in what he called 'the western bomb blister'. This was actually a gun-siting station in a transparent blister on the side of the aircraft. Since he had a view towards the south-west horizon 'in the vicinity of the Bering Strait', he must have been seated in the starboard blister. The sky was clear, with brilliant stars.

Suddenly Menzel saw a bright object shoot in at tremendous speed from the horizon, directly towards the aircraft! His first thought was that it was a meteor or a fireball, and he instinctively ducked. However the object came to a 'sudden skidding stop' about 100 m away (as he thought), thereafter riding along with the aircraft, pacing it and even moving up and down with it. It was flashing red and green lights and had something that looked like a lighted propeller on top. It had a silvery metallic sheen. Clearly it was a flying saucer!

Menzel could scarcely believe his eyes and he thought he might be hallucinating (they had been flying for almost 17 hours). He took off his spectacles, rubbed his eyes and checked for internal reflections. The strange object persisted and he had to accept that it really was outside the aircraft. To his surprise, he found that the object subtended an angle less than that of the eraser on the end of his pencil when held at arm's length. This meant that, if it was 100 m away, it was only about 40 cm in diameter. He then thought it might be one of the radiosonde parachutes that had somehow become caught on the aircraft. However it was nearly 30 minutes since the last release. Just as he was about to call one of the meteorologists, the object flew away and disappeared over the horizon within about 2 s. Its acceleration was instantaneous and enormous. He calculated that it had travelled at about 160 km/s towards the Soviet Union. Now he really was concerned. Was it a Soviet spy device? As he kept his eyes fixed on the point where it had disappeared it suddenly returned, just as before but brighter.

Suddenly Menzel decided that he knew what the object was and that he could explain a great many similar reports (some from the Korean war theatre). It was a mirage of Sirius, the brightest star in the heavens. He believed that Sirius, just below the horizon, was raised by the mirage and distorted into a saucer shape (he did not actually describe the shape of the object and I have seen no sketch). The flashing lights were caused by scintillation and the rushing backwards and forwards was caused by the light being cut off by a mountain in Siberia. The object had appeared to follow the aircraft's every movement because its position remained constant in relation to the aircraft. Later he found that the radiosondes had revealed the existence of a temperature inversion, the necessary cause of the mirage. He was certain that the object was Sirius and claimed to have confirmed it when it briefly 'rose' in the west because of the southwards movement of the aircraft. He boasted that 'only someone familiar with the constellations could have identified the object'.

Menzel gave full details of the incident in two of his books (Menzel and Boyd 1963:60-62; Menzel and Taves 1977:133-135). It is unfortunate and curious that he did not write an article about the incident for a scientific journal. The case is recorded in USAF files as solved, but his identification was later questioned by meteorologist James McDonald, who thought the object was a 'real UFO'. I also question Menzel's identification.

Figure 3:10 shows the probable route of the aircraft and its probable position (70°N; 160°W). At that point on that day (at a height of 6000 m) dawn came at 1739Z. If only Menzel had looked at his wrist-watch we would not need to guess what he meant by 'shortly before dawn', but I will assume 1730Z. Whatever my assumption, the object could not have been Sirius, which was over 30° below the horizon in the north-north-west. So much for familiarity with the constellations (professional astronomers are often unfamiliar with the sky). What then did he see?

Almost certainly Menzel was correct in identifying the object as an astronomical mirage. Unfortunately he misidentified the object involved. There was a first magnitude star near the horizon in the south-west. Spica (magnitude 0·98) lay about 1° above the horizon on an azimuth of 240°. However there is another candidate, which was nearly twice as bright as Spica; the planet Saturn (magnitude 0·3) lay about 3·5° above his horizon to the south-south-west (azimuth 212°). If the object he saw was Spica, why did he not also report seeing Saturn, which was higher in the sky and further forward? The answer must be that the object he saw *was* Saturn. Menzel's idea that he was looking out towards the USSR may be incorrect; the mountain involved may have been in Alaska. Scintillation is certainly more typical of stars than planets, but Spica is a blue star which should have produced some blue flashes. It is unlikely that the slow speed of the aircraft (560 km/h) could have given it sufficient southward movement to compensate for the setting of Spica. However it might just catch up with the more southerly Saturn. If we assume that, 30 minutes later, the aircraft was at 68°N and 155°W, then Saturn was still above Menzel's horizon while Spica was below it. Evidently Menzel saw a mirage of Saturn.

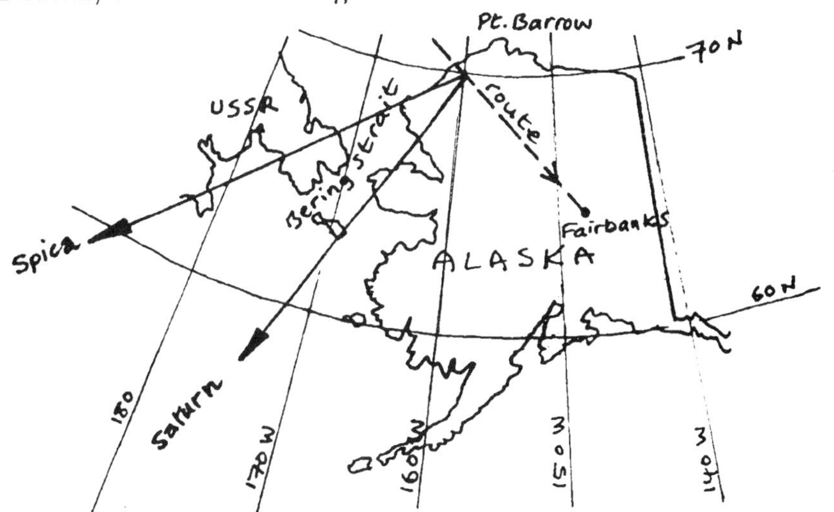

Fig. 3:10 The probable route of Menzel's aircraft, its probable position at the time of his sighting of the mirage and the azimuths of two bright astronomical bodies near the horizon.

Menzel's error of identification is puzzling, but only a minor issue. The more important point is that a responsible and eminent scientist observed how the atmosphere can cause a bright astronomical object (in this case subtending an angle of only 17·4 arcseconds) to appear to be a structured craft only a few hundred metres away. Menzel's estimate of the object's angular size (0·3°) implies that the image of Saturn was magnified by a factor of 62! It is not generally recognized that mirage images can be so enlarged. Nor is it common knowledge that a mirage of an astronomical object can display the peculiar features and appearance reported by Menzel. His surprise at the small angular size indicates that it appeared to be larger, an optical illusion often ignored in analysis of UFO reports.

Although Menzel wrote extensively about the UFO phenomenon and often cited mirages, including those of astronomical objects, as mechanisms which can produce images responsible for UFO reports, he frequently failed to apply the lesson he learned on his polar mission. I shall show that the AMH can explain UFO reports which have defied all other rational explanation.

Reaction to explanations

Rarely is a sceptical investigator thanked for his rational explanation for a UFO report; I believe that it has happened to me only once. Usually my explanations are received with disbelief; in one case I received abuse. Most UFO reporters want their preconceptions endorsed.

Surprisingly I have found sceptics as unreceptive. While ufoists tend to accept a report at face value, sceptics tend to reject a report at almost any cost. The latter will often adopt the first explanation that seems even slightly plausible. They will then not let go of that hypothesis when faced with its defects or its inability to explain the report. Where, as in several case described in this book, the explanation involves new or little known science, sceptics will reject the explanation. Not only is there a UFO myth; there is a counter UFO myth, one in which the witnesses are either liars or hoaxers, or unable to recognize the simplest celestial bodies.

Plate 4:3 Suzette Quick's painting of the object she and her family saw 'sitting' on Chactonbury Downs one evening in 1968 (Anon. 1969). It appears to be a mirage of Mars (which must have been just above the crest of the hill, not below it). ▶

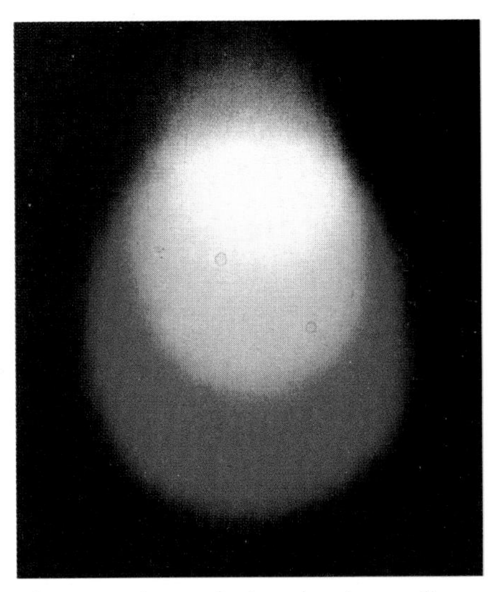

Plate 3:2 Atmospheric refraction as Venus nears the horizon. The different sizes of the coloured images are due to the fact that different wavelengths come to a focus at different positions in the telescope. Photo by Vatican Observatory.

Plate 4:1 Bernard Pobiner's photograph of what was later identified as a 'UFO' over the Cabot Strait off Nova Scotia. In fact it was most probably a mirage of the moon (with an accidental trace across the film).

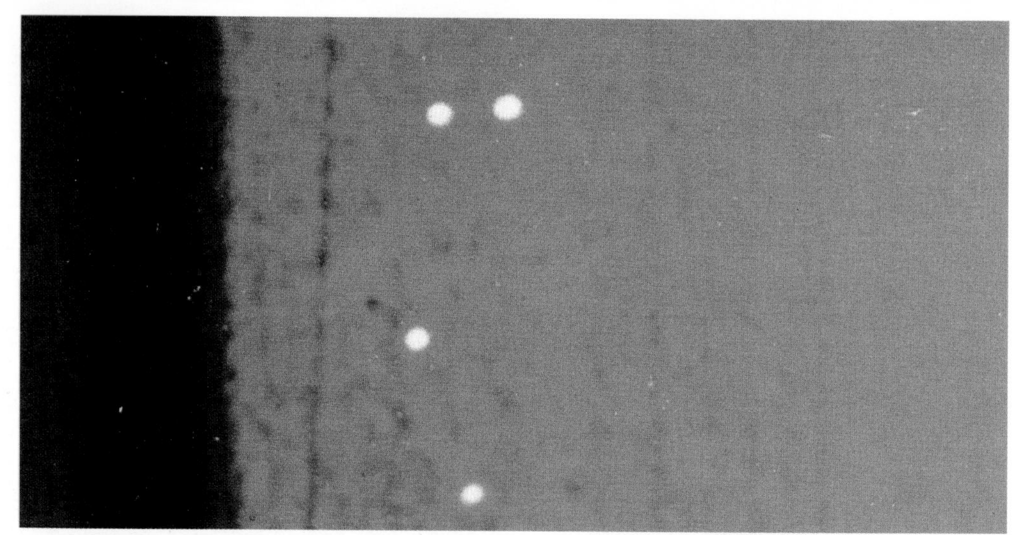

Plate 4:10 Part of a frame from the Tremonton cine film (Story 1980). It probably shows multiple stellar mirages.

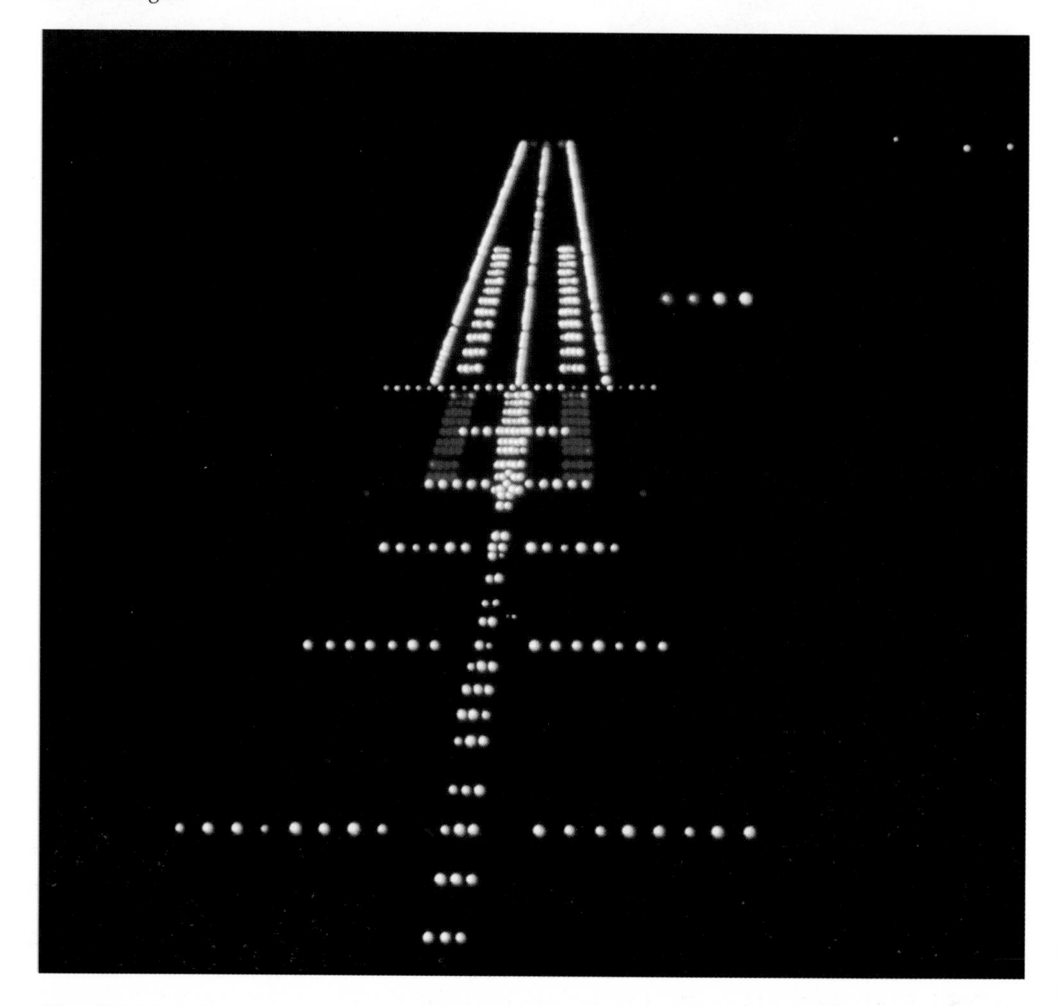

Plate 11:1 Typical modern runway approach lighting pattern. Approach lights are set to an elevation of 5.5°. Sometimes the centre line barrettes are omitted (copyright British Airports Services Ltd.)

Plate 4:2 A painting of a object seen in Tayside (Scotland). It probably shows a mirage of Mars.

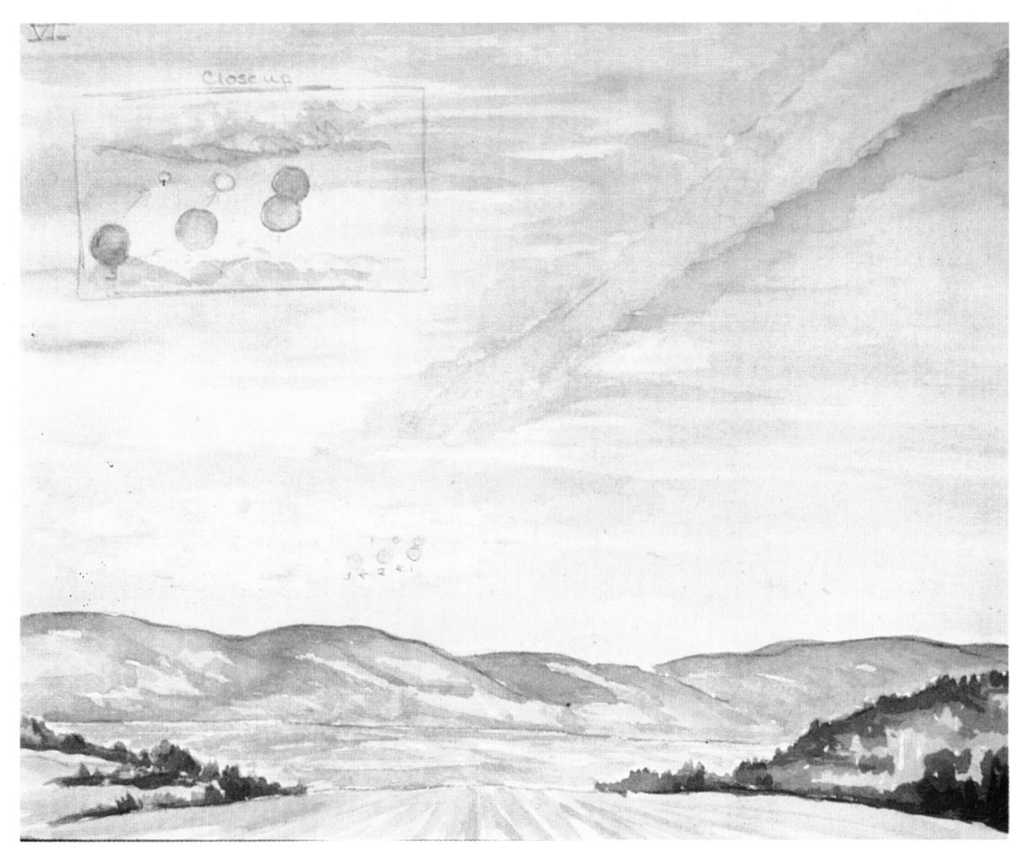

Plate 4:4 A photograph of a sketch showing what a former USAF pilot and his family saw looking west across Skaneatales Lake in upstate New York one evening in 1964 (National Archives and Records Administration). It appears to show a double image mirage of Jupiter.

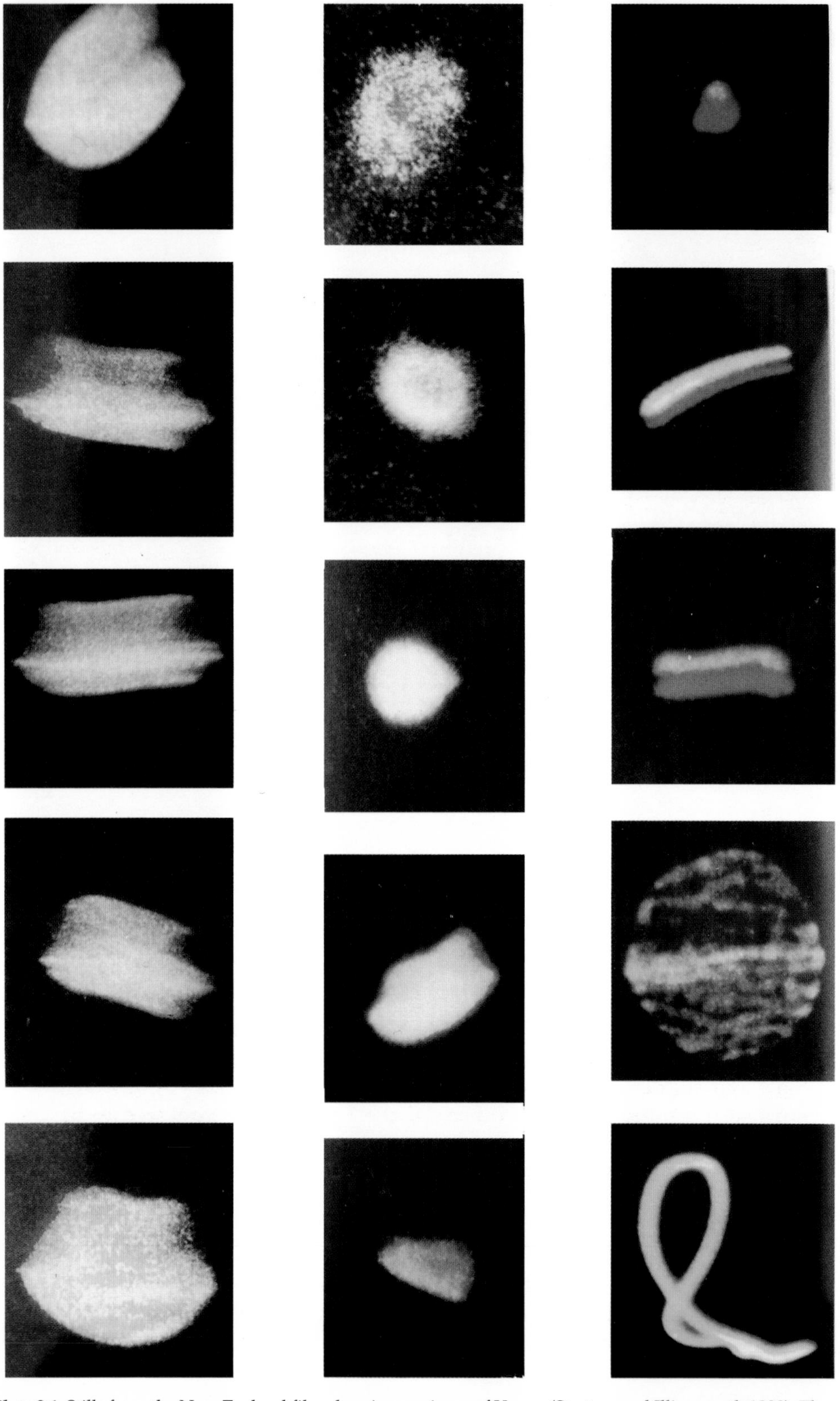

Plate 8:1 Stills from the New Zealand film showing a mirage of Venus (Startup and Illingworth 1980). The smearing is due to various camera movements and the Jupiter-like object is an unfocused image.

4 The major sources of astronomical mirages

While it is very satisfying to find an explanation for a UFO report, it is necessary to be sure that the explanation is correct. Menzel did not check his identification of Sirius (although he had the means to do so). He made another mistake in identifying Sirius as the cause of a UFO report made by the crew of an F-94 on patrol over Odessa (Washington) at 1915L on 10 December 1952 (Menzel and Boyd 1963:62). Even from the aircraft's height of nearly 8 km, Sirius was 10° below the horizon and Menzel did not mention the possibility of a mirage. Others have made incorrect identifications.

I shall now consider which astronomical bodies have caused UFO reports, and examine the identifications that were made.

Reports caused by the Moon

Klass described a case where the crew of a US Navy R5D transport aircraft saw an unusual light at 0055Z while flying from Iceland to Newfoundland on 10 February 1951. They were at a height of about 3000 m, at a position later calculated as 49°50' north and 50°3' west, on a heading of 230° (true), when they saw 'a glow of light below [*sic*] the horizon' about the 2 o'clock position. It maintained this bearing, although the pilot once described it as at 45° to his course. At first the light was yellow, but suddenly it vanished, to be replaced by an orange light which turned 'fiery red', bluish red around the perimeter. It appeared to be approaching them 'at a fantastic speed', but stopped a short distance away. It was tilted about 25° to the horizontal, and appeared as a translucent or metallic saucer-shape about 80 m in diameter with a purple-red fiery edge and a frosted white glow all around. It then retreated and disappeared over the horizon, still on the same azimuth.

Hynek suggested that it might have been the aurora, but Klass noted a remark made by one of the crew. This was that his first impression was that the object was the celestial setting of the Moon. Klass wondered if 'some interactive optical effect' from the thin cloud had made the Moon appear to zoom to and fro. He also wondered if it had been a 'sub-moon', that is, a reflection of the Moon off ice crystals in strata below the aircraft. To check this hypothesis, he asked the US Naval Observatory in Washington for the position of the Moon from the position of the aircraft at that date and time. He was told that the Moon was on an azimuth of 280°, but 1·35° below the horizon (the effect of refraction was not mentioned). It was also six-sevenths dark (crescent). Clearly the object could not have been a sub-moon, but perhaps it was the tip of the crescent Moon. He calculated, taking normal refraction into account, that the tip of the Moon should have been visible to the crew, and argued that if the object was not the Moon it was strange the crew did not report seeing it (Klass 1974:52).

Klass does not appear to have considered that what the crew saw was a *mirage* of the Moon. If the date and the position of the aircraft are correct, the Moon set at 0046Z, and at 0055Z it was only 1·45° below the horizon (allowing for the height of the aircraft and normal refraction). Uncertainty about the exact position of the aircraft means that the Moon could easily have been even nearer to the horizon. A temperature inversion along the line of sight must be presumed.

On 6 August 1971 Bernard Pobiner from New York, on holiday in Nova Scotia, was surprised by the sudden appearance over the Cabot Strait to the east of what (at first) he took to be a brilliant sunrise. However it was late evening (2015 to 2045L, 2315 to 2345Z) and the Sun was setting in the opposite direction. He took two photographs in quick succession (see colour plate 4:1) before the object vanished 'at tremendous speed' (Chibbett 1974). I discovered that the full Moon rose at 2020L on an azimuth of 114° and concluded that this is what he saw (the trail is caused by a slow shutter allowing the Moon's image to track across the film as Pobiner lowered the camera). However, the sudden appearance and disappearance are only consistent with a Novaya Zemlya 'mirage' of the Moon, that is, the Moon was actually below the horizon at the time; at 2015L it was 2° below the horizon.

REPORTS CAUSED BY PLANETS

Mercury

One of the most sensational reports of the 1950s was that made by Father William Gill, an Anglican priest with a mission in Boainai, Papua-New Guinea. He and many others claimed that, on two consecutive evenings, 26-27 June 1959, from about 1845L (0845Z), they saw a large sparkling light in the north-western sky. On 26 June, it (or another object) was visible until 2210L. Sometimes, the object was orange, yellow, or blue, or it displayed an electric blue spotlight; at 2210L it was emitting a red light. Indeed, they could see several 'discs' coming and going through the clouds, and what seemed to be humanoid occupants, one of whom returned their waved greeting. Some of the observers could see portholes or windows in the side of the 'craft'. On the first evening, Gill had looked for Venus, and, on seeing it, had seen the UFO 'above' it. (Story 1980:149). See figure 4:1.

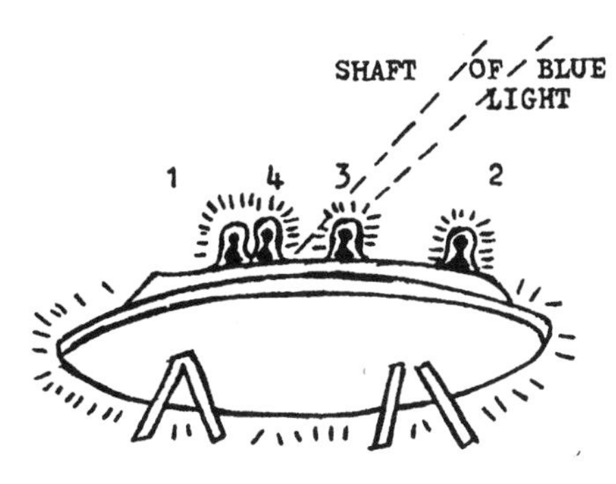

Fig. 4:1 A copy of the sketch made of the object seen by Father Gill in Boainai, showing the order in which the four 'men' appeared (Crutwell 1959). Probably a mirage of Mercury.

Despite the fact that Gill had claimed to have seen Venus and the UFO, Menzel concluded that the UFO was Venus (but see below). He also assumed that Gill was myopic, and (wrongly) that he was without his glasses (ibid.). The Royal Australian Air Force concluded that 'at least three of the lights were planets, e.g. Jupiter, Saturn and Mars', and that 'light refraction and changing position of the planets relative to the observers and the unsettled tropical weather could give the impression of size and movement' (Klass 1974:243).

A sighting lasting several hours is most likely to be of an astronomical object, indeed of several such objects. At that time, three planets were setting in the north-west (south of the equator, planets are seen to the north). Mercury, Mars and Venus were all more or less in line vertically, with Mercury lowest and Venus almost as bright as it can be (at magnitude -4·3). If Gill found Venus at 1845L, he found it at an altitude of 32°. There was no planet above it, but the fainter Mars (magnitude 1·8) was 5° below it and the less faint Mercury (magnitude -0·2) below them both, 9° above the horizon. Perhaps he mistook Mercury for Venus, and Venus for a UFO. Almost certainly Gill and his friends saw a mirage of one or more of these planets. Since mirages almost only occur at low altitude, it seems likely that the first 'sparkling object' was Mercury, which set at 1926L. Because of clouds, observation was not continuous, and it is likely that subsequent observations were of Mars and Venus as they reached low altitude. Mars set at 2046L and Venus at 2104L.

A most detailed UFO report came from 17½-year-old Christopher Avis of Tunbridge Wells in Kent (England). At 0741L (0741Z) on 31 January 1977, he noticed what at first he took to be two strange 'clouds' in the east-south-east (about azimuth 120-125°). Otherwise the sky was 4/5 clear, with only a few stratus clouds and two or three cumulus. The temperature was -1 °C, and there was no wind. The normal clouds were pink-orange, reflecting the light of the Sun which (so he thought) 'was to rise about 20 minutes later'. In contrast, the strange 'clouds' were bright white, discoid, and tilted to the horizon. He made a series of sketches during the next 7 minutes (the duration of the sighting), which are rather like a film strip (see figure 4:2). He thought the 'clouds' were 2-3 km away, and at a height of 1000 m. There was no sound from them (data from BUFORA records).

In fact the Sun was just rising in the east (118°), but it would not have been visible to Avis at that time. Also rising, were Mars and Mercury. Mars was at an altitude of 5° and an azimuth of 136°; Mercury was at an altitude of 8° and an azimuth of 141°. Evidently Avis saw mirages of the two planets (Mars on the left, Mercury on the right). He underestimated the azimuth slightly. Mars was at magnitude 1·3; Mercury much brighter at 0·1. If the base of the mirage was, as indicated on the first sketch, at an altitude of 15°, the whole mirage was elevated at least 10°. However, this altitude may be exaggerated. Avis's detailed sequence gives a fascinating insight into the behaviour of an astronomical mirage. The division of Mercury's image is particularly interesting, showing how twin images can form by stretching and splitting the original image.

Venus

An 'airship' reported over Oakland (California) in 1896 was identified by astronomer Charles Burckhalter of the Chabot Observatory as Mars and Venus in the evening sky. It appeared as a 'winged cigar, projecting a stream of brilliant light from its head' (Menzel and Taves 1977:60). It was probably a mirage of Venus.

Figure 4:3 shows how Venus appeared to a driver on a US interstate highway near Charleston (Virginia) at 0905L on 19 January 1967. The planet (at magnitude -3·7) was only 3° above the horizon, almost in line with the highway.

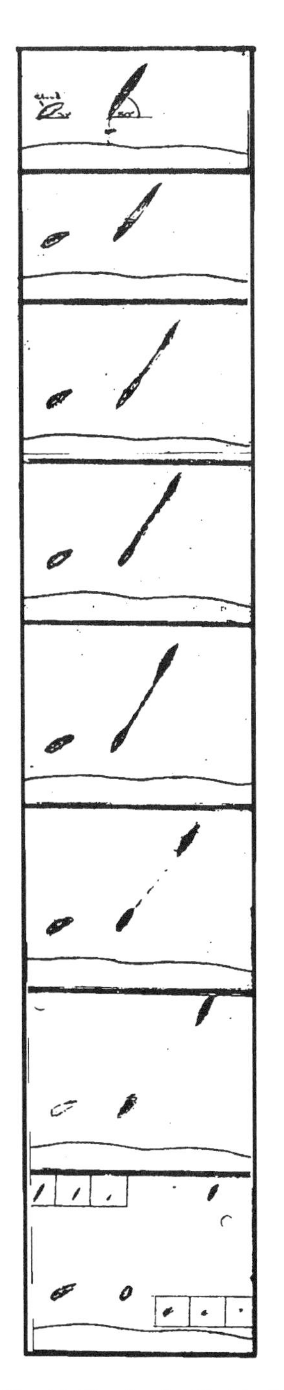

a (0741L)
Two unusual 'clouds' sighted near horizon to south-east.

b (0742L)
Object at right began to lengthen upwards.

c (0743L)
Object at right continued to lengthen and get thinner at centre, Top end brighter and more substantial than the rest.

d (0743L+30 s)
Centre of right object became patchy, but top still moving upwards.

e (0744L)
Centre of right object diffused rapidly and bottom end began to fade slowly. Top still moving upwards and angle to horizon increased to 60°.

f (0744L+30 s)
Centre of right object almost gone; bottom still fading. Top end almost stationary.

g (0745L)
Centre of right object vanished and bottom still fading. Top now began to fade.

h (0746L)
All remains now fading (as inset sketches). Top of right object disappeared at 0746L+50 s and the bottom at 0748L.

Fig. 4:2 Sketches by Christopher Avis showing the behaviour of a mirage of both Mars and Mercury over a period of 7 minutes (BUFORA case files).

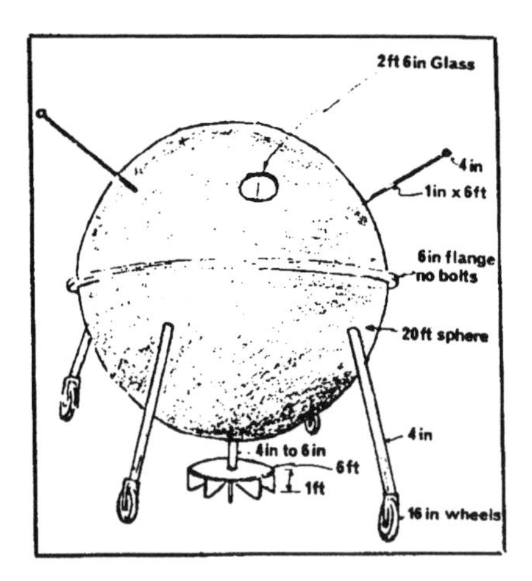

Fig. 4:3 How Venus appeared to Tad Jones as he drove along Interstate Highway 64.

On 10 April 1897, at Evanston (Illinois), a bright light was seen in the west at 2015L (0215Z?) by 'five hundred reputable citizens'. It was as bright as fifty ordinary street lights and was in plain view for fully 45 minutes. Many were certain that it was 'the famous airship'. At the time, an astronomer identified it as Betelgeuse, but Klass suggested that it was Venus, Mars or another bright celestial body (Klass 1974:265). In fact it must have been Venus (or a mirage of it). It was only 6° above the horizon in the west-north-west; Betelgeuse was at an altitude of 30° in the west-south-west.

On the evening of 14 July 1952, an air liner was flying from New York to Miami with ten passengers and a crew of three, including Captain Nash and Pilot Fortenberry. They were at about 2500 m over Chesapeake Bay, approaching Norfolk (Virginia). At about 2012L (0112Z) they saw a brilliant red glow appear in the west, apparently between Newport Mews and the aircraft, and so low that it might have been on the ground. The unidentified light appeared to travel north-east at incredible speed on a horizontal course 1·5 km below the plane. They then saw that the light was actually a procession of six red-orange lights shooting forward like a stream of red tracer bullets. They were sharply defined large discs, arranged in a narrow echelon formation. Suddenly they all flipped up on edge, reversed formation, and flipped back again. They then abruptly changed course and shot away due west (270°), followed by two more discs, apparently from beneath the aircraft. They appeared once more before vanishing, in random order, by climbing above the aircraft. The incident last from 12 to 15 s (Menzel and Boyd 1973:256).

During 1961 and 1962, Menzel tried five different explanations on an unconvinced ufoist, Professor Charles A Maney of Defiance College (Ohio) (Maney 1965). In the end, Menzel had no explanation for the incident. He considered the planet Mercury, but rejected it because it was not bright enough. He also considered a ground light, but could not identify one. However he did conclude that, despite the lack of instrumental evidence, sharp localized discontinuities of both temperature and humidity must have existed over Chesapeake Bay that night.

It is true that Mercury was above the horizon, at 9° altitude and azimuth of 282°. However Menzel appears to have overlooked the fact that Venus (at magnitude -3·8) was only 3° below the horizon on azimuth 300°. From the observers' elevated position, the horizon was depressed 1·6°. This, combined with normal refraction put Venus less than 1° below the observers' horizon. Evidently the pilots saw a multiple mirage of Venus produced by a multiple inversion. Because they were flying a course that was some 20° west of south, the pilots' notion of due west was skewed northward.

Venus (at magnitude -4·4) was the very bright egg-shaped object which 'landed' and terrified the villagers of Llanerchymedd in Anglesey (Wales), from 1915Z on 1 September 1978. At that time it was still 6° above the horizon, but during the next 45 minutes (it set at 2001Z), it seemed to hover and then descend to the ground 'just a hundred feet [30 m] or so away ... beside a tree'. Observers were sure that it illuminated nearby branches, and they claimed to have seen 'two small legs extended from either side of the craft'. Later some boys 'saw some shapes appear in the fields by the side of the landed object', which 'resolved into three 'figures' about six feet [2 m] tall, wearing greyish one-piece suits that were completely covered [*sic*] by balaclava-type helmet'. It was dark by the time the police were called, but nothing was found (Story 1980:211).

A mirage of Venus presented itself as a UFO hovering just over an urban road to an English policeman (Alan Godfrey). At about 0525Z on 28 November 1980 PC Godfrey was driving towards his station in Todmorden (West Yorkshire) when he saw a glowing object which, at first, he thought was a local bus. It lay directly in his path, filling the roadway. He stopped his car and tried to radio his station. Getting no response (perhaps because he was in an area of poor reception), he started to sketch the object (see figure 4:4). It was dome-shaped, like a top, but with what looked like a line of windows around the rim. While the 'windows' were dark, the rest of the object was very bright. He was sure that the light from his car's headlights was reflecting off what looked like the metallic surface of a solid object. He also thought that bushes and trees beside the road were being shaken by the object. Suddenly he was staring into the dark night, driving slowly, further down the road; he had no recollection of the disappearance of the object or of starting the car. Evidently he had been in a trance. He collected a colleague in the town centre and reported the matter at the station (at 0530Z). Later, under hypnosis, he gave an account of an encounter with and examination by aliens (Randles 1981 and 1983b:122 and 147).

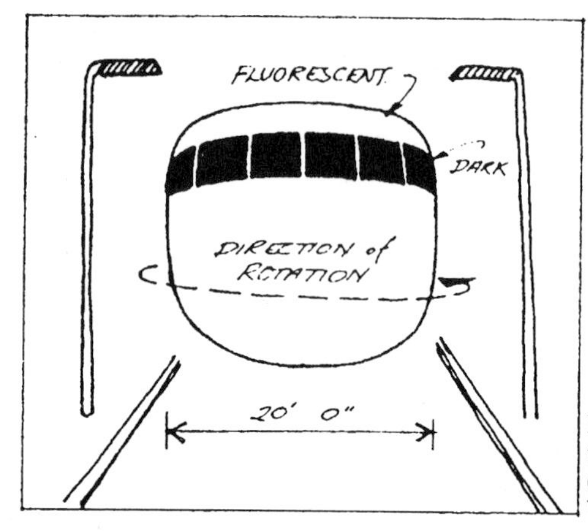

Fig. 4:4 PC Alan Godfrey's sketch of the 'UFO' that he saw at Todmorden (20' is about 6 m). Probably a mirage of Venus.

Venus, at magnitude -3·8, lay directly in line with the road on which Godfrey was driving (116° azimuth) and at only 4° altitude (Campbell 1987a). It appears that the 'UFO' was a mirage of Venus.

Because of its brightness, Venus can often be seen in daylight. A Caltech physicist was once (date unknown) mystified by a bright luminous object much larger than a star or planet which was near to mountains around the Owens Valley in late afternoon. It was found that, at that instant, Venus was just setting below the crest of the Sierra, a place where atmospheric conditions create a 'lee wave'. It was concluded that the image of Venus was 'refracted in a very peculiar way', so producing an unfamiliar image (Story 1981:239). In fact the image must have been a mirage of Venus.

At the Los Alamos atomic laboratory in 1947, a vain attempt was once made to shoot Venus down when it was thought to have been a Japanese spy (or bomb) balloon shining brilliantly in the clear daytime sky. It was only identified by Dr Fermi (Menzel and Taves 1977:11; Klass 1974:90).

During a rocket launch at Vandenberg AFB, a telephoto tracking camera caught an image of a peculiar object. The film stimulated many second-hand rumours that the USAF had 'proof of flying saucers'.

However, triangulation indicated that the object was very distant and an investigation found that it was Venus (Sagan and Page 1972:15).

Venus appears to have been partly responsible for the Gill report (see Mercury).

Mars

In 1978 I was called to investigate a UFO report by a housewife who lived in a rural area near Edzell (Tayside in Scotland). In the middle of August in either 1964 or 1965, she went outside at between 2030-2130Z to fetch in some clothes drying on a line. The sky was clear and it was warm, with no wind. Then she noticed an orange globe 'rise up' over a wood to the west (possible south-west). She thought it travelled slowly south-east at treetop height, until it reached the end of the wood. There it seemed to descend into a clearing and hovered some 2 m from the ground. There appeared to be a yellowish-blue cloud of light around the waist of the globe, and, as it descended, this cloud seemed to take on a more definite form and give off red and green flashes. The cloud gradually resolved itself into a rotating pewter-grey ring in which there were many bright lights, like car headlights, at regular intervals. The speed of rotation gradually slowed, until it stopped altogether, when the flashing ceased also.

She thought that the object was several metres across. Its surface was a bright luminous (fluorescent) orange, looking solid and metallic, and it was surrounded by whitish-yellow light with pale-green edges. Below it there was a dark grey projection, and on top, something that looked like glass or clear plastic.

It was fully a minute before she thought to call her husband. But as she backed towards the door, the object seemed to tilt slightly to one side, rose at an angle up to treetop height, wobbled like a child's top, hesitated a second or so, and continued in an arc to the south-west. She lost sight of it about 600 m away. As an artist, she offered to paint her impression of the object. I accepted the offer and was made a present of the picture (see colour plate 4:2).

Because of lack of precise data I could not make an astronomical check, but I was sure it was an astronomical mirage. Mars was very prominent in those years (c. magnitude 1·1) and set in the west-south-west (azimuth 251°) at 2109L on (for example) 15 August 1965. Consequently the picture may show a mirage of Mars.

Paul Quick was pushing his motor cycle up a lane near his home in Storrington (Sussex in England) about 1845Z on 29 October 1967. Because it was a clear and starry night, he gazed at the sky (looking south, over

Chactonbury Downs); he was surprised to see an object shaped like a rugby ball travelling slowly east before it disappeared behind trees. It was a luminous, bright light and appeared to be 3-5 km away.

He dashed home to alert his family (mother and two sisters) who all then saw a large brightly-coloured ball floating on the Downs. His mother (Suzette) described how the object changed from white to a deep ruby red and looked like a horseshoe upside down. It was flickering, as if trying to attract attention. Suddenly it broke into three separate parts, each a different colour. While the red part remained, the blue and green parts moved to the east. Then all the parts joined up again, into the horseshoe. With one of her daughters, Suzette ran to get a better view from an adjoining field. From there the object looked like a huge ice-cream cornet lying on the Downs, but with bright red ice-cream! It disappeared by 'sliding away'.

The same object was observed by another witness, who watched it through binoculars (Anon. 1968).

As an artist, Suzette Quick was able to paint what she had seen (see colour plate 4:3). It appears to show a mirage of Mars, then at only 5° altitude in the south-west (azimuth 218°).

A witness saw an oval-shaped UFO hovering just over some trees shortly after 2030L (0130Z) on 19 March 1968 at Beallsville (Ohio). The large red object was so bright that it illuminated the road, and it had a band of dimmer red lights flashing around its centre. Suddenly a large tube emerged from the base of the object, moving from side to side, until it came towards the reporter, when a beam of light shot out. The reporter alleged that he was knocked to the ground, and that his jacket caught fire. The UFO just faded away. It was alleged that, during the incident, a light on a nearby pole went out, that a TV set and a dog were affected, and that the reporter suffered second-degree burns (exhibiting a scar three months later). Another witness saw a 'long cylindrical object' at low altitude the same night (Fowler 1979:288).

The 'UFO' was probably a mirage of Mars, then only 3° above the horizon.

Mars appears to have been partly responsible for the Gill report, and it participated in the Avis sighting (see Mercury).

Jupiter

On the afternoon of 7 January 1948, a US pilot (Capt. Thomas Mantell) died after he tried to chase what was thought to be a UFO near Louisville (Kentucky). It appears that (without realizing it) he flew too high without oxygen, and the aircraft crashed after he became unconscious. The incident is so celebrated that it has even been incorporated into an episode of the television series *Star Trek*!

Various explanations have been proposed. Some believe that the object was a Skyhook cosmic ray balloon released by the US Navy under a then classified programme (Klass 1974:36; Menzel and Boyd 1963:38). The USAF claimed that such a balloon was released that day (from Clinton County airport in Ohio), and that it would have drifted over the Godman area, but they gave no time for the release (Steiger 1976:46). However Menzel and Boyd claimed that the records for that day were not available and that the release crew could not recall whether or not a balloon had been released. Before he knew about Skyhook balloons, Menzel thought Mantell had chased a mock sun (Menzel 1953:22). Hynek concluded that Mantell had tried to reach Venus, which, he claimed, was (at magnitude -3·8) six times brighter than the sky (Steiger 1976:43). Hynek allowed that (initially) a Skyhook balloon may have been involved, but the USAF concluded that, although the object seen initially might have been Venus, the object chased by Mantell was a Skyhook balloon.

The course given to Mantell and his flight of three F-51 fighters by Godman AFB varied between 220 and 230° (magnetic?). There is some confusion about the local time, but if it was 1445 EST (1945Z) Venus lay 34° above the horizon on an azimuth of 176°. Not only was Venus too high to be mistaken, it did not lie in the right direction.

Jupiter is a better candidate; it was then only 7° above the horizon on an azimuth of 235° (true). One officer did note the presence of Jupiter in the sky, but he concluded that it was 'impossible to observe with the unaided eye'. Another officer described the object as looking like 'an ice cream cone topped with red'. Mantell described is as 'metallic' and 'of tremendous size'. It seems likely that Mantell chased a mirage of Jupiter.

Jupiter was chased again by the USAF in 1948. Lieutenant George F Gorman was flying an F-51 at 300 m, waiting his turn to land at Hector Airport (Fargo, N. Dakota), at 2100L on 1 October that year (0300Z on 2 October). As he flew in a left circle, he noticed an object that appeared to be travelling east-west at the same speed as himself. It seemed to be the (white) rear navigation light on an aircraft, except that it had no glare and was blinking on and off. However he could see neither wings nor fuselage. He tried in vain to intercept the object, and once thought that it was going to collide with him. He 'chased' the object all the way up to 4200 m, but all the time it seemed to be above him. He lost sight of it at 2127L (Steiger 1976:65).

Initially Menzel thought that Gorman had seen a distant light source reflected by a whirlpool of air over one wing of the aircraft (Menzel

1953:19). Later he suggested that Gorman had seen two objects; a lighted balloon and a mirage of the planet Jupiter (Menzel and Boyd 1963:81). A weather balloon had also been suggested in the Blue Book report (by Hynek?).

Although the Blue Book report opens with the statement that 'there is no conceivable astronomical explanation', as Menzel indicated, there is such an explanation. Jupiter was only 3° above the horizon on an azimuth of 231° (south-west). Furthermore it set at exactly 2127L. A mirage of Jupiter would explain Gorman's extraordinary reaction, and Menzel's uncertainty was not justified. Almost certainly the only object Gorman saw was Jupiter.

At 2245L on 20 August 1949 (0545Z on 21 August), the astronomer Clyde Tombaugh was sitting watching the sky from his house at Las Cruces in New Mexico. There was no Moon, and the sky was so clear that even 6th magnitude stars were visible. He was startled to see a group of six to eight rectangles of light appear almost directly overhead and travel towards the south-south-east. They were of low luminosity, 'window-like' in appearance, and yellowish-green in colour. Altogether they spanned an angle of about 1°. As they moved towards the horizon they became foreshortened, the overall size shrank and the colour turned brownish. They faded from view at an altitude of 35 to 40° (Menzel and Boyd 1963:267). Compare Tombaugh's description with the photograph of the Motunau object (plate 4:8)

It is curious that Tombaugh did not mention seeing Jupiter. It was the only planet above the horizon and very prominent (magnitude -2·5). Furthermore it lay at an altitude of 34°. However it was in the south-south-*west* (azimuth 195°). How could Tombaugh have failed to mention Jupiter? It lay at the same altitude as that at which his rectangles disappeared and it lay more or less in the same direction (he could have made a mistake about the azimuth). This suggests an explanation. Perhaps Tombaugh was looking at a mirage of Jupiter and its major satellites. At the time, the Galilean satellites were all visible, two on either side of the planet. Menzel noted that conditions were 'ideal' for the formation of small, sharply defined temperature inversions (necessary for a mirage, see below).

Jupiter may have been the 'unusually bright bluish white light' seen at 2330L (1430Z) to the north-east from Haneda AFB (Tokyo, Japan) on 5 August 1952. The light was low in the sky at about 30-50° azimuth (McDonald gives '25° to 35°') and disappeared 'after about an hour'. Near the end of the sighting, the object seemed to be higher in the sky (indicating that it was an astronomical object).

The Condon Report suggested that it was the first magnitude star Capella ('magnitude 0·2'), which was 8° above the horizon on an azimuth of 37° (at 2400L), and that the brightness may have been caused by Raman brightening, an interference effect (Gillmor 1969:123). The magnitude of Capella is actually 0·09. McDonald rejected the Condon Report's conclusion for various reasons. He accepted the data on Capella but did not accept that it could have exhibited diffraction brightening. He did note that Jupiter rose at 2300L 'almost due east' (azimuth 69° actually), with a magnitude of '-2·0' (-2·1 actually). Since the reports indicated an object brighter than Venus (he thought that this should read 'Jupiter'), McDonald judged that the object must have appeared about magnitude -3·0, or even brighter, ruling out Jupiter (Sagan and Page 1972:90). However, if Jupiter was seen via mirage and was subject to Raman brightening, it could have appeared to be brighter than usual. At 2330L Jupiter was only 5° above the horizon on an azimuth of 74°.

A 43-year-old former USAF pilot, then a physiotherapist from Cortland, New York State, was picnicking with his wife and children on a hill 550 m above sea level on the east side of Skaneatales Lake (one of the Finger Lakes about 16 km north-west of Homer) on the evening of 11 April 1964. There was a light northerly wind with just a few stratus clouds on the western horizon. About 1800L (2300Z) he noticed contrails left by several jet bombers. Then, about half-an-hour later, he noticed, a little to the north-west, what he thought was a very large contrail from north-east to south-west. It was very white and wide and, at the south-west end, there was a break. Then a very black spiral formation of what appeared to be smoke appeared. The white trail was unusually wide for a jet trail. He concluded that the black portion looked dark because of the angle of the Sun which was just setting behind a hill on the other side of the lake.

The white trail hung in the sky and gradually drifted to the south, slowly dissipating. However, after about 10 minutes, he concluded that the black spiral cloud had slowly moved to the west. Also it had become much darker. Through binoculars (6x25) he could see wisps of smoke streaming out of the black cloud. Suddenly it changed from the horizontal to a vertical position with greater 'smoke' activity; it now resembled a smoking plane slowly falling from the sky, but in a banana shape! It hung there for 2 or 3 minutes and then slowly seemed to sink into the clouds and was obliterated.

After about another 3 minutes, another object appeared. This was a horizontal pencil shape moving from left to right. As he looked at it through his binoculars, there was a flash of white light from one end and it shot forward with incredible speed before stopping suddenly. Then it thickened in the centre, emitting a cloud of 'smoke', and shot backwards. It shortened until it appeared saucer-shaped, fat in the middle and then became a disc. It then slowly divided into two, one above the other, the upper disc gradually getting smaller until it faded altogether. The lower disc headed downwards at 45° towards the spot where the banana-shaped object had been. The object then divided into two again, but the lower object assumed a vertical pencil shape, while the upper oval object faded away. Then the pencil-shaped object faded from sight. The whole episode lasted about 45 minutes and ended just about dusk.

The reporter's wife made sketches of all phases of the event and one of these is reproduced as colour plate 4:4 (showing the object dividing into two). The report and sketches were sent directly to Hynek at Northwestern University (after publicity surrounding the Socorro Case, see chapter 7) and now form part of the Blue Book case files (file 8739).

In January 1965, Hynek wrote to Major Hector Quintanella (then in charge of Blue Book) about the case. He observed that, had the report come from the south-west USA, the object could have been a balloon used for gunnery practice (invisible until it burst into flames). However, he knew of no gunnery practice in New York State. Hynek could find no explanation for what he called 'The Case of the Burning Banana', and it is listed in Blue Book as 'unidentified'.

What a pity that Hynek did not look for an astronomical explanation! He would have found that (at 2342Z when the Sun set) Jupiter lay just 6° above the horizon in the west (azimuth 278°). It would have set at the end of civil twilight when the Sun itself was 6° below the horizon. Evidently all the objects were various mirage images of Jupiter caused by an inversion to the west.

Jacqueline Wingfield and her friend Miss Mortensen were driving near Cappoquin in the south of Ireland on 26 December 1965. There was an absolutely clear sky. Between 1515 and 1530L (1530Z), they saw a strange object 'moving steadily across the sky in front of them'. They stopped the car and Mortensen just had time to take a picture (see plate 4:5) before the object disappeared. Wingfield described it as 'a round solid looking object flying from right to left across the horizon'. Apparently, it trailed a plume like flames behind it, but with no smoke, and there was no sound.

On returning to London, Wingfield reported the incident to her colleague and aviation historian Charles Gibbs-Smith. He took the film for development and examination by a specialist; they concluded that the object was not a conventional aircraft, a balloon, a rocket or a satellite. Nor was it a meteorite. Gibbs-Smith, who wrote to the London *Times* about the incident, thought the photograph showed a flying saucer (Chapman 1970:88).

Plate 4:5 The Cappoquin photograph, which may show a mirage of the rising Jupiter (Chapman 1970).

Although the reporters gave no azimuth, it is notable that Jupiter rose in the north-east (azimuth 49°) at 1531L. It seems most likely therefore that the photograph shows a mirage of Jupiter. The movement attributed to the object may have been induced (see chapter 2).

It seems that a mirage of Jupiter (magnitude -1·9) caught the attention of Michael Bennett, a young farmer at Elsthorpe (New Zealand) some time between 2345 and 2445L (1245Z) on 14 January 1969. In fact his attention was drawn to it because it was moving about erratically. 'The object, which was a point of light but brighter than a star, appeared to be making random patterns; shifting its position, stopping for 5 or 10 s, then moving into another spot ... its glow could be seen behind scattered cloud'. Bennett, a former professional photographer, hunted for a film for his camera, while his wife watched the object. She also saw it 'jump up and down' and 'move from right to left'. She thought it was followed around by two smaller objects, which darted around the main light. Plate 4:6 shows an enlargement from one of Bennett's pictures.

The Bennetts gave the object's altitude as 35° and its azimuth as 50° (magnetic), but local investigators calculated that it was at 10° altitude and 70° azimuth (true) and wondered whether the planet could be seen over a nearby range of mountains (Fulton 1969).

In fact, at 1200Z, the rising Jupiter lay only 13° above the horizon on an azimuth of 81°, and it might have been elevated by the inversion responsible for the mirage. The movements reported by the Bennetts were probably caused by autokinesis, although real movement of the mirage image cannot be excluded. The smaller objects reported by Mrs Bennett may have been some of the Galilean satellites.

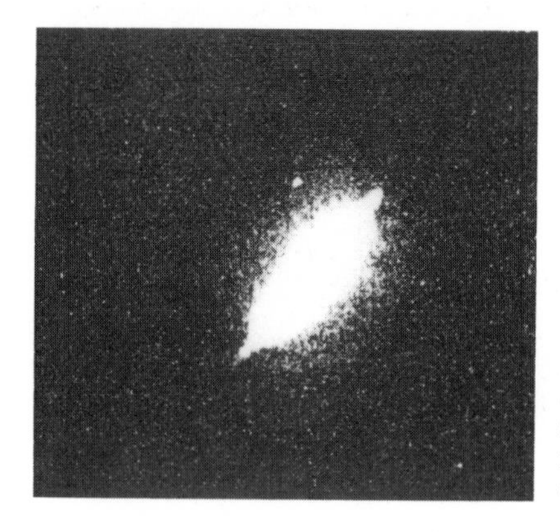

Plate 4:6 A photograph taken in New Zealand in 1969 which probably shows a mirage of Jupiter. The steep angle of the mirage indicates that it was seen on the edge of a temperature inversion.

Although his story is too bizarre to be taken seriously, Joe Simonton's alleged encounter with a silvery object in which there were three dark-skinned men (Story 1980:107) took place at a time (1700Z on 18 April 1970) when Jupiter lay just 2° above the Wisconsin horizon. Stimulated by sight of a mirage of Jupiter, Simonton may have hallucinated the remainder of the story. Or he may just have invented it.

Jupiter may have participated in the Delphos (Kansas) Case; see below (Saturn).

Saturn

At dusk on 13 October 1952, Major William D Leet was co-pilot on a C-54 troop carrier mission out of Tachikawa (Japan) and heading south towards Oshima, when he noticed, in the stratocumulus westward, what appeared to be a perfectly round cloud. Seven minutes later, it took on an elliptical shape and sped off to the west, disappearing in a few seconds toward Mount Fuji. The object seems to have been regarded as a 'foo-fighter' (Hall 1964:24).

Leet appears to have seen a mirage of Saturn, then at magnitude 0·7 and just setting on an azimuth of 264°.

At about 1900L on 2 November 1971 (0100Z on 3 November) Ronald Johnson (16) heard a 'rumble' and looked up to see a very bright object (apparently) about 20 m away (but in a north-east direction), 0·6 m off the ground. He was tending sheep on his parents farm near Delphos (Kansas). He described the object as about 3 m in diameter, with a distinct bulge at the centre. It glowed with multicoloured lights 'like the light of a welder's arc', and had a glow extending below it to the ground. He alleged that it passed over a nearby shed, when the noise changed to a high-pitched sound 'like a jet'. He heard, but did not see, the object fly southward. He ran to fetch his parents, who, on emerging from the house, saw a circular light 'departing' in the south. It is alleged that the object left a mysterious 'glowing' ring on the ground, and that, after the parents touched it, their fingers were numb for several weeks (Phillips 1972).

The case is regarded as a classic and was awarded the *National Enquirer*'s 'Blue Ribbon' as 'the most scientifically valuable evidence' for the existence of extraterrestrial life reported during the year 1972 (Story 1980:98). A panel of scientists, appointed by the newspaper to judge the value of UFO reports, awarded the Johnson family a $5000 prize for their report (Salisbury 1974:134). Klass appears to have thought that the family invented the story and he made no attempt to explain the lights (Klass 1974:312); no other explanation has emerged.

Ronald probably saw a mirage of Saturn, which lay only 1° above the east-north-east horizon (azimuth 66°). The object seen to the 'south' was probably Jupiter, then exactly on the horizon, but in the west-south-west (azimuth 242°). Ronald would have seen Saturn appear to move south as he moved south, towards the house. Later, looking south, the Johnsons may have seen Jupiter and assumed that it was the same object. By the time they returned to the north of the house, Saturn's mirage must have faded. The noise reported by Ronald must have an independent explanation, perhaps machinery around the farm, or an aircraft. He made a false association between it and the mirage.

Any peculiarity in the ground (where Ronald thought a UFO landed) must have been there beforehand. It was later discovered that the 'glowing' was caused by a lighter surface reflecting moonlight. It is thought that the ring was caused by the radial growth of fungus (Story 1980:98) although it may have been caused by a chemical spill. The alleged numbness can have been psychosomatic, the result of believing that the ring was mysterious.

REPORTS CAUSED BY STARS

Sirius

At 2245L (0545Z) on 4 November 1957, an egg-shaped object with a single white light at its base 'came down in a rather steep dive at the east end of runway 26' at Kirtland AFB near Albuquerque (New Mexico). It moved and hovered in the east for about 1 minute, when it raced away upwards on a course of 120° (magnetic?). The USAF concluded that it was a small, powerful, private aircraft flying without a flight plan, that became confused and attempted to land at the wrong airport. There was a radar return normal for such an aircraft (Gillmor 1969:141).

McDonald ridiculed Blue Book's evaluation of the object and was the only person to check the report with the original witnesses (Sagan and Page 1972:115).

Since the local magnetic deviation at the time was about 10° east, 120° magnetic was equivalent to about 110° true, almost exactly the direction of Sirius at the time. The star, almost on the horizon, was probably the cause of a mirage.

Canopus

On the evening of 21 October 1978, Frederick Valentich and his Cessna 182 aircraft disappeared over the Bass Strait (north of Tasmania). At 1906L (0806Z), when at 1370 m, he reported that 'a large aircraft' with 'four bright lights' passed close to him (while he experienced engine trouble and a radio 'blackout'). Three minutes later he reported that it was not an aircraft. It was a long shape which seemed to be at once 'stationary' and 'orbiting on top of me'. 'It has a green light and sort of metallic light on the outside'. He then reported that it had vanished. At 1912L he reported engine trouble, with the UFO hovering on top of him, and gave his call sign. The recording of the conversation ends with 17 s of loud metallic sounds. Neither Valentich nor his aircraft has been found, fuelling speculation by ufoists that aliens made off with both him and his plane (Story 1980:379).

It is not known in which direction Valentich saw the UFO, but, with the Sun setting in the west, he was probably looking south or south-east, the direction in which he was flying. There he could have seen a mirage of Canopus, 5° above his (depressed) horizon, on azimuth 168°.

Evidently his engine was giving trouble, and eventually failed. This must have forced him to try to land on the ocean, a dangerous manoeuvre which evidently killed him. The aircraft would have sunk, but it might still be found if an adequate search of the sea bed were made. The idea that he crashed while trying to avoid what he thought was a hostile spaceship cannot be dismissed.

At about 2100L on the evening of 29 December 1980 (0300Z on 30 December), Betty Cash and Vickie Landrum, with the latter's 7-year-old grandson Colby, were driving south on a lonely highway (FM 1485) towards Huffman (Texas) when they saw an unidentified diamond-shaped object ahead of them. They stopped the car and got out to look at it, but retreated back to the car when the object appeared to spew flames from its base. They claimed to feel its heat and hear a beeping noise. After about 10 minutes the object headed toward the north, accompanied by about 23 (*sic*) Chinook helicopters! Afterwards all three reporters claimed to suffer blisters, hair loss, dizziness, headaches and other symptoms. Landrum claimed that she and Colby suffered photosensitivity, and that Colby suffered nightmares. Cash was hospitalized with cancer. They claimed that these medical problems were caused by radiation from the UFO; in 1985 they tried in vain to sue the US Government for $20 million compensation on the grounds that, if it was not a Government operation, it was an alien one from which the Government should have protected them (Schuessler 1982).

Richard Hall, then editor of the *MUFON UFO Journal*, doubted that the (US) military would test some new radioactive device along a highway near a large urban area 'with reckless disregard for human safety'. However, he saw this as the only alternative to the conclusion that it was a 'luminous, maneuverable, flame-spewing, noise-making radioactive ... UFO' (Klass 1983:274). Klass himself appears to have concluded that the report was a hoax (ibid.), but without any evidence.

At 2100L, Canopus lay at an altitude of 7° on an azimuth of 182°, almost directly in line with the road, which runs absolutely straight for over 6 km due south between forests. The reporters may have had their experience at 2050L, when Canopus lay *exactly* in line with the road. Evidently the reporters saw a mirage of Canopus exhibiting a red base. Because of the surrounding trees, it may have appeared to sit on the road, obstructing the highway.

As Klass has pointed out, some of the reported after-effects (he mentions diarrhoea and increased tooth cavities for young Colby) could have prosaic explanations, and it is important to know the previous medical histories. Some of the symptoms appear to be psychosomatic, or fear or shock responses. Cash's cancer must have been induced many years before. Schuessler has not provided any medical histories. Since the location is near to Houston's airport, it is not surprising that helicopters were seen. It *is* surprising that 23 helicopters moved all at once (and that anyone could count that many). Unfortunately it has not been possible to verify the movement of these aircraft.

Alpha Centauri

In September 1983, Jenny Randles of BUFORA reported that one of her investigators (Philip Taylor), who was then a 'scientist' at the Royal Greenwich Observatory, had explained a report from Vero Beach (Florida) as being caused by sight of Venus. The British pilot of a light aircraft was flying from Norfolk (Virginia) to Miami on 2 March 1982. At about 0505L (1005Z), she was at 2500 m over Vero Beach, heading south, when she saw a bright white light 'ahead (in the south-east)'. At first she thought it was the landing light of another aircraft, but the light remained for 35 minutes 'continually abeam of her'. It took on a spiky appearance, looking like a fuzzy star (*sic*). It seemed to vary its distance; 'several times it moved very rapidly indeed further away, at right angles to the line of sight' (her emphasis). It frequently disappeared in cloud and became 'very hazy'. After reporting the incident, it was suggested that she had seen Venus, then very bright. Because the object seemed too close and its exceptional movement away from her was too fast, she disputed this. Randles reported that Venus was then at an altitude of 11° on an azimuth of 66° ('very low in the south-east'). She called this 'a marvellous example to investigators not to take the witness's statement at face value but to check out the obvious solutions'; she declared that 'any investigator who does not thoroughly check for an astronomical source is not doing his job properly' (Randles 1983a).

Indeed it is a lesson to investigators, but one that teaches that we should not jump to conclusions. Venus was certainly in the south-east (azimuth 114°, not 66°), but 11° is not a very low altitude. For the pilot to mistake it for another aircraft, the light must have been much lower, probably on the horizon. Nor would Venus present a 'spiky' appearance. The possibility should have been considered that it really was a star. The investigators should also have checked the aircraft's course; it was very nearly due south.

In fact a first magnitude star did lie only 1° above the horizon on an azimuth of 186°, almost directly 'ahead' of the aircraft. This star was Alpha Centauri, the third brightest star in the entire sky (magnitude -0·1). Its 'movement' sideways was probably caused by autokinesis.

Vega

Retired electrician Max Krauss (65) was walking north-east along a country road towards Langenschemmern (now called Schemmerhofen) south of Ulm in South Germany at about 1500Z on 9 April 1970. The sky was almost completely overcast, with a strong west wind. Suddenly two muffled sonic booms caused him to look around (to his right), where he saw what looked like a torn-off portion of a skeleton of a plant come whirling along on the opposite side of the road. He waited for the wind to drive it into the ditch, but it carried on, slowly overtaking him. Then he could see that it was no plant; it seemed to be a transparent ball some 40 cm across, with spokes inside it. Sketches of the object and its behaviour were made by Hubert Malthaner (figure 4:5).

Here is Krauss's account (Malthaner 1972):

> From a dark spherical nucleus with hazy edges there came eight radials or spokes ... [which] tapered off towards their outer extremities, their tips extending to the perimeter of the globe, which was almost as clear as glass but non-reflecting ... [It] was rotating on a horizontal axis ... and was floating ... along, rather than rolling, a mere hand's breadth above the road.
>
> As the thing passed me, I increased my pace and stepped out after it...[It] may have rolled along in this way beside me for about 150 metres or so. Then it halted, did a

right-angle turn towards a little stream of water, and stopped there. The rotation stopped too.

What I now saw is beyond my power to comprehend. From the dark centre of the ball there emerged, downwards, something resembling a hosepipe, which bent itself back and upwards like a 'U' and then writhed about sideways several times [see figure 4:5]. In the bend that was nearest to the ball there appeared a gleam like brightly glowing hot iron. The colour grew darker towards the more distant convolutions, and was only visible on the outward facing sides of each convolution of the hosepipe.

The hosepipe started wriggling about like a worm, extended itself, and went down to the ground. I am convinced that it reached into the water. The 'worm' remained there for a short while, and then was drawn back in again. At the same time, the central part of the ball changed colour throughout half its radius, becoming milky, like water just before it boils. The outer shell of the ball now displayed a bluish tinge, somewhat like the ionized air to be seen around electrical high tension generators. Then the strange object slowly started its rotation, gliding movement again, passed across the road, quite close to me, to a point a pace or so into the field. And there it vanished, so absolutely silently, and at such lightning speed, straight into the sky, that I as unable to follow it with my eyes.

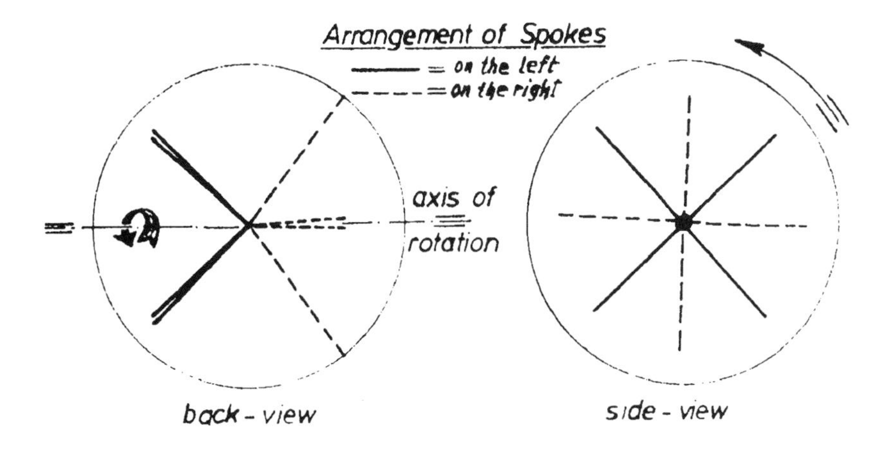

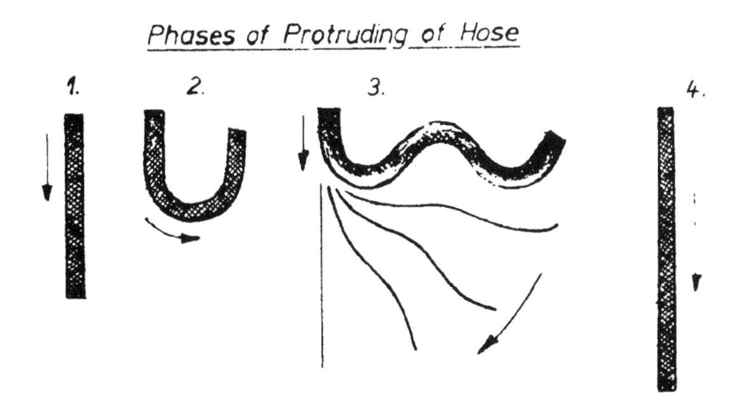

Fig. 4:5 Malthaner's sketches of what Max Krauss reported seeing near Langenschemmern (Germany).

At the time, Vega lay at altitude 6° on azimuth of 325°, the latter being almost exactly the direction in which (according to Malthaner's plan) the object departed (see figure 4:6). It seems that Krauss must have looked left, not right, and that he was on the right-hand side of the road. Krauss may have seen a mirage of Vega, just below the cloud base. The sonic booms were unrelated.

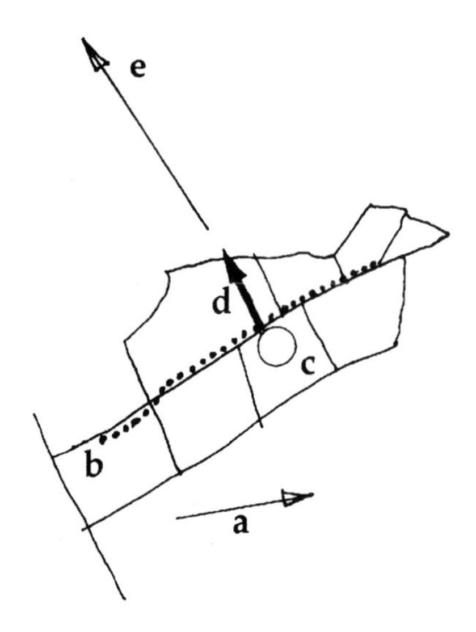

Fig. 4:6 A map of the of the Aufhofen/ Langenschemmern area showing the direction of the wind (a), Krauss's route (b), the point at which the object appeared to take on water (c), the apparent flight path of the object (d) and the direction of Vega at 1500Z (e).

Rigel

As he was leaving his warehouse in South Hill (Virginia), about 2100L (0200Z) on 21 April 1967, C N Crowder saw what he took to be a large balloon with legs sitting on the road in front of him! Suddenly it emitted a brilliant ball of fire from its underside and took off 'like a bullet' into the night. He alleged that it left a section of the road burning, and that he waited for the flames to die down. A burned spot was later found on the road (Klass 1974:115).

After a lengthy investigation, during which he did not consider an astronomical explanation, Klass concluded that the report was a hoax. At the time, Rigel was just setting on an azimuth of 260°. The road in question (Route 747), runs due west (270°), close enough to the azimuth of Rigel for a mirage of it to appear to sit on the road. Red light at the base of the mirage may have appeared as 'fire'; the road may have been burned on an earlier occasion.

Capella

A power failure in Freeport (Texas) enabled officers on the US Coastguard cutter *Legare*, then anchored off Freeport, to see stars much easier. Shortly after the failure, at 0135L (0735Z) on 20 March 1966, they saw a large oval object giving off an orange glow, but surrounded by blue light. It seemed to have ports or windows, which gave off a 'dark orange glow'. One member of the crew gave its direction as 350° (magnetic), and it was observed to rise slowly upwards. At (as they thought) about 300 m high, the orange glow increased and there was a blue flash. Then the glow faded and the object receded very fast, disappearing in seconds.

Klass concluded that the crew had seen a ball-lightning type of plasma created by a short-circuit on the transformer responsible for the power failure (Klass 1974:92). Considering Klass's rejection of the plasma hypothesis, which he adopted in his first book, this conclusion is surprising. However there is an astronomical explanation. Capella lay only 5° above the horizon on azimuth 321° (true). It seems more likely that the crew saw a mirage of Capella.

At 0330L (0230Z) on 25 March 1986, a resident of Soesterberg (Netherlands), who wanted to remain anonymous, was awakened by a loud humming noise. He then noticed beams of light coming through venetian blinds. Looking out, he saw a very bright light, surrounded by a sort of fog. Because it appeared to be close to his car, he thought that the car was on fire. He ran out in panic, climbed into the car, and drove around, trying to attract people's attention. After about 7 minutes, arriving on a military range 4 km away, he got out and saw an 'enormous object' surrounded by a greenish glow. To the left, an oval object was moving among some trees towards the object. He wondered if it could be the same object he had seen earlier. It appeared that he was only 10-15 m away from the object, which was lens-shaped and had windows glowing green. On top there were three, thick green beams of fluorescent light shining upwards into the sky. Behind the windows, he thought he saw humanoids, one of whom gestured with his right hand. Suddenly the object jerked off the ground and, for a moment, hung in the air. It shrank to the size of a dinner plate, and then became a grey spot with a bluish-white glow in the centre, disappearing over a small house on the horizon (azimuth indicated on a plan as about 340°). He got back home at 0415L (Wiersema 1972).

Capella was in that direction; at 0300Z it was at an altitude of 11° on azimuth 342°. However, Pollux, only 8° above the horizon further west (azimuth 307°) may have participated. Evidently what was seen was a mirage of one or both of these stars. The predominant green colour indicates that Capella (peak wavelength 550 nm) was involved.

Altair

Although the UFO reported by (US) ex-President Jimmy Carter has been identified as Venus (Sheaffer 1980:4), it seems that this is a misidentification. It is true that the altitude given by Carter (30°) is not far from that of Venus (24°), but that is about all that does match. Because reporters usually exaggerate altitude by a factor of two or three (see chapter 2), the object may have been only 10-15° high. In fact Carter's sketch of the altitude on NICAP's report form shows it to be about 10°. While Carter reported the object to the west, Venus was in the south-west (237°). The object was reported to be about the same size as the Moon (far too big to be Venus), with variations in size, brightness and colour. At first it was bluish; later it was reddish. Carter had the impression that it approached, moved away, then came close again, and finally that it disappeared into the distance.

The above description is not consistent with a sighting of Venus. However it is consistent with a mirage of a star at low altitude. In fact there was a first magnitude star low in the west at the time. Altair lay only 6° above the horizon just 7° north of due west. It seems probable that this is what Carter and those with him saw.

Aldebaran

A 1948 report by two airline pilots has become a classic. At 0245L (0745Z) on 24 July, the pilots (Chiles and Whitted) were flying an Eastern Airlines DC-3 from Houston (Texas) to Atlanta (Georgia). They were at 1500 m near Montgomery (Alabama) when they saw a dull red glow ahead (but a little above and to the right). In a space of only 10 s, it approached very fast, as if on a collision course, brightened, and seemed to pass just to their right. They described it as like a wingless aircraft, 30 m long, cigar-shaped, and about twice the diameter of a B-29. They had the impression of a brilliantly-lit cabin, underneath which was an intense blue glow. The red glow came from what appeared to be its exhaust. They heard no sound nor felt any air disturbance. The object was also seen by a passenger (Menzel and Boyd 1963:109; Story 1980:71).

In 1953 Menzel thought that they had seen a mirage, but he did not suggest a source. By 1963 he had changed his mind and accepted Hynek's idea that the object was a meteor, an explanation accepted by the USAF in 1959. There was also a suggestion that it was a reflection of the DC-3 off adjacent 'incipient clouds' (Liddel 1953).

Those who claim that the object was a meteor have not produced independent accounts from ground observers. In any case the description is consistent with a mirage of an astronomical object. The colours suggest that the source was a star. Indeed Aldebaran lay about 3° above the pilots' horizon on an azimuth of 72°, slightly to their right (their course was about 70°). It appears that they saw a mirage of the star.

A mirage of Aldebaran appears to have been responsible for the 'Cowichan encounter' (Story 1980:92), in which several nurses at Cowichan District Hospital (British Colombia) reported seeing a flying saucer with occupants about 0500L (1300Z) on 5 January 1970. The object vanished to the north-east, where Aldebaran lay only 2° above the horizon on an azimuth of 293°.

Antares

Antares appeared as a squat cigar (or cone)-shaped object, orange at the bottom, which a Fort William (Highland in Scotland) family thought was coming down Glen Nevis (a valley below Ben Nevis) at about 0300Z on 3 May 1980. Through binoculars, they could see a triangular shape with three panels of orange light and 'revolving' flashing lights. The star lay at an altitude of only 4°, just above mountains at the head of the valley (azimuth 151°). The calm conditions were conducive to a temperature inversion. The sudden disappearance of the mirage led the witnesses to the conclusion that the object had raced away to the west, where they probably mistook Jupiter and Mars (then in close conjunction) for the same object (Campbell 1986b).

Spica

What may be a rare photograph of an astronomical mirage was taken by school caretaker Peter Wood from Stainton near Kendal (Cumbria in England) at 1820Z on 7 July 1977 (see plate 4:7). The object, which was brilliant, appeared to rotate (from right to left) and did not move with the surrounding clouds. He drew his son's attention to the phenomenon, dashed inside to get his camera, and used the last frame on the film. Just after the photograph was taken, it rotated faster, and disappeared by shrinking. As it vanished there was a bright flash of light in the same area (alleged to be about 25-30° altitude). Wood thought that it was a whirlwind cloud. There was no very bright star at the azimuth given (130-140° magnetic). But Spica lay at an altitude of 25° on an azimuth of 176°. It seems likely that Spica was responsible.

At 0615L on 27 October 1979 (1815Z on 26 October), Lou Blackburn was attempting to photograph a friend's boat as it left a tidal river at Motunau (New Zealand). It was his friend's camera (35 mm Olympus), and it had been set (unknown to him) for exposure in daylight. However it

Plate 4:7 A photograph of what may be a stellar mirage (photo Peter Wood).

was dawn, and the scene was in the shadow of hills to the north-east. He exposed several frames at that time, and others later that day. Processing showed that the early frames either did not come out or were grossly underexposed. Only three months later were the slides examined in more detail, when it was noticed that a cluster of lights appeared in the sky on the second frame, to the left of the rising Sun (see plate 4:8). The cluster did not appear on the third frame which was taken 5-10 s later.

The cluster appeared as a sparkling blue light, with diamond-like clarity. Enlargement showed that there were two rows of lights, and that each light was doubled. All the lights were blue, except for two at the lower left which had a creamy tinge. Between the two rows of lights, on the extreme right, there appeared to be a large, purplish hazy spot (see plate 4:9). Local investigators claimed that the azimuth of the bush on the crest of the hill below the cluster was 60° (magnetic) (F and P Dickeson 1981).

Allowing for the local magnetic deviation, the azimuth of the bush is 81° (true), but this may be too small. From the camera data, and the presumed level of the horizon, it can be calculated that the cluster is at an altitude of about 16·5°. The Sun was at 9° altitude on azimuth 99°. The only bright astronomical object in the area was the blue star Spica (15° altitude, 92° azimuth). It appears therefore that the cluster is a mirage of Spica, including multiple images.

Plate 4:8 The uncropped Motunau photograph, which probably shows a mirage of Spica.

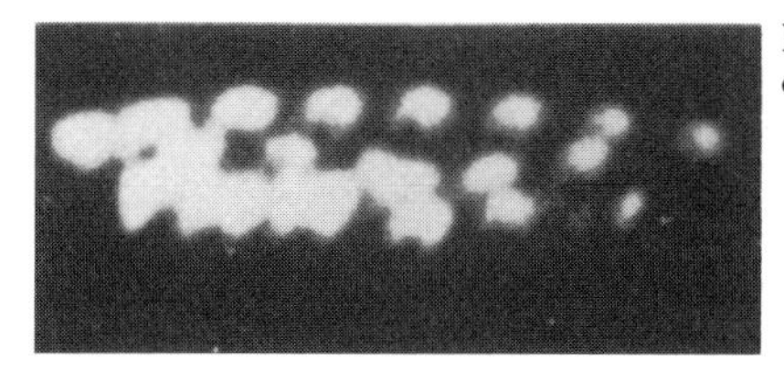

Plate 4:9 An enlargement (70x) of the cluster of lights in plate 4:8

Fomalhaut

A USAF RB-47 jet bomber, equipped with electronic countermeasures and manned by a crew of six, was on a training mission early one morning (see below) in 1957. By 0410L (1010Z) the aircraft was flying at a height of 10·5 km on a course of 265° (true) over Winnsboro (Louisiana). Suddenly the pilots saw 'a very intense white light with a blue tint' coming towards them from the left, 11 o'clock (south-west). It appeared to cut across their path very fast and head away to the right, 2 o'clock (north-west), where it disappeared. At 0439L they sighted a 'huge [red] light', estimated to be 1500 m below about 60° to starboard (325°). An intelligence report claimed that two such red lights were seen, but one pilot could recall seeing only one. At 0440L the pilot changed course (to 320°) to pursue one of these lights. This took the aircraft over Dallas (Texas), where, at 0450L, the light seemed to stop and disappear. At this the pilot made a slow turn to port (see figure 4:7), sighting a 'curious light' to the south-east (north-west, according to Thayer) at 0458L. Attempting (in vain) to get closer to this light, the aircraft descended to 6 km, but, running low on fuel, they had to abandon the chase and head for base. Some anomalous radar signals (not echoes) were thought by the crew to be related to the anomalous lights (Klass 1974:186; Story 1980:297; Gillmor 1969:56 and 261).

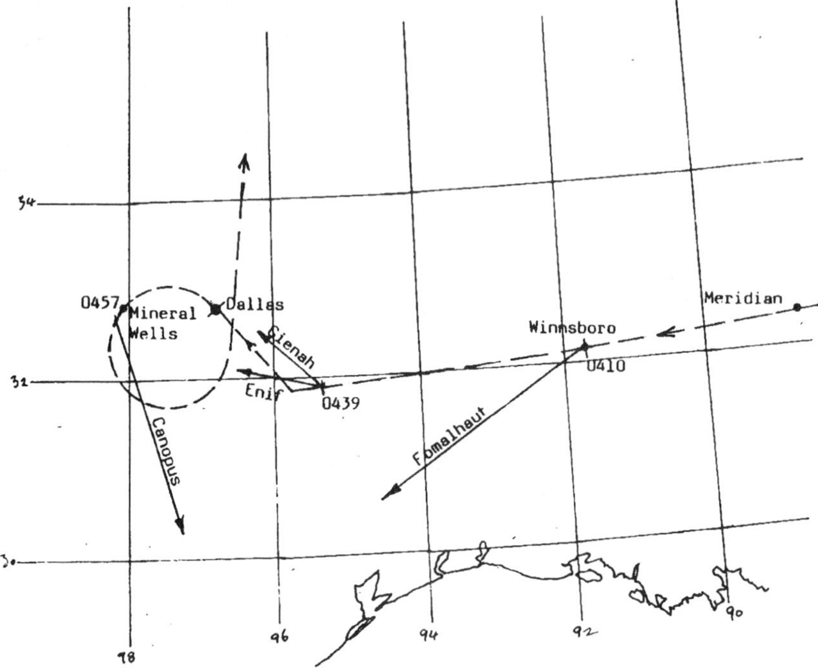

Fig. 4:7 A plan of part of the route of the RB-47 showing the azimuth of various celestial objects at various times.

The case was chosen by a leading aeronautical journal as a sample of the type of observations which form the core of the UFO controversy (McDonald 1971).

Klass explained that the radar signals were caused by a new type of radar, the existence of which seems not to have been known to the crew. He concluded that the light at 0410L was a 'meteor/fireball', but he offered no evidence. Puzzled by the light seen north-west at 0439L, Klass asked Robert Sheaffer if it could be a celestial body. Sheaffer replied that Vega would have been at azimuth 300° and altitude 27°, and he also noted that Rigel was just rising over the horizon on an azimuth of 105°. Klass made no further comment, except to claim that the identification of the light as Vega could 'never be established for sure'.

Menzel accepted Klass's explanation, including his (and Sheaffer's) explanations for the lights seen, although he did suggest that the last light was that of a commercial flight landing at Dallas airport (Menzel and Taves 1977:93). The USAF also concluded that the latter light was that of an air liner (McDonald 1971).

I omitted the date of the incident because of conflict in the sources. According to the Condon Report, whose investigators interviewed all the crew in 1967 and checked their personal flight logs, the event occurred on 19 September (but between midnight and 0300L). According to McDonald, who claimed to have located the Blue Book case files, it occurred on 17 July (Sagan and Page 1972:58). Thayer, who wrote part of the Condon case report, endorsed 17 July (Story 1980), but with no explanation for the discrepancy, not even his own part in it. McDonald referred to, but did not exhibit, a 'three page TWX filed ... at 1557Z on 7/17/57 [17 July] and a four-page case summary...forwarded on 10/17/57 [17 October] ... to Bluebook' (Sagan and Page 1972:58). Blue Book received a summary from Air Defense Command on 25 October, and this delay (more than three months) surprised McDonald (op. cit.:67).

It is curious that one date has two sevens ('17/7'), and the other has two nines ('19/9'). Confusion may have arisen by the misreading of nines for sevens (or vice versa). Perhaps we can decide between them by applying the AMH to both dates and comparing the results.

On 17 July, there were neither planets nor first magnitude stars near the horizon. On the 19 September however, Fomalhaut (a blue-white star) lay at an altitude of -4° on an azimuth of 237°, almost exactly on the pilot's 11 o'clock position. Since the crew could see 4-5° below the horizontal, Fomalhaut should have been visible. According to the Condon Report, a temperature inversion did exist on 19 September. Evidently the object seen at 0410L was a mirage of Fomalhaut and the incident did occur on this date. The three month delay is then reduced to a more reasonable 36 days.

The other objects sighted on 19 September may also have been stars, but not necessarily first magnitude ones. At 0439L, the orange star Enif (magnitude 2·31) was just 1° below the horizon on azimuth 283° and must have disappeared when it was at an altitude of -4° (at 0452L). In fact the red light disappeared at 0450L. At 0452L, another orange star, Gienah (magnitude 2·46), lay at only 1° altitude on azimuth 310°, only 10° from the course taken by the aircraft as it chased a red light shortly after 0440L (see figure 4:7). At 0450L, when the red light stopped and vanished, Gienah was 1° below the horizon, and should still have been visible. However the inversion may have moved or lifted, cutting off the enhanced image. The 'curious light' seen at 0458L seems to have been Canopus, only 1° above the horizon on azimuth 162°.

Sheaffer's identification is inapplicable, not only because it refers to the wrong date, but because neither Rigel nor Vega could have been seen as a red star. Moreover Rigel was in the wrong direction and Vega's high altitude precludes it as a stimulus for the report.

It would be surprising, and somewhat alarming, if a military pilot could not identify the lights of another aircraft. More likely, he knew this was not the case and the USAF is wrong. If it could get the date of the incident wrong, it could get anything wrong.

Deneb

Two bright, elliptical objects were seen and filmed from Great Falls (Montana) at 1125L (1825Z) on 5 or 15 August 1950. At first they were stationary at about 15° altitude in a north-north-west direction, and seemed to tilt momentarily. They also seemed to be rotating. They quickly moved off together, apparently towards the south-west, disappearing in less than 20 s. It has been alleged that the objects were sunlight reflecting off two jet aircraft which were known to be in the area on 15 August. However the cameraman claimed to have seen the aircraft *and* the bright objects, and there is reason to doubt that the film was taken on 15 August. It was also established that the jets should have been identifiable (Story 1980:153).

No azimuth has been given, but a plan in the Condon Report (Gillmor 1969:410) shows it as about 345°. On 5 August, Deneb lay at an altitude of only 3° on azimuth 352°. It seems possible therefore that the objects were duplicate mirage images of Deneb and that they moved because the vertical thermocline responsible moved south. Unfortunately, the weather data given in the Condon Report are for the 15 August.

Unidentified stars

At about 1215L (1615Z), on Sunday 27 July 1975, a Washington (DC) civil servant had his attention drawn to a very bright object 'falling from' the sky in the north-east. He was at his home in Cheverly (Maryland), just east of Washington. He saw an object 'like a bright star' descend with uniform angular motion against a clear blue sky. Suddenly it stopped, oscillated and/or moved sideways slightly; it them remained motionless. He then saw a second, similar object, which seemed to have moved rapidly from the upper left until it was at the same altitude. For a minute or more they remained motionless, during which time he noticed that each one was surrounded by a dark ring like a faint shadow. Each ring was about twice the diameter of each bright object. The second object moved left and right before departing in a uniform, rapid, apparently vertical ascent. It was followed by the first object, which first descended slightly, and then rose out of sight. As they ascended, they shrank in size, taking about 7 s to do so. The objects were also seen by his wife and daughter.

Bruce Maccabee, who investigated, claimed that the objects had been seen about 8° apart horizontally between about 23° and 32° azimuth, and at an altitude of about 25°, plus or minus 5°. The weather was very warm (c. 27 °C), with a clear sky caused by a high pressure system sandwiched between two cold fronts. A cold front lying south-west/ north-east was moving south-east. Visibility was 32 km and the wind was 2 m/s at 160°.

Despite intensive enquiries, Maccabee could find no rational explanation. He could find no other reports of the sighting, and nothing unusual had been reported by pilots in the area or seen on radar. Because flight records are only kept for fifteen days, neither the National Airport (in Washington) nor Andrews AFB (south-east of Washington) could give details of traffic on the day in question. It was established that there could have been three or four landings at National Airport in the period 1200L to 1230L, but these were from the west. The azimuth pointed to NASA's Goddard Space Center (about 10 km away), but nothing happens there on a Sunday. It also pointed in the general direction of Baltimore-Washington Airport (BW), about 34 km away. A Boeing 707 was due to take off from BW at 1200L, but might have been late. Maccabee considered solar reflection ('glint') from an aircraft, but noted that it rarely lasted more than 30 s, and could not explain the sudden movements of the objects. He did not consider mirages (Maccabee 1976).

The behaviour and appearance of the objects indicates that, almost certainly, they were mirages of two stars (or duplicate mirage images of a single star). The dark shadow rings indicate high magnification, probably caused by a thermocline associated with the cold front.

Unfortunately, it is not so easy to identify the star or stars involved. The position described by Maccabee straddles the constellation Draco, slightly below Thuban (α Dra). Slightly to the east (azimuth 45°) lay the constellation of Ursa Major, with Alkaid (η UMa) at 25° altitude and the other stars of The Plough stretching upwards. One of more of these bright stars may have been responsible.

On 2 July 1952, US Navy Warrant Officer, Delbert C Newhouse, with his wife and two children, was driving north on Highway 30, about 11 km north of Tremonton (Utah). At about 1110L (1810Z), his wife drew his attention to a group of ten or twelve bright objects 'off towards the eastern horizon', in an otherwise absolutely clear blue sky. When he found that he could not identified the objects (they bore no relation to anything he had seen before), Newhouse stopped the car and reached for the 16-mm cine camera (with 75 mm telephoto lens) he had in the car. He was an experienced Navy photographer. He loaded the camera and exposed about 9 m of film, aimed at the objects. Newhouse claimed that the objects were approximately 70° above the terrain and that they all had the same motion ('milling around in the sky'), except one which reversed course. Mostly he filmed facing north, but it is reported that the objects vanished to the west. Stills from the film (see colour plate 4:10) show several pairs of white blobs, two pairs in the one exhibited here. The Condon Report gives full details, including the photographic data. According to Richard Baker, Newhouse described them as 'gun metal colored objects shaped like two saucers, one inverted on top of the other', and he estimated that they each subtended an angle of about 0·5°. However, William K Hartmann was unable to confirm this account. In fact Baker's own microscopic measurements showed that the objects typically subtended an angle of about 5·5 to 1·5 arcminutes (Gillmor 1969:418).

The film has been subject to intensive investigation, especially by the USAF and the US Navy on behalf of Blue Book. Neither could identify the objects, but the USAF was certain that they were not aircraft, balloons or birds. The Navy claimed that the objects were internally lit spheres (not objects reflecting sunlight). In 1953, a CIA panel concluded that the objects were birds, but Baker, who made an independent study in 1955, asked why a naval officer would take the trouble to film birds (Sagan and Page 1972:200). Menzel remained convinced that the objects were birds (Menzel and Boyd 1963:130), and even claimed that this had been 'proved conclusively' (Menzel and Taves 1977:192). In the mid '60s the case was considered in detail by William K Hartmann for the Condon team; he also concluded that the objects were birds, and claimed to have seen such sights in Utah. However, he stated that 'the data are not conclusive' (Story 1980:364).

The grouping of the objects in pairs is a strong indication that they are mirages of some bright distant object (or objects). The exact azimuth of the filming is unclear (except that it was northerly). This makes it difficult to understand the statement that the objects were first seen to the east. Nor is the location very clear. Highway 30 twisted and turned as it left Tremonton. However, at a distance of about 11 km, it headed north-north-west (about azimuth 340°). It is most likely therefore that the objects were seen ahead, albeit at first slightly to the right (east). The constellations of Cygnus and Draco lay on the northern horizon, Deneb (α Cyg) only 8° above the horizon on an azimuth of 327°. This may be too far west, and the images may be double mirages of stars in Draco (azimuth about 357°). If Newhouse's estimate of altitude is correct, the stars could have been those of Ursa Minor, including Polaris (α UMi). An alternative source is Vega, which lay 8° below the horizon on an azimuth of 346°, closer to the presumed azimuth of the objects. In this case, the light from Vega would have had to be ducted around the Earth for about 890 km. Whatever the source, it is almost certain that Newhouse filmed mirages of a group of stars.

According to the Condon Report, a high pressure cell from the Pacific Northwest spread over northern Utah during the day. This can have caused a temperature inversion.

This review of many reports shows the power of the AMH; I shall now consider whether or not it (or the MH) can explain some core reports, starting with the first report of 'flying saucers'.

5 The first flying saucers

Most writers on UFOs seem to believe that it is not known what it was that Kenneth Arnold saw on 24 June 1947 (Evans 1987:13). It is certainly true that the incident has never been explained satisfactorily (Story 1980:25). Yet if we cannot explain this seminal case, we can hardly claim to have made much progress in explaining UFO reports.

The pilot's tale

Arnold used a light aircraft to sell fire-fighting equipment over five western states of the USA and, by 1947, he had over 1000 hours flying experience. In January of that year, he bought a new Callair monoplane. On 24 June 1947 he was flying this aircraft from Chehalis to Yakima (Washington), but he took an extra hour to search for a crashed aircraft. Eventually he abandoned the search over a small town called Mineral, and set course at a height of 2800 m for Yakima in the east.

After setting the autopilot, he was able to look about him. The air was crystal clear, with visibility up to 80 km (at least). He noticed a DC4 to his left rear at about 25 km and 4200 m high, but after two or three minutes he was startled by a bright flash to his left, to the north of Mt. Ranier. There he saw a chain of nine peculiar 'aircraft' flying (apparently) from north to south. He estimated that their course was 170° and that they were at approximately his flight level. They were flying in echelon formation but (contrary to USAF practice) with the leader highest, and as if they were all linked together (that is, they all moved at exactly the same speed). He observed that there was a gap between the first four objects and the last five.

Arnold was bothered by the fact that he could see no tail fins on the craft; no aircraft could fly without this distinctive feature. They appeared merely as a thin black lens shape, but every few seconds two or three of them would produce a brilliant blue-white flash which Arnold interpreted as sunlight reflecting off wings as the craft dipped them (although he could see no wings). When flashing, the objects appeared to be completely round (see figure 5:1), although one was darker and a different shape. It was Arnold's attempt to describe this flashing that led to the objects being described by the press as 'flying saucers'. He likened the behaviour to powerboats at speed or saucers skimmed across water, but this does not appear to have been intended to be taken too literally. His simile was intended to illustrate the irregularity of the flashes. He did not allege that the objects made any vertical movements as observed in boats or saucers on water.

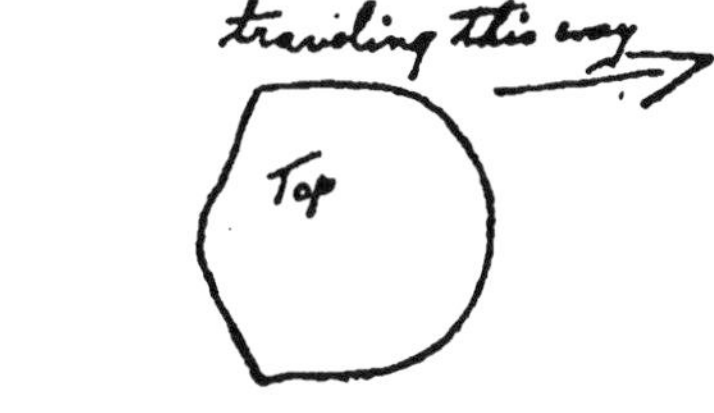

Fig. 5:1 Arnold's original sketch of one of the objects he saw. In addition he noted that they were 'mirror bright' and that their width was about twenty times their thickness (his sketch shows the width only about ten times the thickness).

For a time, the objects disappeared behind Mt. Ranier, but it was just about 1500L (2300Z) when the first one emerged and he realized that he could time them and ascertain their speed. He was amazed that they were flying so close to the mountain tops; they seemed to be flying down the ridge of a mountain range. He estimated that the objects, almost at right angles to his course, were 30 to 40 km away.

He was flying towards a ridge, the length of which he could measure because it had marker peaks, one at each end. Consequently he resolved to time the objects as they passed this ridge. From the time, and the distance between the peaks, he could calculate their speed (assuming he knew their distance). He found that the last object in the chain took 102 s to pass from one peak to the other; he also noticed that, as the first object reached the 'south' peak, the last one was passing the 'north' peak. Later he determined that the peaks were 8 km apart and therefore that the chain of objects was at least that long.

He estimated that he observed the objects for 2½ to 3 minutes, and claimed that, by the time the objects reached Mt. Adams, they were out of his range of vision. For a while he continued to search, but then he made for Yakima, where he reported what he had seen. By the time he reached Pendleton in Oregon, the news media caught up with him and the 'flying saucer' myth was born.

Explanations

There have been many explanations. At the time, Arnold thought that the objects were jet aircraft, as did Hynek in his report to Blue Book (Steiger 1976:35). It was also suggested that the objects were guided missiles from Moses Lake, 112 km to the north-east of Yakima (Arnold and Palmer 1952). It has even been suggested that Arnold saw several small plastic balloons (Gardner 1957:58).

Menzel made several suggestions, but different ones at different times. His first idea was that the objects were either snow ballooning (*sic*) up from the top of ridges or sunlight reflecting off sharp layers of haze or dust (Menzel 1953:8-10). Later he suggested that Arnold had seen mirages of mountain peaks or, less likely, orographic clouds (Menzel and Boyd 1963:6). Finally he tentatively suggested that the cause was drops of rain on the window (Menzel and Taves 1977:6). It is reported that the USAF concluded that the objects were mirages (Steiger 1976:25), but there has been no elaboration or confirmation of this hypothesis. Arnold formed the impression that the USAF knew what the objects were, and that they had good photographs of them. By mid-summer of 1947, he publicized this erroneous impression in magazine articles which gained wide attention. This fostered the 'government conspiracy' myth. The fact that the two officers who visited him were later killed in an airplane crash while investigating another report fuelled further rumours (Sagan and Page 1972:15). Menzel's conclusion was that, because there is 'no grist for analysis other than his report', we shall never know what Arnold saw (Menzel and Taves 1977:81). I shall show that there is 'grist for analysis' and that by grinding it we can fully explain the incident.

Analysis of Arnold's account

In his report to Blue Book, Hynek drew attention to an inconsistency and an error in Arnold's account. The latter's estimate of the size of the objects was not compatible with his estimate of distance (given an assumption about the limit of resolution of the eye) and he had wrongly calculated the speed of the objects from the distance and time given (Steiger 1976: 35). Hynek's criticism was based on the fact that if the limit of resolution of the eye is taken as 3 arcminutes (0·05°), then objects 40 km away would have to be a minimum of 30 m thick (and 600 m long if they were twenty times longer than they were thick). In fact the limit of resolution is usually taken as 1 arcminute (0·016°) and Arnold's sketch shows the objects only about ten times longer than they are thick. It seems that Hynek later retracted these conclusions (Long 1987). However Hynek did not point out (and perhaps did not realize) that Arnold's account of his timing observation is also inconsistent.

Arnold stated that he had 'two definite points' by which he could time the objects. Later he explained that the two points were the northern and southern crests of a ridge which lay between Mt. Ranier and Mt. Adams and towards which he was flying. On later measurement he found that the two crests (he later called them 'mountains') were 8 km apart. However, when he came to report the time the objects took to pass his timing points, he referred to the last object passing 'the southern most high snow-covered crest of Mt. Adams' after 102 s. Now Mt. Adams is some 50 km to the south of his position near Mt. Ranier, and some 80 km from Mt. Ranier. Not only had he reported seeing the objects to the north (to his left) but his statement that the timing points were 8 km apart is irreconcilable with his claim that one of the peaks was Mt. Adams 50 km away to his right. Inexplicably, he also referred twice more to Mt. Adams, albeit in one instance stating that, by that time, the objects were out of his range of vision as far as determining shape and form. In addition, because Mt. Adams rises to 3751 m, nearly 1000 m higher than his flight level, it could not have been one of his timing points; the objects would have been hidden behind it.

A search of the aeronautical chart covering the area immediately to the south of Mt. Ranier (which does lie 'between Mt. Ranier and Mt. Adams') for a ridge with two peaks 8 km apart shows that the only candidate is the Tatoosh Range, which is marked at one end by Pinnacle Peak (2000 m) and at the other by Lookout (1923 m). The two peaks are almost exactly 8 km apart (see figure 5:2). Since this range lies directly east of Mineral it must have been the 'ridge' towards which Arnold was flying.

It seems that the two peaks of the Tatoosh Range have become confused with Mts. Ranier and Adams, probably very early. In his book, Arnold states that the speed calculation made at Pendleton (2650 km/h) astonished him, and he concluded that the distance measurements were being taken 'far too high up on both Mount Ranier and Mount Adams'. But even taking the distance down to 64 km still produced a speed of 2259 km/h (which he wrongly calculated as 2160 km/h). It is these high speeds that have led to the conclusion by some that the objects were extraterrestrial or alien. Yet in his report to the USAF Arnold had clearly stated that he had timed the objects over a distance of only 8 km.

In his account to Blue Book, Arnold does not give the speed at which he calculated the objects were travelling, nor did he reveal how he had calculated it. However, given a speed of 2160 km/h, a course for the objects of 170°, a minimum distance from Arnold of 40 km and two timing peaks 8 km apart, I constructed figure 5:3 (q.v.); this may represent the situation as imagined by Arnold. Note that Mt. Adams does not enter into this concept. Now this interpretation is only feasible if Arnold imagined that he was stationary. However he was a moving observer, travelling at between 164 and 180 km/h (the cruising and maximum speeds respectively of his aircraft). Figure 5:3 demonstrates very clearly that the mysterious objects should have crossed Arnold's course directly in front of him. However he did not report this event. There has to be doubt therefore that Arnold's interpretation of the incident is correct, and I propose to examine another interpretation.

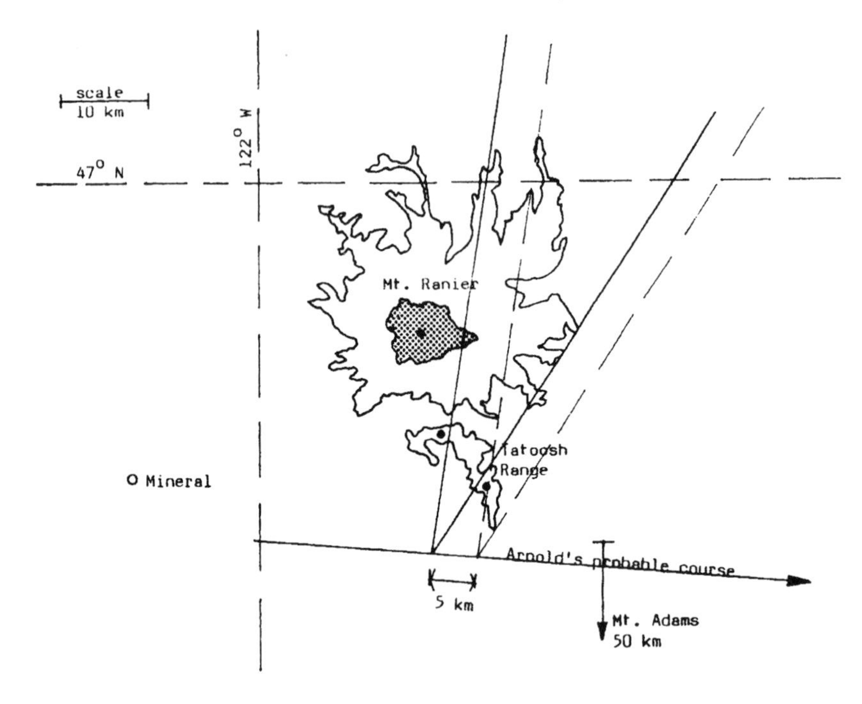

Fig. 5:2 Arnold's probable course from Mineral to Yakima near Mt. Ranier, showing the angle subtended by the mirages of nine Cascade peaks and the peaks of the Tatoosh Range used to time their apparent movement. The shaded area of Mt. Ranier is above his stated flight level and should have hidden the mirages (unless they were elevated) or Arnold was higher than he thought.

Arnold can have had no certain method of determining the course of the objects, but it seems that he deduced it from the graduation in size, the nearest one (apparently) being the largest. The echelon formation, although inverted, must also have given the impression of a southerly course. But, if the objects only appeared to be on a southerly course, they can just as well have been flying a parallel course. In that case, the marker peaks in the Tatoosh Range are only 5 km apart (see figure 5:2). The speed of a very distant object on a parallel course (or any other course for that matter) is very difficult to assess unless one knows what distance it is covering in a given time. All Arnold knew was that the formation took 102 s to pass between his marker peaks (only 5 km apart for a northerly view). If Arnold had calculated the speed that results from covering 5 km in 102 s he would have found that it is 176 km/h, possibly the speed of his own aircraft at the time (which he did not record). This would have alerted him to the possibility that his own movement may have accounted for the apparent movement of the formation. If the formation was very distant it can be regarded as nearly stationary (because of the slow azimuthal change), just as a stationary Moon or planet near the horizon will seem to follow a moving observer. In fact the nine objects could actually have been stationary, but at a great distance. That would explain why they appeared to be fixed together. But what bright stationary objects lay to the north?

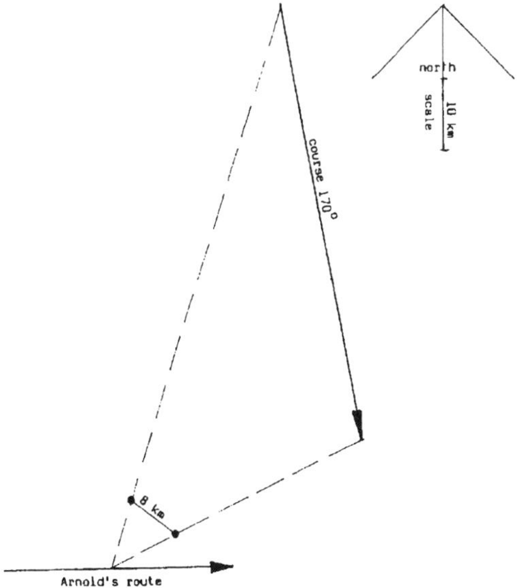

Fig. 5:3 How Arnold may have imagined the strange 'craft' were travelling in relation to his aircraft.

What Arnold saw

Mt. Ranier is part of the Cascade Range of mountains which extends northward towards the Canadian border 250 km away, and which, as it approaches the border, fans out with a proliferation of high mountains in the height range 2 to 3 km (see figure 5:4).

Mt. Stuart, 100 km away in the Wenatchee Mountains, is the start of this chain of peaks. Now Arnold's view northward was across two deep river valleys, that of the Yakima River, about 80 km away, and that of the Skykomish River, about 120 km away. In the calm conditions, it is

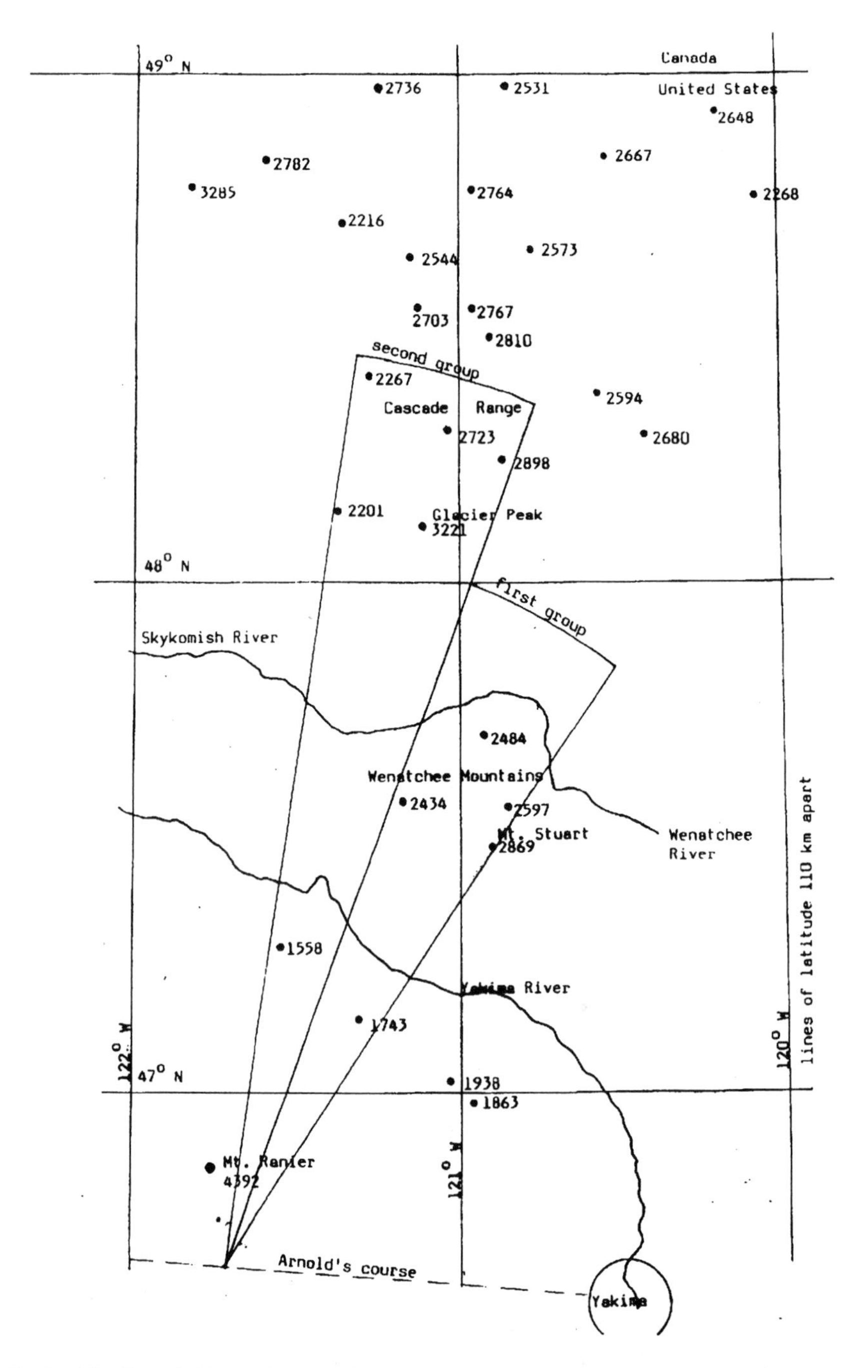

Fig. 5:4 The Cascade Range showing the nine peaks which probably caused Arnold's report.

possible that temperature inversions had formed in either or both of these valleys, so causing mirage effects for anyone viewing objects across them. Arnold can therefore have seen mirages of several of the snow-capped Cascade mountains. They are all more or less permanently covered with snow. Some lower peaks may clear in summer, and this may account for the darker appearance of one object. The blue-white colour Arnold saw is consistent with strongly reflected sunlight off snow. It is evident from figure 5:4 that the first four objects he saw can have been mirages of the four high peaks in the Wenatchee Mountains, 'led' by Mt. Stuart. The second group of five objects can have been mirages of the more distant five mountains around Glacier Peak. They can all have appeared to be flying along the crest of the ridge between Arnold and the Yakima River. The whole group subtends an angle of about 25° in the horizontal plane, and when this angle of view is embraced by the Tatoosh markers it is clear that Arnold must have been 5 km or so south of the direct course from Mineral to Yakima (see figure 5:2).

Although no specific weather data were given at the time, it has since been alleged that there was a wind from the north or north-east and that the air was dry at low elevations with moist air spreading at higher levels (Reed 1958). This moist air is likely to have been warmer than the dry air, so forming inversions over the valleys. The usual thin line mirage can have been enormously brightened as the light rays crossed parts of the inversion(s) where the temperature gradient of the thermocline was steep. The mirage of a peak would appear to flip and brighten as its light crossed areas of strong refraction and focusing.

It is now evident that Menzel had indeed mentioned the best explanation, albeit as one alternative, in 1963. He even showed an illustration of such mountain top mirages (see figure 5:5). Unfortunately he did not develop this idea and later appeared to have abandoned it.

Criticism of the mirage hypothesis

In 1968, McDonald made three specific objections to the mirage hypothesis for Arnold's report. These were (1) that the objects changed angular elevation, (2) that they moved through an azimuthal range of about 90° and (3) that they were observed while the observer's own plane was climbing through an altitude interval of between 150 and 300 m. He noted that it was 'utterly unreasonable to claim that such an observation was satisfactorily explained as a mirage' (Roush 1968:80).

McDonald's idea that the objects changed angular elevation seems to be based on Arnold's statement that 'their elevation could have varied a thousand feet [300 m] one way or another up or down ...'. McDonald may have confused angular elevation with height elevation; clearly Arnold was referring to the height of the objects, which at their great distance, made little difference to their angular elevation (described by Arnold as practically 0°). In any case Arnold was attempting to assess their flight level, not imply that it varied. McDonald's idea that the objects moved through a horizontal right angle is clearly the result of believing that they were travelling from Mt. Ranier to Mt. Adams. I can find no basis for McDonald's claim that Arnold's aircraft was climbing during the sighting. Arnold himself did not claim this. He set the autopilot for level flight. Evidently all McDonald's objections are based on misunderstandings and his criticism has no force.

Fig. 5:5 Menzel's illustration of mountain-top mirages, which might explain the Arnold report (Tacker 1960). Copyright Van Nostrand Reinhold.

To the suggestion that he had seen reflections, 'or even a mirage', Arnold responded that he had observed the objects through an open cockpit window. This deals with internal reflections (and also with raindrops on the window), but it does not counter the mirage hypothesis, which Arnold may not have understood.

It can be objected that Arnold reported seeing the objects outlined 'against the snow' or, as in his book, 'silhouetted against both snow and sky'. There is not enough certainty in this observation for it to have much force. It is not absolutely clear that he was reporting seeing the objects in front of anything but sky.

Conclusions

Evidently there is sufficient 'grist' in the report to find an adequate explanation. Indeed it is an explanation already (apparently) adopted by the USAF, but perhaps without justification, and one suggested by Menzel. Arnold saw mirages of nine snow-capped peaks of the Cascade Range, although they were between 100 and 200 km away from him. However because they were so far away they appeared to be travelling over the nearer mountains. His own movement east caused them to appear to move in the same direction, although he interpreted this as a southwards movement because of their graded size and height (both diminishing to the left). He estimated their speed by timing them between two nearby peaks, but his estimate was erroneous because of his wrong assumption about the objects' distance and their (presumed) course. It was also flawed by reason of his own movement. Subsequently his marker peaks were wrongly identified as Mts. Ranier and Adams. The flashes which first attracted his attention were caused by strong focusing of the mirage rays as they crossed parts of the thermocline(s) where the temperature gradients were steep.

It is interesting to note that (in this case) the MH explains the large number of objects, their precise number, their appearance in two groups (and the number and disposition in each group), the 'echelon' formation (with the highest to the right), the appearance of being fixed together, the shape of the objects and the reason for the flashes, and the apparent speed of the objects. It would be even more interesting to know what other hypothesis could so comprehensively explain this report. The other explanations proposed are utterly inadequate (and some are downright silly). Even some of Menzel's flew in the face of the facts. Billowing snow would have required a high wind and there was no rain to form raindrops on the windows (Menzel anticipated this objection). On the other hand it was Menzel who first suggested a mirage of mountain peaks, albeit based on an idea previously put forward by Tacker (1960:58). It is surprising that Menzel did not develop the idea.

The fact that Arnold's report can be explained as a mirage may be significant. We have already seen that many reports have a similar explanation. Perhaps the probability that the first 'flying saucers' were mirages points to the probability that all (or most) UFO reports can be explained as mirages. I shall show that this is indeed so.

Postscript

An interesting postscript is recorded in the Blue Book files. On hearing of Arnold's report, the editor of the *Idaho Daily Statesman* (published in Boise, Arnold's home town) assigned the paper's aviation editor, David N Johnson, who knew Arnold well, to take the paper's aircraft and look for 'the flying saucers' and photograph them. He was to conduct the patrol as long as he saw fit or until he saw 'a flying disc'.

On the first sortie, on 7 July, Johnson (with Arnold as his passenger) looked in the area where Arnold had been (around Mt. Ranier), but saw nothing. The following day, Johnson flew alone in an AT-6 of the 190th Fighter Squadron, Idaho National Guard, of which he was a member.

Searching now into northern Idaho, north-west Montana, Washington and Oregon, Johnson again saw nothing.

On 9 July, he again took the AT-6, but concentrated his search in Idaho around Boise. At about midday, flying east at about 4260 m, he saw a round, black object to his left (no exact direction given). At first he thought it was a weather balloon, but he was told that the last one had been released at 0830L. He opened the cockpit cover and exposed about 10 s of 8 mm cine film aimed at the object (although he could not see it in the viewfinder). With the naked eye, Johnson could see an object that alternately appeared as a thin, black line and a bright light. It seemed to perform a manoeuvre that looked like a slow barrel roll which, instead of being complete, was broken off at about the 180° point. He lost sight of it as it rolled out at the top. It was observed against a background of cumulus clouds forming over the Camas Prairie, but he could estimate neither its distance nor its speed. He was certain that it was not an aircraft, and no aircraft was known to be in the area. An image of the object was not visible on the developed film (Steiger 1976:36).

Because Johnson's description (almost identical to Arnold's) is typical of a mirage, it is very likely that he also saw a mirage of a snow-covered peak. Indeed, Hyndman Peak (3681 m) lay slightly to his left at a distance of about 180 km. No weather data were given.

6 The Trindade UFO pictures

At about 1220L (1420Z) on 16 January 1958, the sailing ship *Almirante Saldanha* was preparing to weigh anchor near a small rocky island in the South Atlantic Ocean. Ilha da Trindade (Trinity Island) lies about 1100 km off the coast of Brazil, to which it belongs. It was used as a military base for US and Brazilian warships fighting German U-boats during the Second World War. Usually uninhabited, it then possessed a meteorological and oceanographic station as part of Brazil's contribution to International Geophysical Year (IGY). The ship had been converted into a hydrographic unit and was operated by the Hydrography and Navigation Division of the Brazilian Navy. It carried a crew of 300, including several civilian specialists, one of whom was professional photographer Almiro Barauna (42).

The photographer's tale

Barauna claimed that he was on deck along with many of the crew and some of the civilians, forty-eight in all according to Smith (1983). He was preparing to photograph the shore boat and had with him his Rolleiflex 2·8E (set at f/8 and 1/125 s). The sky was bright but rather cloudy and the sea was agitated.

Suddenly Barauna was aware of a disturbance, and his attention was drawn to a bright object moving towards the island. There was great excitement on deck and some shouted that it was a flying saucer. Despite being pushed and pulled by those around him, and nearly falling into the sea, Barauna managed to take six pictures in about 14 s. The first two were taken as the object approached the island. It then disappeared behind a peak on the island, only to reappear a moment later moving in the opposite direction. At this point Barauna obtained his third picture. The object then moved at high speed away from the island but, because of the confusion on deck, Barauna missed it with his next two shots. However he obtained one last picture as the object seemed to stand still before it disappeared in the distance, near the horizon. The four pictures are integrated in plate 6:1, with the mysterious object ringed in each one. This shows that all the images can be linked with a parabola. Plate 6:2 shows enlargements of the object from the third photograph. The shape of the object appears to alter slightly from one photograph to the other. The incident lasted no more than 45 s.

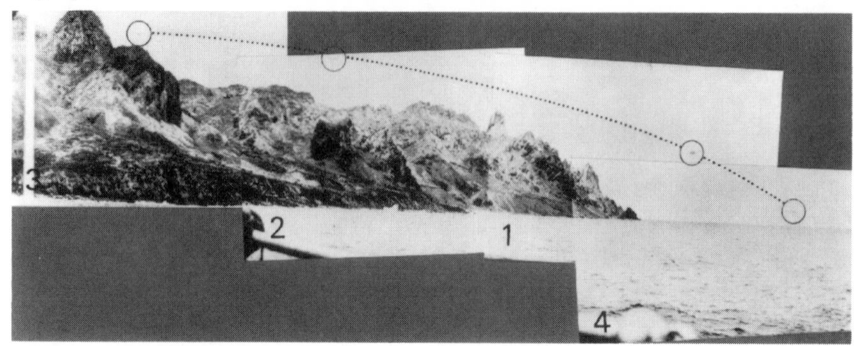

Plate 6:1 A montage from Barauna's four successful photographs showing the northern tip of Ilha da Trindade and the position of the 'flying saucer' (ringed) in each picture Each position lies on a parabolic course, along which the 'object' must have moved. The ring in picture 4 denotes the position of Jupiter. (Pictures from SOBEPS).

Barauna described the object as dark grey in colour, but appearing to be surrounded by a kind of greenish phosphorescent cloud. It glittered or flashed occasionally, but whether from reflected sunlight or its own light he could not tell. He was certain that it was a metal craft. However it moved in a curious way, undulating 'like a bat'! It made no noise.

Confirmation

The object was seen by other civilians who were with Barauna on deck. They included retired Air Force Captain Jose Teobaldo Viegas, who confirmed Barauna's report in a press interview on 22 February. He described how his attention was called to what he thought at first was a 'big seagull':

> The first view was that of a disk shining with a phosphorescent glow which even in daylight appeared to be brighter than the moon. The object was about the apparent size (angular diameter) of a full moon. As it followed its path across the sky, changing to a tilted position, its real shape was clearly outlined against the sky: that of a flattened sphere encircled, at the equator, by a large ring or platform.

Commander Paulo Moreira da Silva, of the Navy's Hydrography and Navigation Service, told the press that the object, which was encircled by a greenish glow, was certainly neither a weather balloon nor a guided missile. Amilar Viera Filho, president of the Icarai Club for

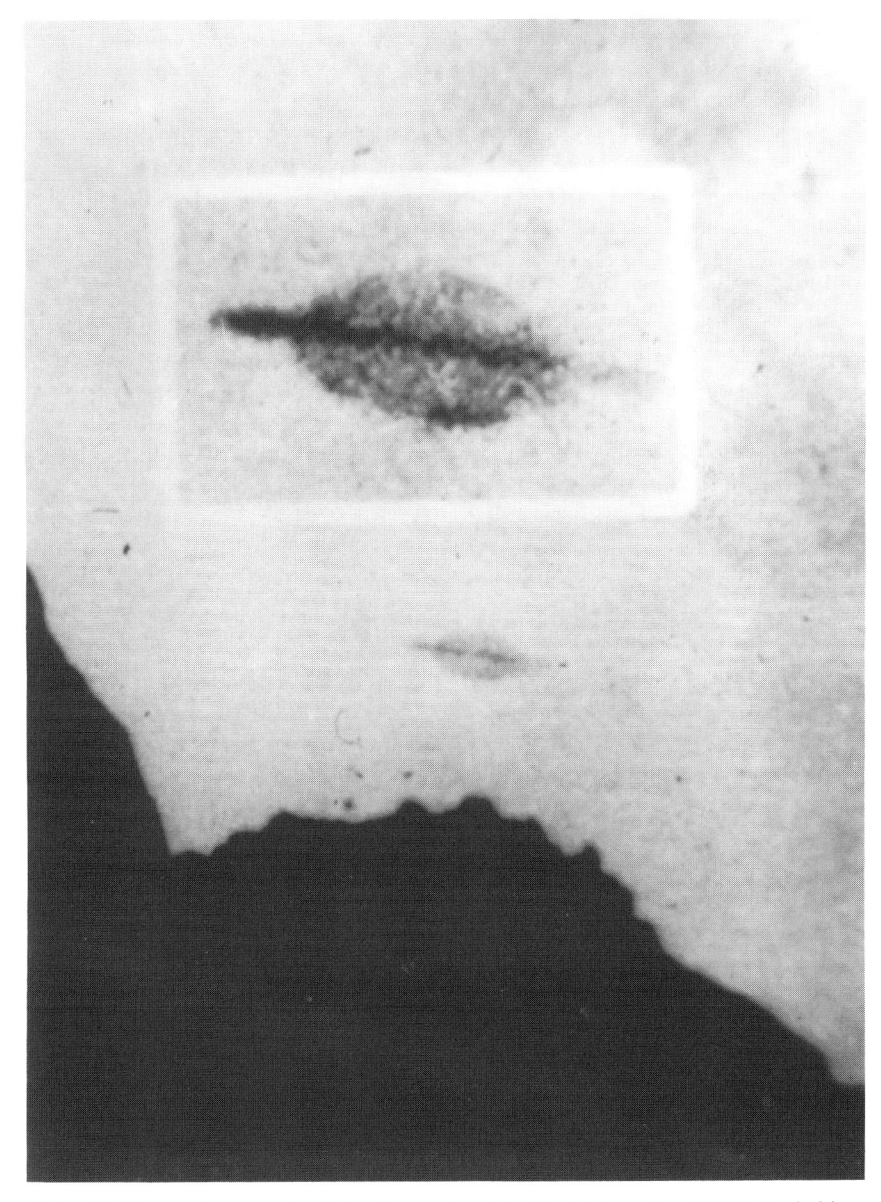

Plate 6:2 Two enlargements of the image in plate 6:1 (picture 3) (APRO). Probably a double/merged mirage of Jupiter.

Submarine Hunting (of which Barauna was also a member) and a member of CACEX Research Division (a Federal Department), could not say whether or not what he had seen was a 'flying saucer'. However it was a grey oval object emitting a fluorescent light. It looked like an object with a polished surface, but it was neither a balloon nor an aircraft. Nor was it a seagull.

Mauro Andrade, an employee of the London Bank of South America, and also a member of Barauna's group, was below deck at the time and so did not see the object. However he confirms that there was commotion on deck and everyone he met told him they had seen a flying saucer.

The official investigation

Following the incident, the captain in charge of the oceanographic station (Carlos Alberto Bascellar) and other officers insisted that the film be developed at once, despite the poor facilities on board and the lack of photographic paper to make prints. A bathroom was transformed into a darkroom and the film was developed by Barauna, under supervision. The settings chosen by Barauna were unsuitable for sky photographs and so the pictures were slightly over-exposed. Nevertheless the mysterious object was certainly visible on the negatives. They were seen and examined by the whole crew, and those who had seen the object agreed that the negatives showed it. Barauna retained the negatives until the ship reached the mainland.

The negatives and subsequent prints were examined by the Brazilian Navy's Photo Reconnaissance Laboratory, and later by a civilian organization (Cruzeiro do Sul Aerophotogrammetric Service). The latter made large prints which were examined by the Ministry of the Navy and the US Embassy. All these experts, and others in the USA, concluded that the pictures were genuine. They found no evidence of a hoax or trickery.

The incident and the pictures caused a sensation in Brazil, and the photographs were given wide press coverage. An enquiry to the Ministry of the Navy by a member of the House of Representatives prompted an investigation. The resulting dossier was never made public, but some details leaked to the press, which also uncovered other information. The incident was not isolated; at least seven other sightings had occurred towards the end of 1957 and early in 1958, one of them in daylight on 7 March 1958. A fifth photograph, taken with a box camera by a sergeant of the garrison prior to 16 January, was part of the dossier, but it was not made public. After receiving an answer to his enquiry, the Representative concerned (Sergio Magalahes) declared that he concluded that an unidentified object was seen by the crew of the NE *Almirante Saldanha* and photographed by Almiro Barauna.

On 21 February 1958, a Navy spokesman made the following announcement:

On the morning of January 16, 1958, over the Island of Trindade, the crew of the school [training?] ship 'Almirante Saldanha' sighted an unidentified aerial object for a few seconds. A civilian who was aboard the ship took some pictures of the object. The Navy has no connection with the case, and its only connection with the occurrence was the fact that the photographer was aboard the school ship, and came back with the ship to Rio.

The same day another spokesman for the Navy High Command released a statement which claimed that 'no officer or sailor from the NE *Almirante Saldanha* witnessed the event'. Barauna's pictures were released to the press by the President of Brazil, Juscelino Kubitschek (Fontes 1960 and Smith 1983).

The UFO hypothesis

The Brazilian Navy appears to have concluded that the object was a real flying craft. Based on time trials and the ship's position relative to the island, they estimated the object's speed at between 900 and 1000 km/h. They also estimated that the object was about 36 m in diameter and about 7 m high. These estimates must have been based on an assumption about the distance of the object (only a few kilometres). However, because the object was not seen in front of any object of known distance, its real distance, and hence its real size and speed, cannot be known.

Perhaps embarrassed by the subsequent publicity, the Brazilian Navy instructed the crew of *Almirante Saldanha* not to talk to the press. Naturally this led to speculation that the Navy knew more about the incident than had been revealed and only encouraged the idea that the object was a flying saucer (or alien craft).

The hoax hypothesis

In 1953 Barauna disputed the authenticity of some photographs taken by Ed Keffel at Barra da Tijuca (Brazil), writing an article for a popular magazine in which he demonstrated how the photographs could have been obtained. This has led some sceptics to discredit Barauna. Menzel devoted over nine pages of his second book (Menzel and Boyd 1963:206-216) to the Trindade incident, concluding that it was a hoax. He repeated the conclusion in his final book (Menzel and Taves 1977:193-4). His case against Barauna was that (1) he had no connection with the Brazilian Navy, (2) he was a professional photographer noted particularly as an expert at trick photography, (3) only two persons are recorded as eyewitnesses, both of them personal friends of Barauna and neither having any connection with the Navy, and (4) he had ample time and many opportunities to fake the pictures. In addition Menzel noted that the camera he used could easily be used for double exposures (a series of pictures of a model 'saucer' could have been pre-exposed) and that the pictures themselves show internal inconsistencies. Furthermore, Menzel was impressed by the fact that the Brazilian Navy Ministry never accepted the pictures as authentic and that some of Brazil's leading astronomers agreed with his sceptical conclusion. This hypothesis is still the belief of most sceptics and also of some ufoists.

Menzel's case amounts to a claim that because Barauna might have faked the pictures he must have done so. This does not follow. A hoax hypothesis requires evidence just as much as any other hypothesis. The fact that Barauna and his friends were not Navy personnel is not relevant. The lack of evidence from Navy personnel is explained by the Navy's order (effectively classifying the incident). Barauna's behaviour is not consistent with a hoax; he took several pictures and immediately claimed to have done so. Moreover, it is very unlikely that he pre-exposed six pictures of different (but similar) model 'saucers' (missing twice) and then added pictures of Ilha da Trindade so that, when integrated, the model in each picture lies on a parabolic curve. He could hardly have arranged this. Finally why would Barauna, Filho and Viegas describe such a curious object, 'flying like a bat'?

In fact there is no evidence that the pictures were faked and the circumstances make it extremely unlikely. The photographer and his friends were greatly outnumbered by the crew on deck (making it difficult to persuade the larger number that there was a UFO in the sky). Menzel's adoption of the hoax hypothesis may have resulted from the lack of any realistic alternative, but it flies in the face of a statement by the Navy confirming the incident. Menzel should have considered the mirage hypothesis he championed elsewhere.

The mirage hypothesis

If the pictures are genuine, and they do not show a solid craft, then they may show a natural phenomenon. The principal clue to the identity of that phenomenon is the position in the sky where the 'object' is reported to have disappeared.

Plans of the island are usually shown (inexplicably) inverted, so that the object appears to have been seen to the east. In fact, as figure 6:1 shows, the 'object' disappeared near the horizon just south of due west. At that very moment, the planet Jupiter was setting at that same point. The giant planet (magnitude -1·7) lay just 1° above the horizon on an azimuth of 259°. Normally Jupiter (or any planet) would be invisible in daylight. That a bright object was seen to disappear at that point indicates that something had made Jupiter visible. Something had also enlarged it, changed its shape and thrown the image around the sky. Only a mirage can have been responsible.

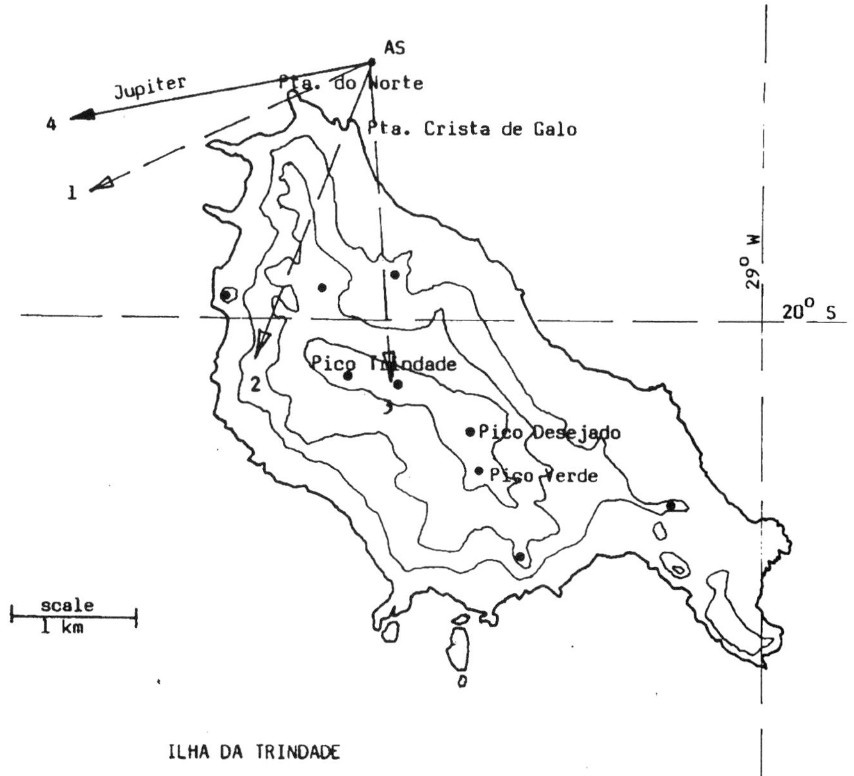

Fig. 6:1 A plan of Ilha da Trindade showing the probable position of *Almirante Saldanha* (AS) and the direction of the four photographs taken by Almiro Barauna.

What Barauna's pictures appear to show is a double merged and magnified image of Jupiter, seen via mirage. The two 'domes' in the image are the upright and inverted images of the same part of a magnified image of Jupiter (see figure 6:2).

Viegas's estimate of the size of the image can be verified from the pictures. From the focal length of the camera (80 mm) and the film size (60 mm square), we can calculate that the central 'dome' on the clearest image is about 0·5° high and 1° wide. The full Moon is about half a degree wide. So the magnified image is, at least, the size of the full Moon (as Viegas claimed), indicating magnification by a factor of fifty times in the vertical direction and one hundred times in the horizontal!

The movement of the image indicates that a temperature inversion had folded down to the south-west so that its surface was nearly vertical. Figure 6:3 shows how the vertical component of the thermocline could contain a wave which drifted first one way and then another.

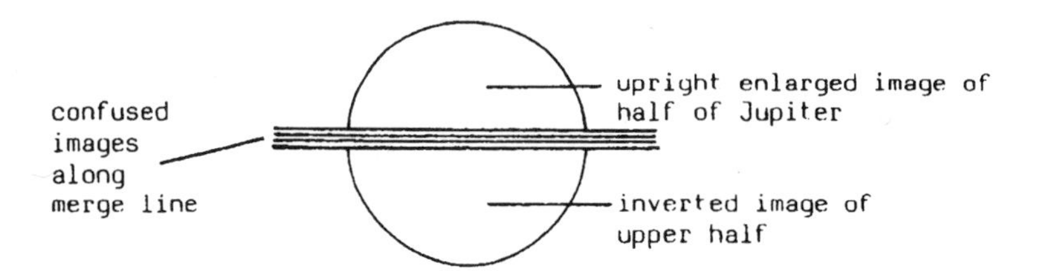

Fig. 6:2 How a mirage can produce the image in the Trindade pictures.

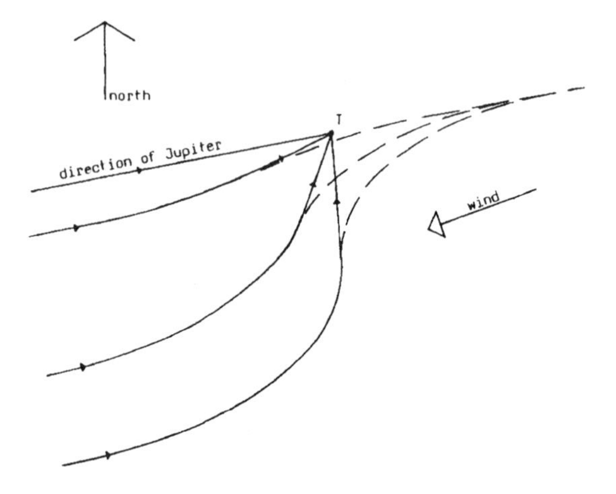

Fig. 6:3 One way in which a dynamic wave in a vertical thermocline (broken line) can move a mirage image laterally. Light is ducted around the concave part of the thermocline but emerges where the curvature changes so that it can be seen by an observer at Trindade (T). The scale of this diagram is necessarily very small.

The accounts indicate that the wave moved to the south and then back again to the north, taking the mirage with it. The concave part of the thermocline could duct the image around until the change in curvature allowed it to be seen by anyone in the line of sight. The exact line of the thermocline cannot be determined but it is evident that the ship lay at a point that enabled the crew to see the image. Whether or not there was only one such point we cannot tell. The thermocline would have been curved in two directions, like a shallow bubble. This is why, besides being displaced laterally, the mirage is elevated. In fact the image reached a maximum elevation of about 22°. The regular 'course' of the image indicates regular curvature of the thermocline, the radius of curvature decreasing with increasing angle from Jupiter. Necessarily the curvature of such a thermocline must be gradual and the inversion responsible must have been spread out across a large area of the ocean. The IGY surface weather chart for 1200Z that day shows a large anticyclone centred south-south-east of Trindade. This could have involved an inversion at a height of about 1 km.

The bat-like movement of the image indicates that there were ripples in the inversion layer. Whether the image was 'dark-grey' (Barauna) or 'brighter than the moon' (Viegas), an enlarged image of Jupiter in daylight may well have looked like reflecting grey metal. The pictures do not show a bright object, but that could be the result of the glittering or flashing reported by Barauna. If the image flashed very brightly occasionally (and if it did so during exposure of the film) then a dark image could be recorded because of the Clayden effect (a failure of the high intensity reciprocity law). Such flashes could be caused by strong focusing in the thermocline or an interference effect known as Raman brightening. The green cloud was probably caused by differential refraction, similar to the green flash. Although the sky was cloudy, it was not completely obscured (as some of the pictures show). It must be assumed that Jupiter was not obscured on the horizon. All the clouds must have been higher than the inversion.

Few alternative explanations are available and we are driven to conclude that the object *was* a mirage of Jupiter (however unlikely that may seem). Such a mirage completely explains the object's appearance (especially its changeable appearance) and its behaviour. It explains why it was seen when it was, why its appearance was so fleeting and why the object made no noise (Campbell 1989a).

If the pictures show such a mirage they are probably unique (and valuable); I know of no similar pictures. Barauna has most probably captured pictures of a very rare natural phenomenon, one not yet catalogued by science.

Criticism of the mirage hypothesis

Dr Willy Smith of the UNICAT project objected that a mirage of Jupiter could not have been seen because 'the sky was overcast'. He also claimed that a stationary Jupiter could not produce a moving image and that such a mirage could not have been seen more than 1-2° above the horizon (Smith undated).

The photographs show that, although there was some cloud, it was not overcast. More important, there is no evidence that cloud obscured the western horizon. Smith's other objections have already been covered in chapter 3.

7 The star over Socorro

The report from Socorro in New Mexico is probably the most notorious of all UFO reports. It was the only occupant case accepted as credible by both McDonald and NICAP, and it has been selected by many as the definitive 'Close Encounter of the Third Kind' (CE3) case, one which is both strange and reliable. Hynek described it as 'one of the classics of UFO literature', and he often challenged sceptics to explain it. It is labelled by the USAF as 'unexplained'. In fact it is the only combination landing, trace and occupant case listed as unidentified in Blue Book files, and it seems to have been the case that caused Hynek's volt-face (Jacobs 1975). Although it was ignored by the Condon Report, most ufoists have found the case convincing and have given it pre-eminence. However Ronald Story was sceptical of the report's authenticity and thought that it did not deserve the high credibility rating that it receives (Story 1981:72).

The policeman's tale

In Socorro, the 24 April 1964 was a hot sunny day with just a few scattered clouds and a strong wind. At about 1745L (but see below) New Mexico State Police patrolman Lonnie Zamora was chasing a speeding (black) car south out of the town. He thought it was driven by a youth of seventeen. While doing so he heard a roaring noise and saw a flame slowly descending in the sky to the south-west (*sic*). The flame, which he thought was about a kilometre away, was 'bluish and sort of orange' and narrower at the top than at the bottom. He thought that it was about 3° wide, twice as wide at the bottom as at the top, and that the height was about four times the top width. He did not notice any object on top of the flame and its base was hidden by a low mesa (hill). His immediate thought was that a dynamite shack beyond the mesa had blown up. However the noise was not that of an explosion; for a period of 10 s it changed from high frequency to low frequency. The noise lasted as long as he saw the flame, which had by now disappeared behind the mesa.

To reach the dynamite shack, he had turned on to a gravel road (see figure 7:1) which led up the mesa and which his car only climbed with difficulty. On reaching the top, he stopped for about 2 s to search for the shack. Instead he saw a shiny object 'to [the] south' about 150 to 200 m away off the road. At first he thought it was a white car on end in an arroyo (gully), but its appearance was more like aluminium and its shape was a vertical oval, with no windows or doors. It also had two 'legs' slanting outwards to the ground at the base (see figure 7:2a). He thought that some youths might have been responsible. Indeed he thought he saw two short people in white overalls very close to the object; one seemed to turn in his direction and look startled.

He concentrated on the road as he drove nearer and did not see the people again. He reported a possible accident and stopped the car. As he got out, he dropped the radio microphone and heard two or three loud 'thumps' about 1 s (or less) apart. He had hardly begun to walk towards the object when he heard a very loud roar, starting at low frequency and rising quickly to high frequency. At the same time the mysterious object was rising upwards. He could now see flames under the object; the flames were light blue, but 'sort of orange' at the base. At this point he turned and ran, bumping into the car and losing his glasses (prescription with green sun-glasses). He ran to the north, putting the car between himself and the object. He noted some kind of red 'insignia' in the middle of the object and later sketched it (figures 7:2b and 7:2c).

As he kept running to the north, he glanced back twice to see the object rise up to the level of the car. The noise had stopped. The object then retreated directly away from him very rapidly and at the same height, just clearing the dynamite shack. Keeping an eye on it, he ran back to the car and collected his glasses from the ground. He called the police radio operator to see if he could see anything, telling him 'it looks like a balloon'. By now the object was very small and seemed to just clear a mountain (Box Canyon or Six Mile Canyon Mountain, he was not sure which), where it disappeared. He estimated he had been out of the car for only 20 s.

After telling the operator of the incident, and where he was, he went down to where he thought the object had stood, finding the brush burning in several places (Steiger 1976:115-21; Powers 1966).

The official investigation

Sergeant M S Chavez arrived with Socorro County Undersheriff Jim Luckie and other police officers. They found Zamora pale and sweating and clearly very frightened. Together they examined the arroyo, where

Zamora pointed out some 'burning' bushes. Hynek later established that although the bushes were charred, they were not burning at the time (Steiger 1976:133). Chavez noted some marks in the ground which were thought to have been made by the landing pads of the 'craft'.

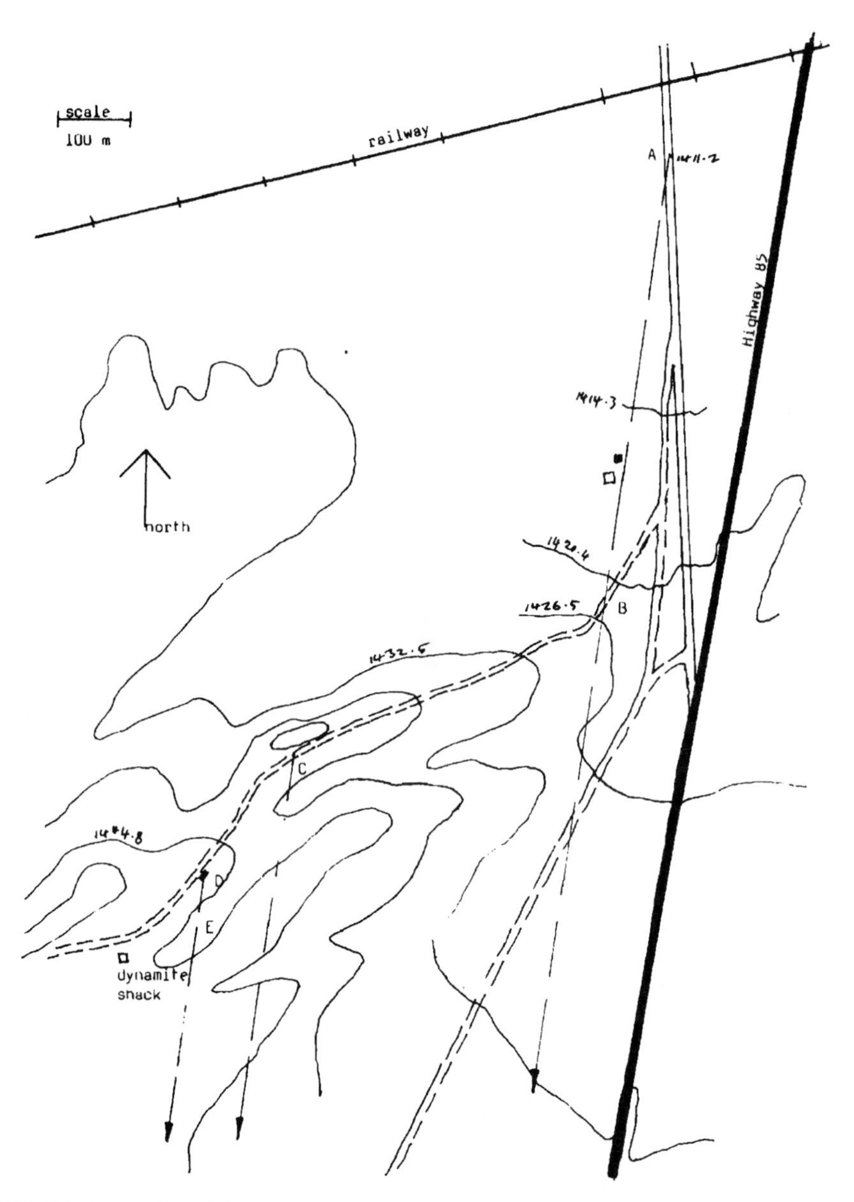

Fig. 7:1 A true plan of the area of Socorro involved in the Zamora UFO report showing the azimuth to Canopus from various points (heights in metres; contours at about 6 m intervals)

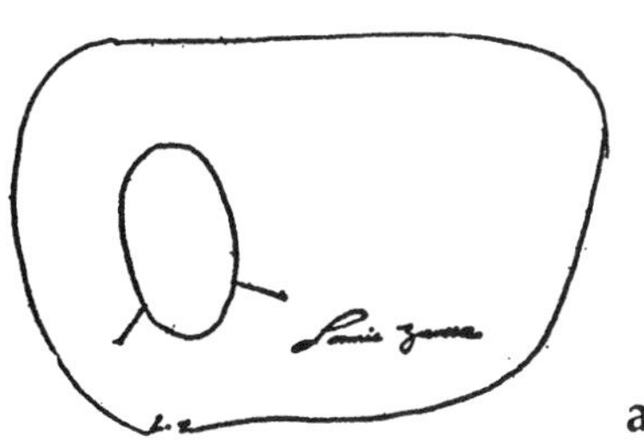

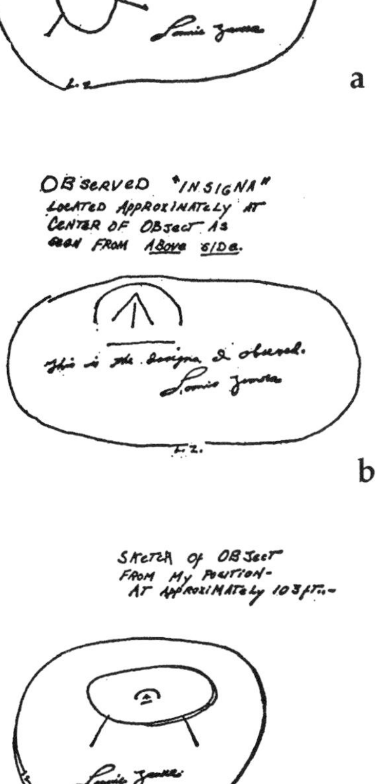

Fig. 7:2 Lonnie Zamora's sketches of the object he saw at Socorro. **a**: his first view of the object (from point C on figure 7:1); **b**: the 'insignia'; and **c**: the object and the 'insignia' (from Steiger 1976).

Chavez notified the local military authorities, who sent Captain Richard T Holder, Up-Range Commander from the nearby Stallion Range Center. He was accompanied by FBI Special Agent D Arthur Byrnes (or Burns), who happened to be in Socorro at the time, and a Sergeant Castle. Holder and Byrnes measured and recorded what they took to be the landing traces of some aerial craft and its occupants. The principal marks appeared to be impressions left by four rectangular pads, but in an eccentric arrangement.

The USAF sent investigators from Wright-Patterson AFB in Ohio, and also diverted Hynek to Socorro from Las Cruces (on behalf of Blue

Book). Hynek made a second visit four months later, and a third in March the following year.

The Air Force established that there were no unidentified helicopters or aircraft in the area and that observers at radar installations had observed no unusual or unidentified targets. Attempts to discover if a research vehicle had been tested in the area met with no success. NASA's prototype lunar lander had been delivered to Edwards AFB, but it was not operational at the time. There was no unusual meteorological activity; certainly no thunderstorms. There was no evidence of markings of any sort in the area other than the shallow depressions in the arroyo. Laboratory analysis of soil samples disclosed no foreign material or radiation above normal for the surrounding area. Analysis of the burned bush showed no traces of propellant. No other eyewitnesses were discovered (Steiger 1976:109, 112), but see below. The FBI reported that the incident was not known to be connected with the military or a contemporary operation known as Cloud Gap (a joint programme to learn about the problems of inspecting and enforcing the arms control agreement).

A CIA report on the incident, dated 28 May 1964, concluded, among other things, that the sighting could not be attributed to atmospheric or astronomical phenomena. It also concluded that the object was not an interplanetary space vehicle.

Hynek could find no rational explanation. He later asked one of his astronomy students, who came from Socorro and who had submitted a term paper on the incident, to do everything he could to find 'an obvious natural explanation of the sighting'. The student was unsuccessful.

Sceptical investigations

A more sceptical investigation was conducted by Klass. He found that Zamora had not necessarily seen people near the object; what he saw looked more like two pairs of overalls hanging from a clothes line and flapping in the wind (according to Ray Stanford, this was not true). Klass concluded that Zamora's impression that the object had legs was caused by misperception of the branches of two strategically-placed bushes. In any case, if the object had four legs then Zamora ought to have seen at least three (this is not necessarily true). Discrepancies in the number, location and shape of the alleged landing-pad marks led Klass to the conclusion that investigators had imagined some if not all of them. The marks could have been made by rocks, or they were burrows.

Klass noted that Zamora's two-way radio had given trouble that day, and that it was 'dead' when he tried to use it later.

During his second interview with Hynek, Zamora changed his account by omitting mention of the flame (on first sighting), even though that removed the cause for him to abandon his chase. Klass considered the possibility that Zamora had in fact seen '*only the flame*' (his emphasis) and that his mind had subsequently supplied spurious information about the noise, perhaps as a result of seeing space rocket launches on television or in movies.

Klass went to Socorro believing that Zamora might have seen an atmospheric plasma related to ball lightning. However, while he was there, a professor at the New Mexico Institute of Mining and Technology suggested to him that it might have been a hoax. Warming to this idea, Klass noted that, since the incident, the gravel road had been graded and improved and that the site was on land owned by the mayor. Furthermore it was 'conveniently' situated between two major highways and there were plans to make it a major tourist attraction. Also, part of a UFO movie was made in the town. A hoax (or fraud) is Klass's current explanation for this report; he believes that Zamora invented the story on instruction from the mayor (Klass 1968:ch. 18-19 and 1974:105-114). Klass claims that Zamora's credibility vanished when he interviewed him, and that a recording he made of the interview convinces those who hear it that Zamora is an unreliable witness.

From the police radio log, Klass established that Zamora's first call must have been received about 1717L, not 1745L (Klass 1977). If one allows 10 minutes from the time of first sighting to the first radio report, Zamora must have first seen the object at 1707L (0007Z on 25 April).

The fraud hypothesis

If Zamora's story is incredible, it is not much easier to believe Klass's explanation. Klass has to explain why Zamora would make up such a tale. As a State policeman, Zamora was not employed by the town of Socorro, or the mayor.

The Blue Book file reveals that Menzel and Hynek corresponded over the case, the former suggesting that it was either a hoax or a hallucination (Steiger 1976:113). Hynek tried in vain to find fault with Zamora's story, but told Menzel that he could not substantiate the latter's ideas, even though he wished he could. Not only did Zamora not behave as if he was lying, he had an excellent reputation. Hynek concluded 'the guy doesn't drink, cavort with women, or recite poetry ... he has none of the marks of a crackpot ... [and] I would feel that [he] is incapable of perpetrating a hoax'. Professor Lincoln LaPaz (Institute of Meteoritics, University of New Mexico), who knew Zamora, testified to his honesty (Jacobs 1975:191). Major Hector Quintanella, then head of Blue Book, noted (in a then classified CIA document) that 'there is ... no question about Zamora's reliability. He is a serious officer, a pillar of his church and a man well versed in recognizing airborne vehicles in his area.'

(Fawcett and Greenwood 1984:140). Burt, who also visited Socorro, was impressed by Zamora's 'matter-of-fact reporting of the event' (Burt 1970:60).

Nor is the circumstantial evidence favourable to the fraud hypothesis. Klass himself noted that, after three years, there were no signposts to the site and no announcements for tourists in the town. Nevertheless he regarded this as evidence that the fraud had been recognized. The failure to promote the 'landing' should be viewed in light of the fact that Socorro does not even promote its proximity to the site of the first nuclear explosion!

The fraud hypothesis explains neither the origin of the report nor its details. For example, it does not explain why Zamora did not describe a conventional flying saucer, with windows and waving occupants. Why did the 'craft' appear to be supported on rockets? The latter are not a feature of the saucer stereotype. Why did the 'craft' depart by flying horizontally directly away from Zamora? This means of departure is hardly one that Zamora would invent.

Zamora's reputation, the circumstances, the objects and events he described and his reaction to them are all inconsistent with the fraud hypothesis.

Other hypotheses

As indicated above, some believe that Zamora saw some type of secret vehicle, the existence of which was (and perhaps still is) unknown to the official investigators. It has been suggested that the object was a rocket-propelled remotely piloted vehicle (RPV), carrying two technicians (Boyce 1981:117).

Some think Zamora saw an alien spacecraft or a paranormal phenomenon. Good (1991:104) was told that an alien craft landed at Socorro by mistake!

However there is 'an obvious natural explanation'.

The mirage hypothesis

Evidently it did not occur to Hynek and his astronomy student to look for an astronomical explanation. If they had done so, they would have found that Canopus, the second brightest star in the whole sky, was then setting along the southern horizon. At 1707L it lay at an altitude of only about 3° (discounting refraction) on an azimuth of 187° (almost due south).

Naturally the star could not have been visible except via a mirage, magnifying its image. This would have required a temperature inversion in the valley of the Rio Grande south of Socorro. No upper air weather data are available and the surface data are sparse. Hynek reported that there was a very strong south-west wind, but Klass asked how he knew this when there was no weather station in Socorro. In fact temperatures were recorded by someone in Socorro (the maximum that day was 24 °C). However the nearest wind data come from Elephant Butte Dam, 100 km south. Although they give neither direction nor maximum speed, they do indicate that winds were stronger on that day than on other days that week. A strong wind blowing from the south-west across the Chupadera Mountains could have caused an inversion in the Rio Grande valley.

The AMH can explain many features of the report, not least the fact that it was made at all. It explains why the report was made on that day, and at that time. For a brief period such a mirage was visible from Socorro. It can explain why the 'flame' was blue at the top and orange at the bottom; atmospheric refraction had spread the star's light into a spectrum, with (as usual) the longer wavelengths at the bottom. It can explain why Zamora could see no object at the top of the 'flame'; there was no object. It can explain why the 'flame' seemed to be descending. Zamora saw it just over the crest of the mesa which he was approaching; the result would have been that the mirage only seemed to descend as the horizon rose.

The mirage hypothesis tells us that the 'craft' which Zamora reported in the arroyo was in fact the same mirage which he had earlier identified as a 'flame'. In different circumstances he interpreted the image differently. Figure 7:1 shows that not until point C would Zamora have caught sight of the mirage again, after losing it behind the mesa. Now it seemed to be a nearby vehicle, perhaps at first a car off the road. He must have imagined that there were people (or youths) near it; after all he had been chasing a youth in a car. There may be some truth in the notion that he mistook bushes for people or legs, but the possibility that the 'legs' (people?) were produced by the mirage should not be excluded. It cannot be easy to tell what you see when looking straight into a mirage.

Because he was concentrating on the road between points C and D he cannot have noticed that the mirage travelled west with him. The fact that the road turned more to the south must have resulted in the image becoming so slow moving that he thought it was stationary (in the arroyo at E).

The mirage hypothesis can explain the subsequent alleged movements of the 'craft'. Zamora must have climbed down into the arroyo without noticing that the image was following him down. When he heard a frightening noise (discussed below), which he associated with the object, he turned and scrambled out. Looking back he would have seen the mirage rise up, but only because of his own movement. If Zamora ran due north (as he claimed) then the object would have appeared 'directly over the place where it rose from' (as he also claimed). However if he saw it just over the dynamite shack then he must have run to the north-west, or circled to the west as he retreated. Since he was then lower than the car, the mirage can have appeared at about the same level as the car. Now the mirage itself makes a move. It fades (probably because Canopus is setting), causing the image to shrink, but Zamora interprets this as rapid movement directly away from him. If, as it faded, he was also moving west, then the mirage can have appeared to fly over the dynamite shack. This may account for the impression he gave others that the object disappeared to the south-west.

Zamora's report that the object had a red insignia may derive from an observation made while he was without his spectacles. In that case the detail need not be taken too seriously. However the red colour was surely caused by the red component in the spectrum of the mirage.

Once it was believed that a strange craft had landed in the arroyo, a search was bound to find signs that seemed to confirm that belief. Almost certainly the bushes had been burned on a previous occasion, perhaps as someone set fire to rubbish. The marks alleged to have been made by pads were probably caused by someone lifting stones. It is known that FBI agent Byrnes moved rocks to mark what he thought were indentations. Perhaps he created new 'pad prints' in the process.

Sounds off

Naturally the mirage hypothesis does not explain the sounds which Zamora reported, and which he associated with the phenomenon he saw. A clue to the source of these sounds lies in Klass's report that the car's two-way radio was faulty (no report on the condition of the radio has been published). It should also be noted that the car's windows were open throughout the incident.

It seems evident that the 'thumps' heard at the time he dropped the microphone were caused by the microphone itself hitting either the car or the ground. The sound could have been that of the impact being relayed back through the speaker. Some information on the type of radio might throw some light on this (it might have been a Pye 'Bantam', widely used by US police).

The character of the roar and its change of pitch suggest that it was un-squelched loss-of-signal noise from the radio, perhaps through failure of the squelch gate, or through Zamora setting the gate too high.

It may be, as Klass suggested, that Zamora heard no sound when he first saw the mirage. However it is unlikely that Zamora imagined the noises. It is possible that he unconsciously transferred the sounds from the latter sighting to the former. However it is also possible that, coincidentally, the radio did produce a roar just as he first saw the mirage. It seems very likely that the radio was responsible for the noises heard in the arroyo. The fact that he heard the noise as he moved away from the car suggests that his body induced a reaction in the radio. Because his attention was entirely directed towards the strange sight, it was natural that he would associate a simultaneous strange sound with the sight.

There is a report that hundreds of people on the south side of Socorro heard 'a roaring noise', but two who were interviewed gave the time as 1750 to 1755L (Stanford 1978:81).

Criticism of the mirage hypothesis

In March 1986, I sent an article about this incident to Kendrick Frazier, editor of *The Skeptical Inquirer*, the journal of the (US) Committee for the Scientific Investigation of Claims of the Paranormal (CSICOP). Frazier lives in Albuquerque, only about 120 km north of Socorro. Clearly interested, he referred it to Klass, Chairman of CSICOP's UFO Subcommittee, and to another (anonymous) referee.

The latter considered that my article was 'utterly without merit' and that my idea, that a star can be seen in daylight, was 'absurd'.

Klass took more trouble in outlining his objections, although he regarded my hypothesis as so flawed that he hardly knew where to begin. He claimed (1) that Canopus must have been hidden behind the mesa (although he could not be bothered to look at a map to check), (2) that the azimuth of the reported object was 30 to 40° away from the azimuth of Canopus, that is, south-west, not south, (3) that on subsequent days Zamora did not point to Canopus as the UFO (although it must have been visible), and (4) that there were no reports from other witnesses.

Consequently Frazier rejected my article. My response to the criticisms was passed to Klass, who then wrote directly to me.

Klass claimed that, from where Zamora first saw the object, the top of the mesa was at an altitude of 3·6°. He wrote 'CLEARLY THE MESA PREVENTED ZAMORA FROM SEEING CANOPUS AT THAT TIME' (his upper case; letter 23 May 1986). Later I discovered that Klass had made an error of 13·1 m in the height which he attributed to Zamora. In fact the crest of the mesa was at an altitude of only 2·8°. In any case, normal refraction would have lifted the mirage at least 0·6°, possibly more, and the inversion could have lifted it even more. Klass subsequently accepted the correction to the altitude of the mesa, but with no apology for his error; he suggested that we should not 'quibble over a "few feet" of elevation' (letter 4 July 1986), ignoring the importance he had previously attached to the matter.

The direction in which Zamora reported the departure of the object is critical for the mirage hypothesis; if it departed to the south-west it could not have been Canopus. Power's and Hynek's versions of Zamora's account differ from Steiger's by including the words 'in a southwest direction' (and also by including four additional sentences). But, as Steiger has it, Zamora merely claimed that the object disappeared over a mountain, the name of which was uncertain. According to Blue Book, the object 'flew off in a southerly direction'. This conclusion is confirmed by a CIA report only made public in 1984. The report states that the object disappeared 'over a point on Highway 85 about 6 miles [9·6 km] away' (Fawcett and Greenwood 1984:139). Highway 85 runs almost due south (see figure 7:1). The idea that the object departed to the south-west derives only from Zamora's impression that it was moving in that direction.

The maps in Blue Book and others (see below) show that, after he had climbed the mesa, Zamora saw the object 244 m away to the west-south-west (about 255° azimuth), so contradicting his written evidence. Klass took a photograph from what was alleged to be the same point and arranged for a man to hold a large bath towel in the arroyo where Zamora claimed the object sat (Klass 1968:Plate 10a). The man can just be distinguished below the lowest point in the distant mountains. Examination of the USGS Quads (maps) shows that this pass bears about 205° from the site of the photograph (see figure 7:3). This is a long way from west, or even south-west, although neither is it south. Zamora may not have been able to remember exactly where he was when he first saw the object 'in the arroyo'.

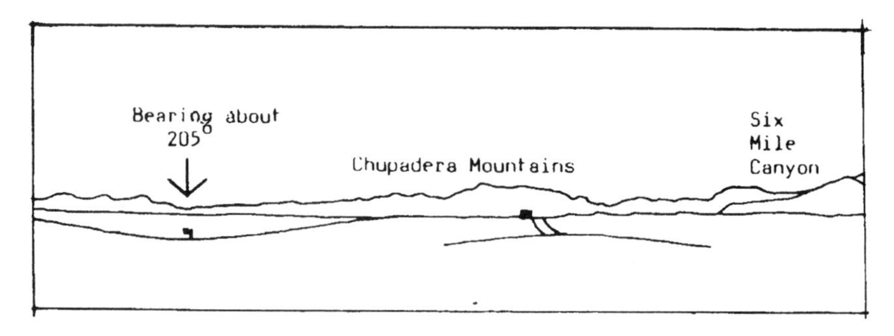

Fig. 7:3 A sketch of part of Klass's photograph taken from the point where Zamora saw the object for the second time. A man standing in the arroyo (where the object was alleged to have landed) bears about 205°.

Evidently all the maps are in error, and Zamora did see the object to the south, as he stated. A mirage of Canopus can have appeared over the mountains, but further south.

Klass's third objection is hardly worthy of comment. A mirage is a rare event and it is not likely to have been repeated on subsequent days. In any case, since Zamora did not know that he was looking at a mirage of a star, he could not have pointed to the star as the cause.

Klass's fourth objection is dealt with below.

On the whole, I was unable to reason with Klass. Because he resorted to gratuitous sarcasm and quoted large extracts from Zamora's account (as if I did not know it) in an attempt to demolish my hypothesis, I terminated the correspondence on this matter in July 1986.

The other witness

Hynek interviewed a Socorro petrol station attendant who told him that a tourist stopped at his station about the time of the incident. This tourist reported being buzzed by a low-flying aircraft just south of the town. On being told that helicopters often flew in the area, the tourist remarked, 'if that was a helicopter, it's the damndest [*sic*] helicopter I ever saw. It seems he was in some sort of trouble because he landed just over the hill, and a little later I saw a police car going out toward it' (Steiger 1976:113). Stanford identified this 'attendant' as Opal Grinder, the manager of Whiting Bros. service station at 1409 N. California Street, and he published the latter's affidavit in his book. According to Grinder, the motorist, who was accompanied by his wife and children, saw the 'aircraft' cross the highway from east to west in line with a junk yard (see below). Stanford himself (in a dramatized account) states that the family saw the egg-shaped object though the windscreen (but somewhat to the right) as they drove north (Stanford 1978:20-23). Klass was very critical of Grinder's report, noting that his original account did not mention any wife or children and that the time given by the tourist did not agree with the time recorded in the police radio log (Klass 1977).

In 1968, Paul Kies and Larry Kratzer from Iowa reported that they had spoken that day to a Socorro petrol station attendant about 'a shiny reflection' they had seen from a point about 1·5 km south-west of the town. Kratzer thought it might have been a junkyard. They placed the time at about 1700 Iowa time, which they (or Richard Hall) equated to '6 P.M. MST' (Story 1980:341-344). In fact 1700 CST is 1600 MST (L), so not only is there a discrepancy in time of 77 minutes, but Kies and Kratzer must have been on Highway 60, which runs south-west from Socorro. These discrepancies, and the fact that two businessmen travelling alone can hardly be confused with a family group, lead to the conclusion that neither Kies and Kratzer was the man who spoke to Grinder. Nevertheless one has to express surprise that anyone would mention what they thought was a bright reflection to a pump attendant.

Perhaps they did see the mirage, and the time and their location have not been recalled correctly.

Kies and Kratzer may have seen something shining in the compound containing a large variety of aircraft, and parts of aircraft, owned by the New Mexico Institute of Mining and Technology. A gleam from this compound caught the eyes of later investigators (Firestone and Firestone 1982).

The accounts obtained by Hynek and Stanford do indicate that a tourist (with or without a family) did see the mirage. However, unless the mirage was seen in the rear view mirror, he would have to have been travelling *south* on Highway 85 (California Street was then part of the Highway as it ran through the town). His direction of travel may have become reversed. If the mirage was reducing at the time, it may have appeared to have flown over the car from the north (or north-east) and headed south (or south-west).

An astronomical mirage ought to have been visible to other people in Socorro. Indeed, Nep Lopez, the Sheriff's Office radio operator, told Holder that approximately (*sic*) three reports of a blue flame had been received by telephone (Powers 1966). Unfortunately the identities of these callers have not been published (or were not recorded).

The evidence that there were other witnesses supports Zamora's account and is inconsistent with hypotheses which claim that there was fraud or that the account is the result of a hallucination.

A note on maps

Several maps of the area of the incident have been drawn, but they do not all agree. The Blue Book report contains two very similar maps which appear to have been drawn by two people in collusion (Steiger 1976:108 and 117). One is reproduced with Zamora's account (implying that it is his plan) and the other appears in a separate account (implying that it was drawn by whoever wrote the account). Klass sent me copies of these maps, but with 'Zamora' written at the foot of one and 'Holder' written at the foot of the other. However, the one marked 'Zamora' was not the one published with Zamora's account. Both maps refer to the actions and experiences of the 'witness', indicating that neither was drawn by Zamora, who did not report making a plan. If one plan was drawn by Captain Holder then the other may have been drawn by Special Agent Byrnes, so explaining the evident collusion.

The differences between the two maps are curious. Both agree that Zamora was chasing a speeding car at 1745L on Old Rodeo Street. But while one places the hearing of a noise ('roar' in one, 'explosion' in the other) on that street, the other places it on the road to the airport. One map claims that the airport road was 'rough gravel', and the other indicates that Zamora only turned off onto that road because he heard a noise (no mention of seeing anything unusual). Neither map is to scale and both distort the true layout of the main features. In particular, both take the gravel road north of a hill when the USGS Quad shows it to the south of the same hill.

Klass exhibited a copy of the USGS 1:24000 Quad on which he had marked various incident points which agree broadly with one of the Blue Book maps. However the scale is small and little detail can be seen (Klass 1968:Plate 9). Stanford also published a map, a larger scale plan set in a small scale layout. Although he shows contours, they do not correspond to the USGS Quad, and nor does his road layout (Stanford 1978:21). My own plan (figure 7:1) is based on the USGS Quad and shows the true layout of the area and the azimuth of Canopus as seen from various positions.

Conclusions

The case is an excellent example of how several rare events can combine to give a convincing impression that something occurred which did not occur. Astronomical mirages are rare, and Zamora had no reason to recognize one. His error of identification is understandable. It is unfortunate that a fault with his radio reinforced the mental set into which he had fallen. It is less surprising that a search for corroboration found marks which appeared to support his report.

Those who investigated the incident, particularly Hynek, have less excuse for not recognizing the cause. However astronomers are not generally familiar with meteorological phenomena. It is not clear why the CIA dismissed atmospheric or astronomical phenomena.

The tenacity with which sceptics have clung to the fraud hypothesis demonstrates how dogma can triumph over reason. The mirage hypothesis explains the incident more completely than the fraud hypothesis, and yet it was rejected.

Almost certainly Zamora's 'spacecraft' was a mirage of Canopus.

8 Venus down under

By 3 January 1979, a film taken a few days earlier by a New Zealand film crew had been shown on television all over the world. It was claimed that it showed a UFO (although the film crew did not claim to know what that is). In Britain, it was shown as the lead item on BBC-TV news at 2000L on 31 December 1978, and it was discussed in several subsequent TV and radio programmes. It was headline news in newspapers and on television around the world, but largely ignored by scientific journals.

The incident generated two books, one by the pilot of the aircraft from which the film was taken (Startup 1980), and one by the Australian TV reporter who organized the film crew (Fogarty 1982). It also featured as a major item in books about UFOs and generated very many articles. Klass described it as 'the best-documented UFO incident' and suggested that it might seem to qualify as 'the most impressive UFO case of all time' (Klass 1983). The cover blurb on Fogarty's book claimed that his story is that behind 'the world's first verified film encounter with an unidentified flying object'. In fact the case assumed importance only because of the interest of an American physicist (Maccabee) and his propagation of it.

The Woodbourne report

The incident which was filmed was one of many reported by both pilots and ground observers between 20 and 31 December 1978. There are too many reports to deal with here, and in most cases there is insufficient information to make a safe identification. However there is one exception.

Some peculiar lights were observed by officers at Woodbourne Royal New Zealand Air Force Base near Blenheim (South Island) on the night of 20/21 December 1978 and diagrams of these lights were published (see figure 8:1). Startup and Illingworth gave the time as 2355L (1055Z)

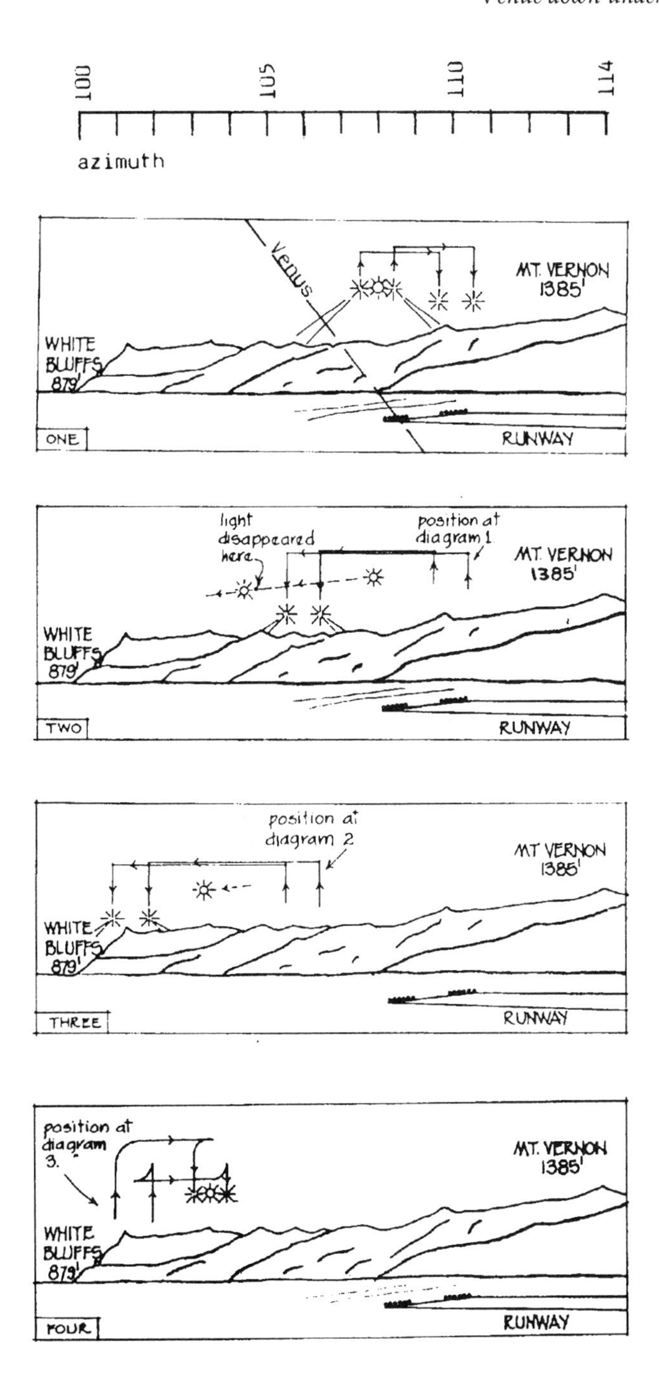

Fig. 8:1 Diagrams of the movement of UFOs as seen from Woodbourne aerodrome at about 0335L (1435Z) on 21 December 1978 (from Startup and Illingworth 1980). The rising course of Venus (without refraction) is shown in diagram ONE

to 0045L and Ireland gave it as 2350L (although he also mentioned a similar report made a few hours later). They appeared to be the lights of a freighter going north toward Wellington, but they moved upwards and around in a rectangular pattern, but at random speed. There appeared to be one large bright orange light and two less intense white lights. At one stage the lights appeared to rush towards the observers, but generally they seemed to move northward; eventually they faded. According to Ireland, the lights were on an azimuth of 60° true, for which reason he attributed the phenomenon to Jupiter, which rose at 2320L on 65°. However the published diagrams show that the lights were seen between 100° and 114° azimuth, agreeing with Ireland's description of a 'very bright light' observed low in the sky east of Woodbourne aerodrome at 0335L (1434Z) on 21 December (which he identified as Venus). This coincided with reports of a 'massive, ... bright orb, pear-shaped with a reddish tinge' seen from an aircraft as it climbed through cloud at 0328L. Startup claimed that Ireland had the wrong direction and gave it as 115° to 135° true. My azimuths are from a published map of the area.

I could find no astronomical explanation for the objects shown in the sketches until I took the time to be 0335L. Then it was obvious that the rising Venus was responsible (and that there had been confusion between the reports). Venus rose at 0331L on an azimuth of 109°; at 0335L it was about 0·5° above the horizon on 108°. But it could not have been visible directly because of the intervening hills. This (and the peculiar behaviour of the lights) suggests that what was seen was a superior mirage of Venus, perhaps producing multiple images. This may explain why the image fell instead of rising; the image and its movement was inverted. Since Venus was 5° above the horizon when it reached azimuth 104° (at 0400L), and so was directly visible over the hills, it must be that the sketches have the images too far to the left (in relation to the hills) and that the time given is that of the disappearance of the lights. It is more likely that the mirage began when Venus was a few degrees below the horizon and that it disappeared when Venus reached the horizon. Some of the movements described resemble the autokinetic phenomenon and so may not have been real.

Filming a UFO

The main incident occurred as an Argosy freighter was returning north after delivering newspapers to Christchurch in South Island. Because of previous reports of UFOs from the pilots, an Australian journalist (Fogarty), who was on holiday in New Zealand, collected a film crew and travelled in the hold of the aircraft, and occasionally in the cockpit. There were no seats for passengers. During the flight south from

Wellington several unidentified lights were seen and ground radar reported several unidentified targets (probably conventional anomalies). Contrary to popular belief, the lights were not identified with the radar targets.

The aircraft took off from Christchurch airport at 0216L (1316Z) on 31 December 1978 on a course 54° true along an air route known as Moto (see figure 8:2, which shows the aircraft's probable route). The pilot was Bill Startup, with Robert Guard as co-pilot. The rate of climb was about 5 m/s, with the air speed about 80 m/s (both increasing with height). There was a following wind of about 8 m/s, giving an initial ground speed of about 88 m/s.

At about 0219L, when the aircraft was about 16 km from Christchurch and at a height of about 850 m, just breaking through low cloud over the land, a very bright light was observed. It was either about 10-30° to starboard (Maccabee 1979) or seen 'through a starboard window' (Fogarty 1982). Fogarty noticed that it was 'apparently keeping track with the aircraft'. The light was either 'about at the height of the plane' (Maccabee 1979) or '*below* the aircraft' (Klass 1983, his emphasis).

Fogarty reported seeing two lights initially, one above the other, the upper light being the brighter. He claimed that he had to stand very close to the window to see the second light 'much further below'. He did not see the lower light again, and later concluded that it had been a reflection of the upper light in the sea or on a cloud bank. As the cameraman (David Crockett) began filming, Fogarty began his commentary: 'We are now about 3 minutes out of Christchurch airport and on our starboard side we can see two very bright lights ... one much brighter than the other. The only way to describe it ... it's like a very very bright star ...'.

About 0221L, when the aircraft was about 28 km from Christchurch and at about 1830 m, the aircraft's own radar was switched on and set to the 32 km range (the light was thought to be that close) and map mode. The radar was MEL's E190 Weather Radar operating at 9375 MHz and 15 kW (with no MTI capability). Surprisingly it showed a strong target about 30° to starboard and just inside the 32 km range ring (or at 18 km according to Maccabee). Guard and Dennis Grant (a Christchurch newspaper reporter acting as sound recordist) were sure that the azimuth of the radar target was the same as that of the bright light. The pilots estimated that the size of the radar blip was three to five times larger than the blip usually received from a large fishing vessel. They concluded that the bright object was also responsible for the huge radar echo and excitement mounted. The object did not appear on the Christchurch airport radar, probably because it was below that radar's lower limit. Fogarty spoke into the microphone again:

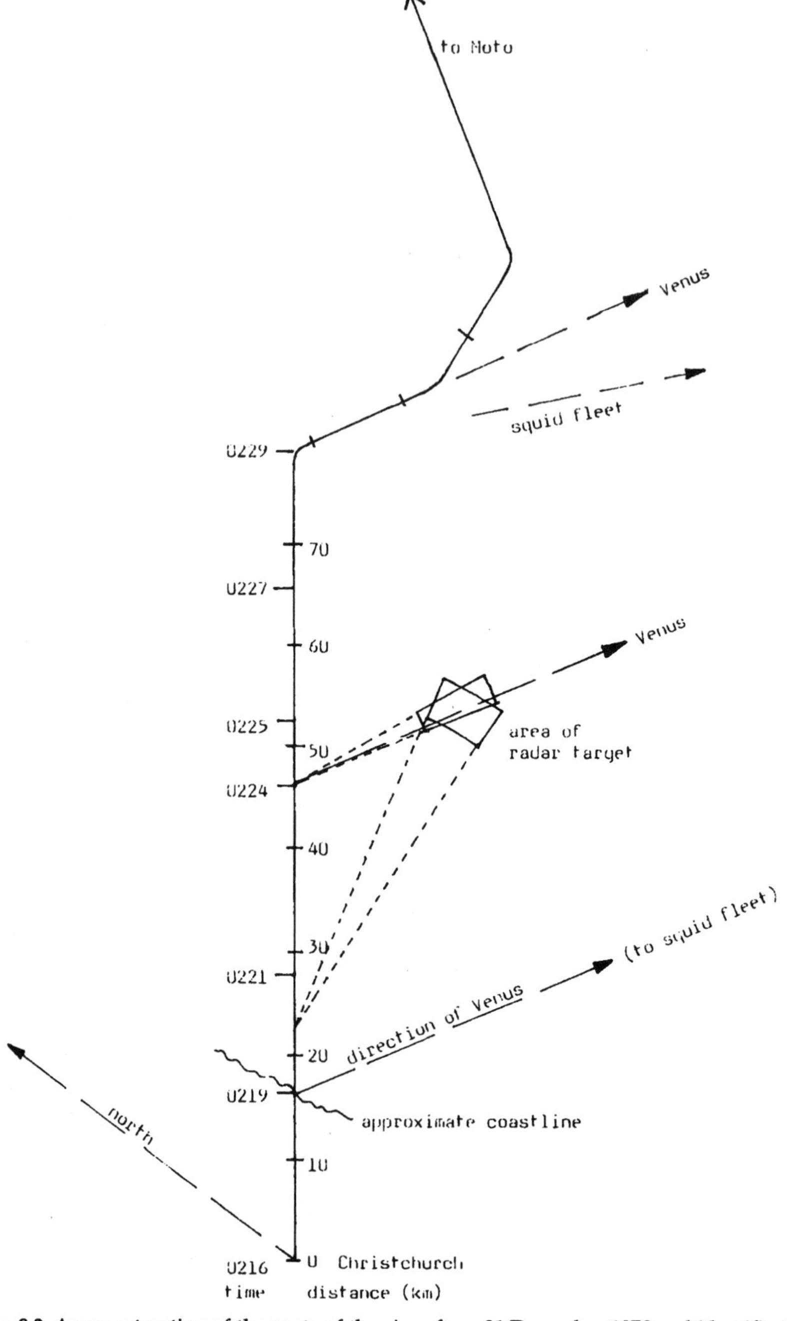

Fig. 8:2 A reconstruction of the route of the aircraft on 31 December 1978 and identification of the visual and radar targets.

Those two lights appear to be travelling with us. They're still off the starboard wing. The brighter one is still above the other and it's moved a little further ahead. It's extremely bright, much brighter than any of the other stars in the sky. Now it's just dimmed. ... it's gone, it's back again. It appears to be going behind cloud. I can't make out whether in fact it is going behind cloud or whether in fact the light is just dimming ... no, it's such a bright light...it's lighting up the clouds around it.

At about 0225L, the target disappeared from the radar screen on a bearing of 60° to starboard, but the pilot did not change course (the aircraft was still on autopilot). Two minutes later Guard called Wellington airport to inform them that he had a 'great big target sitting at 3 o'clock'. Fogarty noted that the object appeared as a roundish bright light, yellowish-white in colour. At first Startup thought it was the full Moon (until he realized that there were no lunar features), but Guard described it as 'a squashed orange'; it had an orange tinge like the rising Moon and it shimmered around its edge. Klass reported that the object changed from a thin ellipse to a 'distorted triangle', to an ellipse growing in thickness until it appeared as a roughly circular blob, frequently distorted. Crockett, looking at it through his camera viewfinder, saw it become 'flattened and longish, bright at the bottom'. Fogarty continued: 'the bright object is still with us ... just off our starboard side ... it's extremely bright ... it's very hard with the naked eye to pick up any details because the light is so bright. It must have been following us now for close to 10-12 minutes'.

At 0229L, when the aircraft reached its cruising height (about 3960 m), Startup disengaged the autopilot so that he could turn the aircraft to head towards the light. We do not know the new course, but it is alleged that he had to make a 90° turn (Maccabee 1979). The aircraft was then aimed at the bright object, but now under manual control, and not as steady as it had been with the autopilot. The result was that Fogarty reported various movements of the object unaware that it was the aircraft which was moving. No compass reading was given and no target appeared on the radar. Fogarty said, 'it has got to be something; it's certainly not the planet Venus as many people would like you to believe'.

After one or two minutes Startup turned the aircraft on to a course of 87° true for a short time before resuming a course for the reporting point at Kaikoura East, where he would rejoin Moto. It was during this part of the flight that Crockett captured the planet-like images that made headline and television news, stills of which are shown in colour plate 8:1. Fogarty's last sight of the object was out of the far right window as the aircraft banked left; he claimed that he was 'looking almost straight down on it'.

The cine equipment and the film

The camera, a Bolex H16 EBM electric 16 mm Reflex movie camera, was loaded with Fujicolor 8425 (ISO 400) reversal film. Initially Crockett used a Kern Vario-Switar 16-100 zoom lens at f/1·9, but on the journey north he also used a Sun Macro-Zoom 80-240 mm lens at f/4. On the northern leg the film was exposed at 10 frames per second.

It was later discovered that the 80-240 zoom lens was out of adjustment and that distant objects were out of focus when it was set to 'infinity'.

The sequence of the film taken on the northward journey runs to 255 frames showing a very bright object filmed unsteadily. About one quarter of the frames show reddening along the lower perimeter of the object and yellowing along the upper perimeter (see colour plate 8:1).

Explanations

At first, the public relations officer of the New Zealand Ministry of Defence identified the object as Venus. However a report issued later by the Department of Scientific and Industrial Research (Ireland 1979) concluded that, although many of the lights seen were 'generally unusual views of either terrestrial sources such as lighthouses, navigation beacons and city lights, or the planets Venus and Jupiter seen through an unusually clear atmosphere', the object seen on the climb out of Christchurch was 'most likely a squid boat [see below] seen under quite normal viewing conditions'. Vince Ford (research officer for the Research School of Physical Science of the Australian National University) told Fogarty that although a small group of Mount Stromlo scientists thought that the photographs were 'definitely planets magnified by "atmospheric shimmer"', the planet in question was Jupiter. Later Ford realized his mistake (Jupiter lay well above the horizon to the north-east), but he could think of no other astronomical object which would fit the report. Amateur astronomer Robert Lanigan-O'Keefe persistently told Fogarty that the object was Jupiter, apparently because he could see its moons in the pictures. David Mabin, head of the Mount John Observatory in New Zealand was almost sure that the object was Venus, although later he opted for Jupiter. Many chose Jupiter because some of the pictures showed a banded object, mistaking the bands for Jupiter's cloud belts. In fact these details can hardly be made out with powerful telescopes and the familiar pictures came via NASA's Voyager probes. The banded image was later explained by the misaligned zoom lens; it was an unfocused image of the unidentified object. British Astronomer Royal Sir Martin Ryle suspected a hoax, while broadcaster Patrick Moore suggested a reflection off a balloon or an unscheduled aircraft.

Other explanations included light reflected off flocks of mutton birds or off fields of cabbages! On ABC-TV in New York in 1981, a geologist (Brian Brady of the US Bureau of Mines) suggested that the camera may have caught earthquake lights generated by the movement of the Alpine Fault which runs through South Island (although nowhere near the plane's flight path). He has not published any data to justify this idea.

The squid boat hypothesis

A Japanese squid fishing fleet was in New Zealand waters at the time, most of the boats concentrated in an area about 240 km east-south-east of Christchurch. These boats use very powerful lights to attract squid to the surface and a satellite photograph shows the output of the lights exceeding that of either Christchurch or Wellington (Sheaffer 1980). Both Klass and Sheaffer adopted this squid boat hypothesis, arguing that since (*sic*) the observers reported only the UFO then the latter must have been the squid fleet. In fact Fogarty did report two lights, the lower of which could have been the squid fleet.

Sheaffer's satellite photograph shows the squid fleet as a luminous patch about 30 km across. Apart from the fact that, at a distance of 240 km, a body that wide subtends an angle of 7·4°, nearly fifteen times the diameter of the full Moon, the fleet must have presented not a disc but a horizontal line of light. This is not consistent with the description and pictures of the UFO. In any case, when the UFO was first seen, and the aircraft was only 850 m high, the horizon was only 104 km away. At this point the fleet would have been invisible unless it was seen via abnormal refraction (mirage), which is what a Canadian scientist suggested (Lehn 1980). Even if visible, the light from the fleet would have appeared to move aft about 13° in the 10 minutes between 0219L and 0229L. The observers emphasized that the UFO kept pace with them. The squid boat hypothesis does not explain why the aircraft flew past the radar target instead of aiming for it to identify it. If the UFO was the squid fleet then it could be filmed in similar circumstances for comparison; this has not been done. It has been argued that a veteran pilot familiar with his route would not be puzzled by sight of something which he had seen many times before. Why would he think the lights of squid boats unusual?

Maccabee rejected the squid boat hypothesis on the grounds that the image would not have been bright enough. He claimed that the illumination was equivalent to 250 kcd at 16 km, whereas the fleet produced an output of 300 to 400 kcd at 260 km. By the inverse square law, 3-4 x 10^5 cd at 260 km is equivalent to only 1·3 kcd at 16 km. However Maccabee's assumption that the source was 16 km away is based on the radar target's distance.

The radar target

Like the crew and film team, Maccabee assumed that the radar target and the visible object were one and the same. However the evidence points to the conclusion that this was not so. In map mode the radar was aimed downwards ahead of the aircraft so that it could scan the surface. Its half-power points (the effective limits of the main beam) were 3° and 15° below the axis of the aircraft. Although the plane was nose-up during the climb it is likely that the radar could see down to 11° below the horizontal. Consequently a surface vessel at 32 km would show as a blip on the aircraft's radar but would not show on the radar at Christchurch. This vessel does not have to have been a squid boat; unfortunately there does not seem to have been any attempt to locate the vessel responsible. Such a vessel would disappear from the radar at about 15 km because it would fall inside the limit of the beam when the aircraft was in level flight. A large vessel about 13 km to the right of the aircraft's track (see figure 8:2) would explain the radar data. Figure 8:2 shows that, at one point, the direction of the light (if it was Venus) and that of the radar target must have coincided, convincing the observers that they were indeed one and the same object.

Maccabee explained non-simultaneous discrepancies between the position of the radar target and the visual UFO (as one object) as caused by movement of the object. Indeed he made much of the fact that one frame of the film shows a looped image (see colour plate 8:1). From the fact that the camera exposed each image for only 0·044 s he deduced that this loop could not be caused by camera movement and so must show movement of the object. However he seems to have been unaware that the shutter of the camera did not close automatically when the camera stopped. Consequently the loop can have been caused when Crockett stopped filming, even if he did so only momentarily.

The Venus hypothesis

Several times is has been suggested that the UFO was Venus. The planet was at its brightest (magnitude -4·6) in the south-east (azimuth 122°), as shown in figure 8:2. At least it was bright enough and in the right direction (more or less) to be the UFO. It was also the right colour; plate 3:2 shows a central colour similar to that of the UFO. Some of the images of the UFO also show a red base, indicating that it was an astronomical object. However Venus had not yet risen and it was too small. It was still 10° below the horizon to a surface observer (neglecting normal atmospheric refraction). To an observer at a height of 850 m (and allowing for normal refraction) it should have been about 8° below the horizon. Its apparent diameter was only 31·5 arcseconds (about 0·01°), ten times smaller than the object on the film.

Lehn suggested that the UFO was a Novaya Zemlya mirage of a squid boat. However it could have been a Novaya Zemlya mirage of Venus. A mirage would explain how Venus could be visible and ten times larger than normal. In this case the light from Venus must have been ducted around the Earth for nearly 1000 km! That would explain the strong orange colour of the image; the extra distance through the atmosphere would increase Rayleigh scattering. It would also explain variations in size and shape of the image and its shimmer. If the UFO was Venus, that would explain how it appeared to keep pace with the aircraft throughout the period of observation, and why it lay on the horizon.

If the UFO was Venus, it must have been 66-68° to starboard (about 2 o'clock) at all times (until the aircraft turned). At 0224L Venus was almost in the same direction as the radar target when the latter disappeared. This may explain the false association between the UFO and the target. It is evident that, when he turned the aircraft (presumably on to 120°), the pilot flew that course only so long as necessary to locate a target at the last recorded distance of the radar target. When nothing was found, he abandoned the search and resumed his course northward.

A mirage of Venus would have required a temperature inversion over a very wide area of ocean to the south-east. At a Defence Department inquiry on 5 January 1979, Dr D C Thompson of the Meteorological Services at Kelburn explained that 'there were inversions around', perhaps formed by the light wind from the west. Ireland drew attention to the long history of optical mirages and temperature inversions in the area and also gave weather data. Maccabee has shown that, on 30 December 1978, conditions were such as to allow radar rays to follow the curvature of the Earth. Ireland stated that super (radar) refraction occurred on the following morning and that conditions were 'conducive' to the production of optical mirage effects. In addition Ireland noted that the atmosphere was very clear, not only because of lack of dust but because of exceptionally stable conditions (there was little scintillation). The air was so clear and stable that two to three times more stars than usual could be seen (Ireland 1979).

It is surprising that Ireland did not recognize that these exceptional circumstances were conducive to the production of a mirage of Venus (which he identified as the cause of so many other UFO reports of the period). It is ironic therefore that he attributed the report to sight of a single squid boat.

Criticism of the Venus hypothesis

Maccabee rejected the Venus hypothesis mainly on the basis that it was 'not visible' and 'in the wrong direction'. He also observed that, on the horizon, its brightness would be reduced by a factor of 100 or more by atmospheric extinction. It is evident that he did not consider a mirage hypothesis, which overcomes his objections (except for direction about which he must be mistaken).

Lehn's article (1980) prompted Dr T W Rackham of the University of Manchester's Nuffield Radio Astronomy Laboratories (Jodrell Bank) to write to Lehn in June 1980. Rackham had been studying the film and an accompanying dossier sent to Sir Bernard Lovell. Rackham compared the appearance of the image with that of Venus published by O'Connell of the Vatican Observatory (see colour plate 3:2) and wondered if the mirage mechanism described by Lehn could result in Venus being seen when it was 8° below the horizon. He wondered why most of the light was not absorbed by the great depth of atmosphere involved. Lehn replied that what Rackham proposed was 'an interesting possibility'. An atmospheric duct could have produced the effect, although it would have had to be very long (he thought 500-600 km) and absorption would dim the image severely. Lehn proposed to test the hypothesis on a computer simulation, but at the date of writing he had not done so.

My Venus-mirage hypothesis (Campbell 1990a) was noted (and summarized) in the Fall 1990 issue of *The Skeptical Inquirer*. This prompted systems analyst Robert Sheaffer to disparage the idea in the Spring 1991 issue of the latter journal, but, apparently, without first obtaining a copy of the article. Sarcastically, he suggested that Venus could only have been seen through a transparent Earth, and he referred to the limit of mirage displacement (1°) described by meteorologist William Viezee (Gillmor 1969:625). He claimed that it was not necessary to hypothesize 'mega-mirages of a kind unknown to science to explain the appearance of a brilliant light source'. He implied that I had 'grabbed' at an inappropriate explanation without employing critical thinking and that I gave grounds to critics of scepticism. I replied by pointing to Viezee's own calculation (Gillmor 1969:617), that, with an inversion temperature gradient of +11·6 °C/100 m, the curvature of light rays is 33 arcseconds/km, equal to the curvature of the Earth's surface. The light did not have to refract 8°; it only had to follow the curvature of the Earth. My reply was not published. Nor was an article I sent for consideration by *The New Zealand Skeptic*.

9 Venus down in the forest

While I was BUFORA's Scottish Investigations Co-ordinator, a major CE2 incident was reported only 16 km away from my home. This presented an opportunity to investigate at first hand; most of the case reports in this book have been solved remotely, from my armchair. Furthermore the case offered the opportunity to test the notion that the more one knew about an incident the less strange it became. Overseas cases might only seem strange because distance lends enchantment and prevents access to information which would show the incidents to be more prosaic. Whatever conclusions I reached in this local case might be extrapolated to cases world-wide. The case was so extraordinary and complicated that BUFORA published my initial report as its first Case History (Campbell 1982a).

On the evening of 9 November 1979, I was telephoned at home by a journalist from a major Scottish daily newspaper. He informed me that a forestry worker at Livingston (a new town some 20 km west of Edinburgh) had been attacked by small furry creatures which had emerged from a transparent spacecraft. The craft was alleged to have left tracks in the ground! To say that I was sceptical would be an understatement; I could hardly believe it, and was sure that someone had made a mistake. It was then dark and the witness had gone to England. However I resolved to give it my full attention as soon as I could.

The following morning, two Scottish daily newspapers brought fuller details, confirming most of what I had been told. The reports revealed that the local police were investigating. Consequently I made myself known to them and was invited to visit their local headquarters in Bathgate. This I did that morning, discussing the incident with the superintendent in charge and glimpsing the routine police report (I obtained a copy later). Clearly they were baffled.

I was then taken to the scene of the incident, a forest clearing. There I was shown some anomalous marks or tracks (by that time fenced off) which, I was told, had been found where the 'spacecraft' had landed (see plate 9:1). The police were photographing and measuring the marks while I was there (see figure 9:1). Nevertheless I took some photographs, including plate 9:2.

Plate 9:1 One of 'track' marks at Livingston the morning after the incident (photo by Alistair Sutherland).

Only on 27 November 1979 was I able to speak to the person involved in the incident, foreman forester Robert David Taylor.

The forester's tale

Taylor, 61 at the time of the incident, had worked as a forester all his life on the land in Scotland. For 16 years he had worked in the Forestry Department of Livingston Development Corporation, the new town authority. On the morning of Friday 9 November 1979, he was inspecting a forest plantation in the north of the town near, but not within sight of, the M8 motorway. He was alone except for his dog, a red setter. At about 1015L (1015Z) he rounded a corner in the forest track and was confronted by the most amazing sight. A large domed object appeared to be hovering stationary just above the ground (see figure 9:2)! It did not seem to be rotating and no sound was audible. The colour was uniformly dark grey, with an appearance similar to that of emery paper (many small bright highlights set against a darker background). The surface of the object periodically changed, in different places, to become smooth and shiny. He thought it was attempting to camouflage itself. It seemed to be about 6 m in diameter and stood about 4 m high. It appeared to be mounted on an equatorial flange or rim, like the brim of a hat. Protruding from the upper edge of the flange were what appeared to be regularly spaced stems surmounted by propellers. These appendages did not move and the propellers did not rotate. Just above the flange on the surface of the dome were darker, regularly-spaced, circular patches. No other features were visible.

After only a few seconds, two smaller spiked spheres (see figure 9:2) rushed towards him. They were of the same appearance as the dome, but only 0·5 to 1·0 m in diameter. They seemed to roll forwards on a horizontal axis with only the ends of the spikes touching the ground. The number of spikes is uncertain, but Taylor recalls that they made a sucking or plopping sound when they touched the ground. He did not see where they came from, but they stopped one either side of him and each attached a spike to his trousers! Immediately he felt himself being pulled forward, towards the dome. He claimed that his feet (in rubber boots) were dragging on the ground. As the spheres reached him, he was overwhelmed by a very strong, acrid choking smell. Struggling for breath, and trying to resist the pull of the spheres, he lost consciousness.

When he recovered, none of the objects could be seen. Only his dog was with him; it was racing about and barking. When he tried to speak to the dog, he found that he had lost his voice. He also found that he could not stand. So he crawled on his hands and knees for about 90 m back along the way he had come. After that, he managed to stand and walk unsteadily to where he had left his pick-up truck. There he tried to contact his headquarters via the two-way radio, but he still could not speak. He attempted to turn the truck around, but got it stuck in soft ground and had to abandon it. He then walked home, a distance of about 1870 m via a short cut across fields and woods, arriving home about 1115L. His voice returned on the way. He was very thirsty and suffering from a frontal headache which lasted for several hours. His thirst lasted for two days. He could still taste the smell and he had a pain in his chin and felt sick.

Consequences

When she saw that he was covered in mud and heard that he had been attacked, his wife wanted to call the police. He restrained her and explained the nature of the incident. However he allowed her to call his supervisor and head of the Forestry Department, Malcolm Drummond. While she did this he took a bath.

Drummond called a doctor and made straight for Taylor's house, interviewing him in his bath! Taylor explained that there must be marks on the ground where the spacecraft (he was sure that's what it was) had sat. Drummond set off to look but could not find the clearing. Meanwhile the doctor had arrived.

Dr Gordon Adams found a graze on Taylor's left leg, and a slight graze under his chin. He could find no sign of head injury or brain compression. Taylor's temperature, blood pressure, heart and lungs were normal. However he ordered an ambulance to take him to a nearby hospital for a head X-ray and an interview with a psychiatrist.

Taylor then set off with Drummond to show him where the incident had occurred and to look for evidence. It was then that the ground markings were discovered and the police were called.

While Taylor and his wife later went by ambulance to hospital, they were kept waiting so long that they left without him being examined. He felt well, and they wanted to go away for the weekend to visit relatives.

Meanwhile the press learned of the incident, and it became UK news the following Sunday. I have never seen so much press coverage of a UFO report. It received wide publicity and interest throughout Britain and the world, and it has featured on television and in many books. In the autumn of 1991, Livingston Development Corporation commemorated the event by placing a plaque set in a huge boulder on the site (see opposite). Unfortunately the plaque was stolen three months later and at the time of writing it has not been replaced.

THIS IS THE SITE REFERRED TO IN
ARTHUR C CLARKE'S 'MYSTERIOUS WORLD'
WHICH DESCRIBES AN ENCOUNTER
BETWEEN A FORESTRY WORKER OUT
WALKING AND WHAT APPEARED TO HIM
AS AN UNIDENTIFIED FLYING OBJECT

LDC 1991

The police investigation

The local police had never before experienced such a case and were mystified. It is to their credit that they never questioned the honesty of the report, at least not once they heard character references and saw the ground marks. Apart from measuring and recording the marks, they took statements from Taylor, his wife and the doctor.

In any case of alleged assault, Scottish police are required to have the clothing involved sent for forensic examination. This examination showed that both Taylor's trousers and his long johns had been torn on each hip (one tear corresponding to where he had a graze on his leg). These tears had been noticed by Taylor's wife on his return. The tears were consistent with the material having been pulled up while the trousers were being worn.

The forensic scientists also found traces of a powder similar to maize starch on the trousers. They did not know that this was caused by the fact that the trousers had been transported to the laboratory in an old shopping bag.

No evidence was found of helicopter movements in the area that day, or the previous day. One policeman made a search of the area around the clearing to see if there were signs of a mobile crane that might have been used to lower something into the clearing. He found nothing.

The ground markings

These were of two types (see figure 9:1). There were two parallel ladder-like 'tracks', each about 2·5 m long and the same distance apart. Each 'rung' of the ladder was about 2 or 3 cm wide and deep, and about 30 cm long, and the area of grass between each 'rung' was evenly flattened, but not as deeply as the 'rungs'. Although the 'tracks' appeared to be impressions made by a heavy object, the indentations were only in the grass; the ground beneath the grass did not appear to have been indented or crushed at all. I was able to confirm this later when the grass had been flattened by snow and had withered. However, individual blades of grass were bent around the square 'rung' and they did not lose this form even after 24 hours.

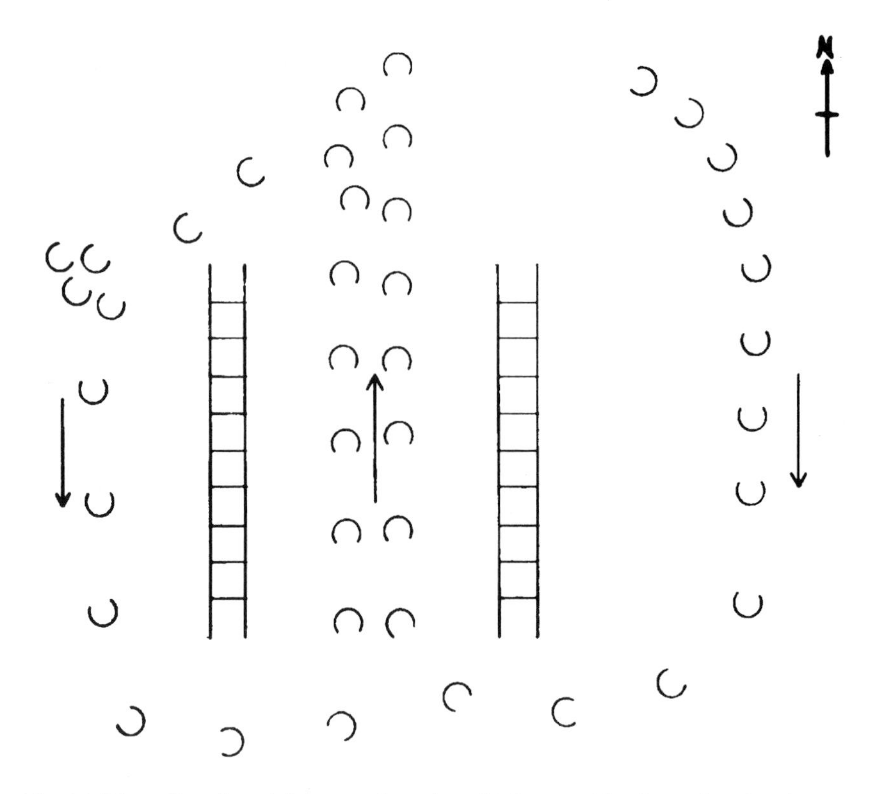

Fig. 9:1 The police plan of the ground marks at Livingston. The 'horseshoes' and arrows indicate the direction in which the holes were angled. The north pointer is incorrectly oriented.

There were also forty holes surrounding the 'tracks'. These holes, about 10 cm across, and even less deep, exposed fresh soil. All seemed to be at an angle of about 30° to the horizontal. The direction of the angle of inclination was consistent, that is to say the holes all faced in the same direction, towards the next hole in the circuit (there were two circuits). One circuit of holes ran clockwise and one ran anticlockwise, but they seemed to match up between the 'tracks'. In some of the holes it could be seen that blades of grass had been cut. There was no obvious impression of an implement in the holes. None of the grass was burned or scorched; fresh grass growing on the site in 1980 seemed quite normal and showed no sign of the incident. The grass and the ground beneath it were damp; in fact when I first saw the site it was covered in hoar frost.

The witness

Taylor was known for his honesty and responsibility. He was not the sort of person to invent a tale or play a practical joke. In fact he was of phlegmatic disposition and has reacted to the experience as if it were a minor traffic accident. He does not appear to have been changed by the event. He had heard of flying saucers, but had no interest in the subject and his house contained hardly any books, let alone any on UFOs. Many told me that they would not have believed the report from anyone else. The subsequent conviction that aliens attempted to abduct him does not seem to have changed or disturbed him, although afterwards he always carried a camera in case they came back.

He drank very little alcohol, and none during working hours. He did smoke cigarettes. He described his health as good, although he was troubled by poor appetite, which he attributed to the condition of his liver (possible cirrhosis caused by heavy drinking in the past). In 1965 he suffered viral meningitis, from which he made a good recovery. In 1977 he was hospitalized with mild hepatitis. He had undergone two operations, a herniorrhaphy and an operation on his neck for cervical spondylosis. He had no history of head injury, and he did not normally suffer from headaches, dizziness or blackouts. He did suffer from angina and high blood pressure; he was taking medication for the latter. He weighed 73 kg and was 1·8 m tall. His hearing was good and he needed spectacles only for reading.

My own investigation

Convinced that a simple explanation would eventually be found, I busied myself with obtaining as much data as possible.

One line of enquiry was the strange smell Taylor reported. An odd feature was the fact that, although he claimed that it persisted when he got home, his wife could not detect it. He likened it to that of burning brake linings. Tests with samples of ozone (O_3), nitrogen dioxide (NO_2) and hydrogen sulphide (H_2S) showed that the last came closest to matching the strange smell (although none was identical).

A soil sample was tested, but was found to contain only the normal elements, the distribution of which differed only slightly from that of a control sample from the same site. The radioactivity of the samples was normal.

In order to check Taylor's route home and to find how long he could have been unconscious, I traced and timed this route. There seemed to be nowhere on the route where Taylor had to climb, so tearing his trousers. The time taken on this route indicated that Taylor must have been unconscious for about 20 minutes.

Taylor himself was unable to produce a sketch of what he saw. The first attempt was made by David Hammond, then a student architect and the fiancé of his youngest daughter. This sketch showed the 'UFO' standing on four slender legs, but Taylor strenuously denied that he saw any legs. He agreed that the general form shown in the amended sketch (figure 9:2, where the legs have not been completely removed) did represent what he saw.

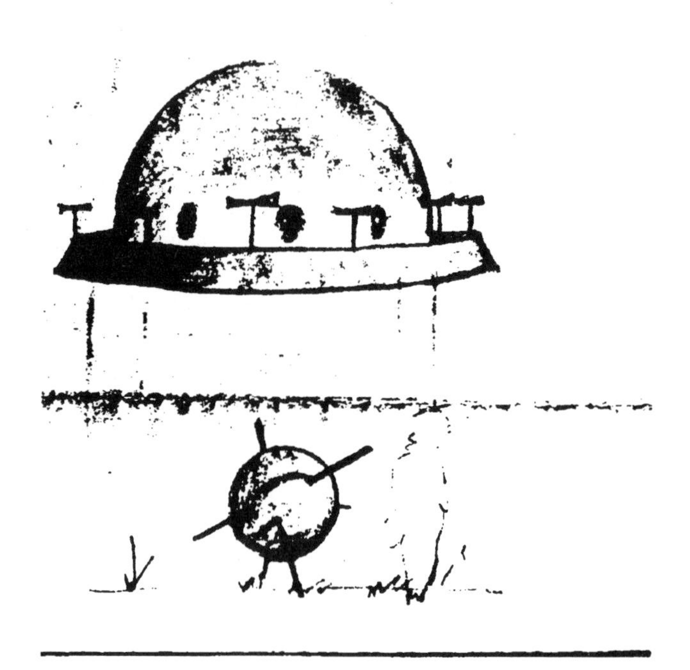

Fig. 9:2 A sketch of the 'spacecraft' and one of the 'robots' that accompanied it, as described by Robert Taylor and drawn by David Hammond.

The ground markings reminded me of the impression obtained by leaving equipment lying in grass while the latter is growing. This idea was reinforced by the fact that the underlying soil was not impressed. Also there were indications that a vehicle had turned the corner of the clearing. All this suggested that some fairly light equipment had been stored in the clearing during the summer when the grass was growing.

At first I could not imagine what the equipment was. However, on my first visit to the site, I had seen stacks of PVC pipes in an adjacent field. Enquiries revealed that, during the late summer, the local water authority had been laying a cable duct within 100 m of the clearing. They complete this work by 9 October. It seemed very likely that they had stored two stacks of the pipes in the clearing. The 'rungs' of the 'tracks' would have been caused by the wooden bands used to hold the stacks together. The holes might have been caused by the use of some implement, perhaps a pick, to remove the bottom timbers of the bands.

Although I traced the men employed on this operation, and although they admitted that they had travelled though the clearing, they denied having stored anything there. I suspected that they were not telling the truth, perhaps because they were not supposed to have used the clearing for that purpose. Taylor himself could not recall having seen anything lying there on previous visits. Nevertheless I remained convinced that the marks were caused in the manner described above. It was the simplest explanation.

As to what Taylor had seen, I was completely baffled for a long time and resigned to never being able to solve the case. At one time I considered that Taylor had seen some unusual meteorological phenomenon such as ball lightning. However there was no storm to justify this hypothesis. Moreover, at that time I was attempting to explain all features of the report by one phenomenon. The ball lightning hypothesis was overstretched to do this and had to be abandoned.

Investigation by others

A team from the UFO Investigation Network (UFOIN) also visited Taylor and inspected the site of the incident. They saw it as the landing of a spacecraft and concluded that the smaller objects were 'devices'. They were sure that the 'craft' had rested upon the ground and caused impressions in it. They reported that the Taylor was 'mesmerized by the object's totally alien appearance', and that he had been 'assaulted' by the devices. They made numerous enquiries in an attempt to establish whether or not 'folklore, mystical, or UFO type events' had been associated with the area in the past (Keatman and Collins 1979-1980).

Medical hypotheses

At that time, Dr Patricia Hannaford, founder of the Edinburgh University UFO Research Society (when she was a student), was a member of the local branch of BUFORA. As a physician, she was qualified to advise me on medical aspects of the case. After hearing Taylor's story and interviewing him, she suggested that his collapse was caused by an isolated fit of temporal lobe epilepsy. Indeed, she also suggested that the fit explained the whole incident, including the objects he reported seeing.

An epileptic attack usually starts with an aura lasting several seconds or minutes. This aura commonly involves bizarre and varied hallucinations, particularly visual and olfactory, and old memories may intrude into consciousness. Hallucinations of smell are powerful and unpleasant. Loss of consciousness may then occur as the fit becomes generalized, and deep sleep follows. Afterwards there may be confusion, drowsiness, headache, aching limbs and a period of altered consciousness. Such a *grand mal* fit may be caused by one of the following:
1. Damage to the temporal lobe as a late effect of viral meningitis;
2. Impaired blood supply as the result of cerebrovascular disease, a transient ischaemic attack or a cardiac arrhythmia:
   or
3. A space-occupying lesion in the brain.

Less likely causes are the onset of idiopathic epilepsy or some unknown outside agency.

Hannaford commented that, in this case, because of the suddenness of the onset, the lack of prodromal symptoms such as sweating, dizziness or nausea, and the length of the period of unconsciousness, a vasovagal attack was most unlikely. A cerebrovascular accident was also unlikely, in view of the lack of evidence of subsequent neurological damage and the rapid recovery. A transient ischaemic attack, which is caused by a brief impairment of the blood supply as the result of a spasm or minor blockage of the blood supply, was a possibility, but it usually causes focal neurological signs such as one-sided weakness. A cardiac arrythmia producing sudden loss of blood supply was also a possibility. Both these occur without warning and may cause varying periods of consciousness, usually short.

Clearly the best explanation for Taylor's collapse and his symptoms was an isolated epileptic attack. Previous meningitis left him susceptible to such an attack and the report of a strong and unpleasant smell which no one else could detect makes it almost certain that this was the cause. Such an attack explains, not only the period of unconsciousness, but his headache, his dry throat and the paralysis of his vocal chords and legs (Todd's paralysis). During the attack, he would have been shouting and thrashing around. However Taylor was not an epileptic and had never before (so far as he knew) suffered such an attack. A subsequent examination at a major hospital in Edinburgh showed no abnormal brain activity. Consequently I now sought the cause of the attack. Was it, as Hannaford believed, a spontaneous fit in which the objects 'seen' were hallucinations forming part of the aura? Or was there an external stimulus?

The stimulus for the fit

One of the outstanding problems in the study of epilepsy is what triggers a seizure. By far the majority of fits are idiopathic (they occur without apparent cause), yet clearly every fit must have a cause. Some experts distinguish between the *predisposing cause* and the *precipitating cause.* It is clear that in this case the predisposing cause was the scar in Taylor's meninges. But what was the precipitating cause?

Precipitating causes (sometimes called 'precipitants') can include sleep, lack of sleep, alcohol, stress and worry (including intense fear, pain or rage), mood, intercurrent illness, drugs and the external stimuli that cause reflex epilepsy (sometimes called 'sensory precipitation'). Reflex epilepsies include photosensitive epilepsy, in which the seizure is a response to flickering or flashing lights or a reflection.

One expert claims that only rarely does a subject have hallucinations that invoke two organs of sense. If this is correct then the fact that Taylor suffered an olfactory hallucination (the powerful smell) makes it unlikely that he simultaneously suffered a visual hallucination. This conclusion is reinforced by consideration of the areas of the brain that must have been involved. Since speech and motor functions were affected, the left temporal lobe must have been involved. However, visual hallucinations can only occur if the occipital lobe is stimulated. These two lobes are widely separated and it is not likely that a disturbance in the temporal lobe would affect the occipital lobe. Consequently I concluded that it was most unlikely that the objects Taylor reported seeing were hallucinations. In any case they did not consist of the flickering and dancing lights usually reported.

If Taylor did not hallucinate the 'spaceship' and its 'robots' then he must have seen them. Surely it was not mere coincidence that he suffered such an attack just as he rounded a corner and was able to survey a scene that had previously been hidden from him. The attack could have been stimulated by some very unusual and perhaps alarming sight. But what could it have been?

The mirage hypothesis

Somewhen in the mid '80s, I obtained an astronomical computer programme that enabled me to explain many cases as sightings of astronomical objects. One day, out of desperation, I used it to find what bright astronomical objects might be near the horizon at the time Taylor saw his 'UFO'. To my surprise, I found that *two* planets were rising exactly in Taylor's line of sight as he rounded the corner and looked across the clearing. Plate 9:2 (q.v.) shows that Taylor had a clear view to Deer Hill (see figure 9:3). Venus (magnitude -3·7) lay at an altitude of only 3°

(neglecting refraction) on an azimuth of 138°, while Mercury (magnitude 0·4) lay close by at an altitude of 2° (neglecting refraction) on an azimuth of 139°.

Plate 9:2 The site of the incident at Livingston the morning after (the fence was erected to prtect the marks). This is the direction in which the witness saw his 'spaceship'.

In normal circumstances both planets would have been invisible, not only because it was daylight, but because the crest of Deer Hill lay at an altitude of 5°15' (from Taylor's position). However, if they were visible, it can only have been via mirage, a mechanism that can elevate the source. It is feasible that one or both planets could have been visible, magnified and lifted just over the crest of Deer Hill. But a temperature inversion would have been necessary.

If Taylor was looking at Venus (or less likely Mercury), then his view was across the valley of the River Almond, beyond Deer Hill. At that time, Britain lay on the edge of an anticyclone which brought relative calm and low wind speeds (25 km/h from the north-west). At Edinburgh Airport 13 km away, the minimum temperature the previous night was -1 °C. A satellite photograph shows that, at 0920L, Livingston lay near the edge of a cloud bank with clear skies to the north-west. By 1015L this cloud must have cleared, and warm air can have overlain colder air in the valley. It is quite likely therefore that an inversion had formed in the Almond valley by 1015L. Unfortunately no upper air data are available to confirm this.

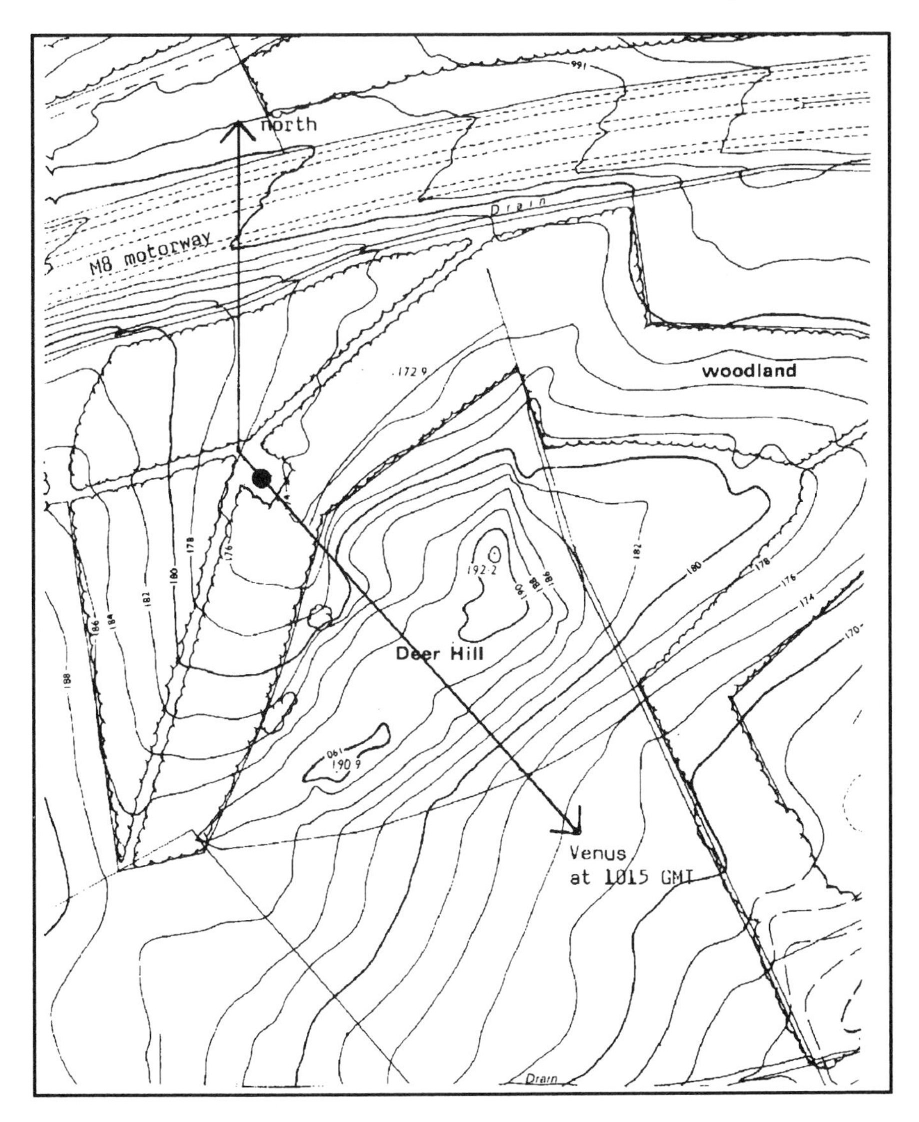

Fig. 9:3 A plan of the site of the Livingston incident showing the direction of Venus at 1015L. The black disc marks the alleged position of the UFO (and the location of the ground marks). Plan by courtesy of Livingston Development Corporation. Contours are at 2 m intervals.

The mirage hypothesis explains why Taylor suffered an epileptic attack when and where he did. Rounding a corner he was confronted by a hemispherical enlargement of the image of Venus appearing to be in the clearing in front of him (although in fact it was in the sky just above the hill). Its extended image would change in appearance as the light from Venus was refracted along different paths in the atmosphere. The cause of the two 'robots' is not clear, but perhaps Mercury also participated in the mirage. The 'spokes' may have been caused by corneal fibres and astigmatism as the pupils of his eyes opening in heightened interest. A combination of surprise, fear and the unusual sight may have been enough to trigger the epileptic seizure. Some of the images may have become distorted in the aural phase of the attack.

Criticism of the mirage hypothesis

Publication of the AMH (Campbell 1986a) brought criticism from aeronautical engineer T R Dutton in the next issue of *The Journal of Transient Aerial Phenomena.*

Dutton, who believes that UFOs are real alien vehicles, considered the hypothesis 'utter nonsense'. He thought that the Sun (on an azimuth of 160° and at an altitude of 15°) must have obscured any sight of the planets. Even if Venus had been visible it could not have resembled the non-luminous 'craft', which had 'structural form and technological features'. It was alleged that I had produced no evidence that Taylor suffered an epileptic attack. Dutton would not accept that there was a simple explanation for the ground marks and trouser tears, and he preferred the conclusion in the Case History (that the cause was ball lightning). He concluded that I was impugning the integrity of the witness.

I have never suggested that Taylor lied; on the contrary, I have made it plain that I believed him incapable of inventing the account. On the other hand I have been at pains to point out that we are not obliged to believe that the object was what Taylor thought it was. Dutton's failure to see the evidence for an epileptic attack showed that he had not read the Case History very carefully. Nor, if he thought they could not produce low-illumination images with 'structure', did he understand mirages. He had a better point concerning the Sun, which was even closer than he thought; azimuth 155° and altitude 14°. However, because the Sun was low and to Taylor's right, it was hidden from him by dense fir trees, even at the point where he entered the clearing. Consequently he was shielded from its light, and able to see the mirage of Venus.

In 1988 I submitted an article about the case to Wendy Grossman, then editor of *The British and Irish Skeptic* (now *The Skeptic*). Because she found 'so little support' for my mirage hypothesis, she had reservations about it and was reluctant to publish it without 'some kind of scientific backing'. In an attempt to obtain such backing I consulted Professor R V Jones (then retired), whom I knew slightly and who had followed the UFO mystery with interest for many years. He thought the hypothesis interesting, especially since Venus was so very nearly in the right direction. He also thought my article worth publishing, if only to show what trouble an investigator was prepared to take in order to explain a report.

However he saw conflict between the report of a 'very bright' image and its size; he thought that an increase in size should have reduced the brightness. A mirage of Venus was not physically impossible and he suggested that, if the atmospheric refraction was over a large enough area, then the effect on the observer could have been that of an object of finite size and of appreciable brilliance. In fact Taylor had not reported a bright object; he had reported that it was dark grey (but with bright points). Consequently the report was consistent with an extended image of Venus, including the reduction in its brightness.

Early in 1989 I received a formal rejection of my article from Dr Steve Donnelly, the new editor of *The British and Irish Skeptic* and a physicist. He considered that the whole incident was explained by an epileptic attack and reminded me that such attacks do not have to be triggered by flashing lights, but that (when they are) the flashes have to be regular, not irregular as in the scintillation of a low altitude planet. He did not consider that the AMH was plausible and he did not know of any documented cases where a superior mirage was magnified. In any case, he argued, magnification would result in the light intensity (*sic*) being spread out over the whole area of the magnified image, giving rise to an image so faint that it would not be visible in daylight. He thought that it would be wrong to publish 'such a weak, apparently "scientific" hypothesis with so little evidence to back it up'.

I had not claimed that the object Taylor saw was flashing or that the attack had been brought about by such flashing. Donnelly seemed to regard the attack as idiopathic, ignoring the need to identify a precipitating cause. His ignorance of similar cases was understandable, although his error regarding the use of the word 'intensity' and the difference between his conclusion and that of Professor Jones were not. A 'faint' image would not be an invisible image and, because it would be darker than the sky, it should be visible as a dark object (as reported by Taylor).

Subsequent correspondence with Donnelly produced an undertaking to consider publication of my article if I described the exact mechanism which I claim gave rise to the magnified and relatively undistorted superior daylight mirage of Venus. He also required me to provide at least one reference to an article in a refereed scientific journal where magnified undistorted superior mirages have been observed, and at least one reference to an article in a refereed medical or scientific journal stating both that *grand mal* attacks require an external trigger and that the victims invariably dream of fond memories and loved ones! He likened the probability that the atmosphere could form a magnifying lens to that of anti-gravity.

I considered that too many obstacles were being put in my way and that it was not reasonable of Donnelly to make demands which were not customarily made in his journal, which is not itself refereed. In any case he was demanding evidence of phenomena which (it seemed likely) I was myself providing. He had also ignored Professor Jones's recommendation that the article should be published. Consequently I did not attempt to pursue the matter.

Implications for foreign reports

If a local report which I had fully investigated was found to be both reliable and strange (although not as strange as described initially), then similar foreign reports could not easily be dismissed as hoaxes or invention. However the discovery that this case could have been caused by an astronomical mirage alerted me to the possibility that this might also be the explanation in foreign cases. UFO reports may generally be both reliable and explicable, although by no commonly accepted mechanism.

10 The Air Force hunts a UFO

An unusual insight into the conduct of an investigation by the USAF of a report made by its own personnel comes from Suffolk (England). A US television programme about the incident (*Unsolved Mysteries*) described it as the 'best-documented' UFO case in USAF history.

Hearing a rumour of an incident in December 1980 at RAF Woodbridge (then occupied by the US 81st Tactical Fighter Wing, supervised from the nearby Bentwaters base), two local ufoists, Brenda Butler and Dot Street, made quite a nuisance of themselves by questioning anyone and everyone; they even interviewed the base commanders (USAF and RAF) and advertised for witnesses. Denials were taken as 'cover-up', and only made them more convinced that something was being concealed. The rumour was summarized by a journalist as follows:

> On the night of December 30, 1980, a spaceship supposedly crashed in the forest near the Bentwaters/Woodbridge Royal Air Force Base, a NATO installation in England. Three silver-suited aliens, each three feet [1 m] tall and hovering above the ground in a beam of light, repaired the damaged craft while conversing with an American base commander. Four hours later, repairs complete, the spaceship shot off at tremendous speed [Mishara 1983].

Mishara claimed to have obtained his information from a former Deputy Base Commander, now a general.

The case develops

Butler and Street were given sketchy directions to what was alleged to be the crash site, a recently felled area of Rendlesham Forest only 1 km from the end of the Woodbridge runway. The felling was interpreted as an attempt to conceal the incident, and the lack of vegetation was attributed to 'radiation'. Here they thought that their car was mysteriously accelerated by an unknown force.

In her first account of the incident, Street concluded that it occurred on the evening of 28 December 1980, when a local farmer, woken by his restless cattle, heard an unusually loud noise and noticed that the sky was 'a[s] bright as day' (Street 1982). This farmer was never identified.

During 1981, after hearing that military radar had tracked a UFO which crashed in Rendlesham Forest, Jenny Randles, BUFORA's Director of Investigations, began to take an active interest in the case. The following year she wrote two articles (Randles 1982a and 1982b); in one of which she claimed that the USAF had filmed the UFO on the ground. Meanwhile, investigation by an independent UFO group from Swindon (SCUFORI) cast doubt on the claims made by Butler and Street and convinced sceptics that there was no foundation to the reports (Mrzyglod and Shipp 1983).

Among the readers of Randles's articles were Larry Fawcett and Barry Greenwood of Citizens Against UFO Secrecy (CAUS) in the USA. They realized that a story they had heard from a young ex-serviceman was related to the incident. Larry Warren, who at first used the pseudonym 'Art Wallace', approached them after reading about the investigations in England; at the time he had been a security policeman at Bentwaters.

Warren alleged that, while he had been on duty at 0100L on a night 'either on or very near to' 30 December 1980, he had been ordered to help take a gas-powered trailer-mounted light ('Light-all') into Rendlesham Forest. As he and colleagues approached a clearing they noticed a 'brightness' in the distance and the sound of helicopters overhead. He saw large movie cameras and many military and plainclothes personnel 'milling about watching something'. This was an object like a huge transparent aspirin tablet hovering just above the ground. It was 15 m in diameter and was filled with a bright pulsating yellow mist. Over a radio, he heard someone say 'here it comes', at which point he saw a red light appear from behind a tree. The light came to hover over the 'tablet' and silently broke into a shower of particles, upon which the 'tablet' was replaced by a bright white domed disc with budding wings. After turning to say something to a colleague, he awoke lying on his bed in the barracks. He was fully dressed and muddy up to his knees. He was told that he had come in at 0400L. Only gradually did he recall the earlier (alleged) events.

Later Warren was debriefed, told not to talk about the night's events, and shown a film about UFOs. He alleged that the version of the story 'leaked' to the British mass media, detailing alien meetings in the forest and landing marks on the ground, was deliberately contrived to mislead the public and preserve secrecy.

CAUS filed for documents under the US Freedom of Information Act and were, at first, told that there were no records. However they were told that there was 'some strange activity near RAF Bentwaters at the appropriate time in question'. Eventually a copy of a memorandum from the then Deputy Base Commander was produced. This astonishing document (see Appendix 1) appeared to support Warren's story. What was equally astonishing was that, according to the supplier (513th CSG) the copy was supplied by the British Ministry of Defence (MoD) who had denied all knowledge of the incident (Fawcett and Greenwood 1984:215-218).

The Halt memorandum impressed CAUS and created a sensation in British UFO circles. Here was a senior USAF officer stating, not only that a metallic craft had been seen in the forest (although not by him), but that (by implication) it had left marks and radiation, both of which he witnessed. Moreover he and other officers had seen anomalous lights which neither he nor they could identify. All this tended to corroborate the earlier and more sensational report. The lack of any mention of a crash, repairs or aliens was attributed by ufoists to censorship.

Colonel Halt himself, still at Bentwaters, was embarrassed. However he did confirm that it was his memorandum and that he stood by what he had written. The story became headline news in Britain during October and November 1983, when the press carried sensational accounts (including Warren's) and extracts from the memorandum. Sceptics were baffled.

Explanations

Suddenly some rational explanations emerged. Because events outside the base were the concern of the civilian police, Butler and Street had asked the local police to check their records for 27-30 December. Surprisingly this had produced nothing, leading the team to become even more suspicious of a cover-up. Then, as a result of the publicity, a local newspaper discovered that the police *had* been called to RAF Woodbridge; but the call came at 0411L on *26* December. Furthermore the records showed that, although a patrol car had gone into the forest, the officers in it had seen nothing except the light from a lighthouse at Orford Ness (8·6 km away to the east). At 1030L the same day, the police received another call to see where a craft might have landed. Evidently someone at Bentwaters took the matter seriously. However the police thought that the marks could have been made by an animal.

Ian Ridpath, a science writer with an interest in UFOs, had already looked in vain for a conventional stimulus for the night's events. He now discovered that, at 0250L on 26 December, a very bright fireball (large meteor) had been seen over the North Sea to the east of Suffolk and Kent. According to the British Astronomical Association, it flared at a height of 180-120 km on an azimuth (from Woodbridge) of 100-120° (see their Newsletter No. 4, February 1981). Evidently the patrolmen at Woodbridge had seen this fireball and had assumed, as many people do, that it was an object falling in flames a short distance away (into Rendlesham Forest). It seems possible (if there is any truth in the report) that this object was also the 'UFO' that was tracked by radar; radar could have detected the ionized trail of the fireball. On a visit to the area, Ridpath encountered a forester who suggested, not only that the lights seen through the trees were the beam from the lighthouse, but that the marks were old rabbit burrows. Ridpath himself concluded that the radiation readings were normal (natural background) and that the latter lights (mentioned in the Halt memorandum) had been stars. This hypothesis was explained in a newspaper article (Ridpath 1985), and in *The Skeptical Inquirer* (Ridpath 1986).

Ufoists were shocked and outraged. Although a fireball could have stimulated the first report (assuming that Halt had the wrong date, which they doubted), they refused to accept that anyone would be fooled by such a familiar landmark as a lighthouse. They ridiculed Ridpath's explanation and clung to their beliefs.

The tape recording

The investigators had heard that Halt had recorded a commentary on his nocturnal exploration, and they were encouraged to hear that it justified their beliefs. They were told that it recorded the 'shock, amazement and terror at this fantastic occurrence' and that it ended with the words 'Oh my God, it's a m ...'! Naturally they concluded that the unfinished word was 'machine'. It was alleged that elsewhere Halt could be heard crying out 'here they come! ... quick men ... run!', words that were followed by the sounds of shouting and panic. The investigators never expected to hear the tape, believing that it was closely guarded. However, after publication of their book (Butler, Street and Randles 1984) the Pentagon released copies of the tape (see transcript in Appendix 2).

As might be expected, the tape did not substantiate the fanciful beliefs of ufoists (a fact that led some to conclude that it was faked). On the other hand it contains information that is not only interesting for its own sake, but which explains the incident.

Because of the discrepancy between the date of the fireball and the date given in Halt's memorandum, we cannot tell on what date the recording was made (perhaps the night of 28/29 December). However it is certain that it was contemporaneous with events described by Halt in the second and third paragraphs of his memorandum (the date of the animal 'frenzy' seems to have become transposed). Among the various items of equipment mentioned are the 'Light-all' floodlight and a 'Starscope' (or 'Starlight scope'), which appears to be an infra-red detector.

It is evident that Halt's team were not skilled in the use of some of the equipment, especially the Geiger-counter, which they appear to have thought was giving significant readings. It is also apparent that they thought they were examining the site of the crash of an alien craft and that it was radioactive. It is not clear why a second expedition was mounted at night. One explanation could be that the USAF had no right to examine the area; another that they hoped to see the craft again. It may be that they could only use the Starscope at night (there would be too much heat during the day). The 'burn marks' on the trees, which Halt and his colleagues saw as evidence that a craft had crashed, were explained to Ridpath as resin exuding from cuts made by foresters two months before to indicate trees to be felled. The tape provides a fascinating insight into the operation of a small military team attempting a scientific investigation. It also shows very clearly how people who are convinced that they are at the site of a mysterious event will find what they consider to be evidence for that event.

The lightship hypothesis

Ridpath concluded that, on each occasion, the light seen was that of the Orford Ness lighthouse, whose characteristic pattern is one white flash every 5 s. But that light lies on a bearing of 100° magnetic (see figure 10:1). Halt's two lights lay on a bearing between 110° and 120° magnetic (at the time the magnetic deviation for south-east England was 5° west).

It is more likely that he was looking at the light of the Shipwash lightship, which lay on a bearing of 115° magnetic and whose characteristic pattern is three close flashes every 20 s (see Table 10:1). Shipwash lay 18·2 km away and is ten times less powerful than Orford Ness. While this makes it less easy to see, it also makes confusion between the two lights very unlikely. Halt and his team would have been familiar with the light of Orford Ness and could not have mistaken it. In fact they must have ignored it (unless the second light they saw was that from Orford Ness). They would not have been so familiar with the light from Shipwash, which may have been enhanced by mirage. Shipwash lay well within the usual limit of visibility (29 km) for a light with an output of 10,000 cd. Halt's light was red or yellow while the Orford Ness light is white. Trinity House have not told me the colour of the Shipwash light, but their failure to mention that it is white suggests that this was not the case. In any event, its light would be reddened by the greater distance it had to travel.

If the second light reported by the team was not Orford Ness, then it may have been the star Spica, at an altitude of 1° (neglecting refraction) in line with Shipwash at 0155Z (Campbell 1985b). Ridpath concluded that the second light was Shipwash. The relative ease with which these beacons could be seen from within the forest would depend on the layout and density of the trees lying between the observers and the beacons. From some positions the powerful Orford Ness may have been invisible.

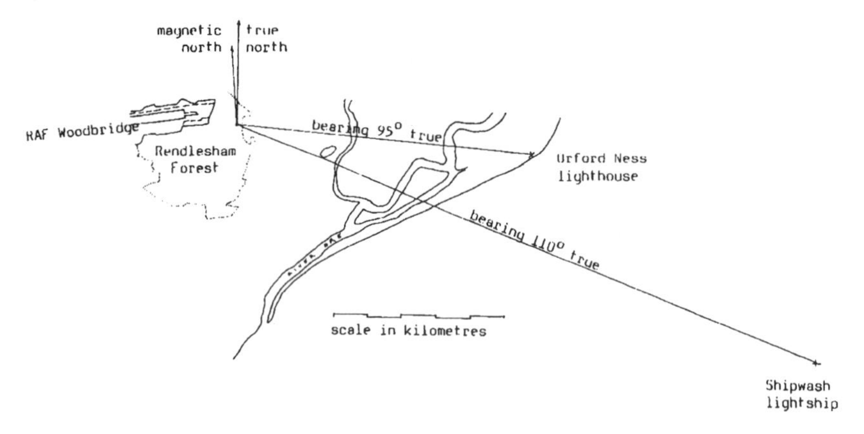

Fig. 10:1 The true bearings of the lighthouse and the lightship from Rendlesham Forest.

Explanations for other features of the report

Ridpath was almost certainly correct in concluding that the other lights reported were stars (although they may have been mirages of the stars concerned). Deneb and Vega lay near the horizon in the north-north-east, while Sirius was towards the south-west horizon (altitude 12°; azimuth 222°).

It seems likely that Halt and his team were themselves responsible for some of the other reports. They must have disturbed the animals, and their own floodlight(s) must have produced the light seen by the farmer, and that seen by Warren.

Not only can stars have been misreported during this incident. The planets Jupiter and Saturn were at close (less than 1°) conjunction in the south-east and can have appeared to hover over the forest before the Moon rose.

Criticism of the lightship hypothesis

Early in 1986, I sent an article describing the case, and my conclusions, to the editor of *The Skeptical Inquirer* (Kendrick Frazier). At about the same time Frazier had been considering re-publishing Ridpath's newspaper article. Ridpath, to whom he showed my article, suggested the publication of both articles, although mine in a shortened form.

Frazier did not take this advice; instead he referred my article to Klass. Because he could not understand my objective or viewpoint, Klass was 'distressed'. It seems that he could not tell whether I was for or against belief in UFOs (as if that mattered). He advised against publication because of my 'fallacious conclusions and inferences'. These were: my conclusion that there had been obsessive official secrecy; that Halt was now a general; that the USAF took a serious view of the incident; that the incompetence of the base personnel was disturbing and that the USAF had learned nothing about dealing with UFO reports.

Klass was wrong on all counts. Obsessive official secrecy is endemic everywhere, and especially so in Britain, where the MoD told Randles practically nothing and denied that they had any documents relating to events at Woodbridge. Only via the USA's Freedom of Information Act had the veil of secrecy been penetrated; the United Kingdom has no equivalent legislation. I had not claimed that Halt was then a general; I was referring to Mishara's informant. If the USAF had not taken a serious view of the report they would not have called the local police and (later) mounted an expedition in the dead of night. Nor would Halt have written a report. Klass even challenged my astonishment that the USAF officers took the idea of a UFO landing seriously, and he tried to justify the failure of the USAF to apply the lessons learned decades before. No doubt he was sensitive to criticism of his country's armed forces, especially the USAF (Klass was a senior editor for *Aviation Week and Space Technology*).

In subsequent correspondence, Klass tried to justify identification of the light as that of Orford Ness lighthouse. He had noted that, at one point in the tape recording, a period of 5 s can be marked between a voice saying 'there it is again' and 'there it is' (see annotation on the transcript). Knowing that the period of the Orford Ness light is 5 s (but knowing nothing else), Klass concluded that the light must have been that of Orford Ness, and Ridpath has followed this idea. However this hypothesis does not explain why the light was so small, or why it disappeared from time to time (a few seconds later Halt asked 'is it back again?'). Apparently Klass was unaware of the pattern of the Shipwash light, with its three flashes 2·5 s apart. If the second flash was not noticed then the observed flashes would indeed be 5 s apart. Furthermore the 15 s eclipse of Shipwash is evident in the recording, as is the 20 s overall period (see annotation). Although I drew Klass's attention to this, he later labelled my hypothesis 'HOGWASH' and offered to make a wager as to whether the recording shows 'AT LEAST TWO SINGLE FLASHES SEPARATED BY FIVE SECONDS OR THREE SUCCESSIVE FLASHES REPEATED EVERY 20 SECONDS' (his upper case and emphasis; letter 10 July 1986). I ignored this offer, partly because it was ambiguously worded and partly because it was not clear who would adjudicate. It was also silly and not in the spirit of scientific enquiry.

Conclusions

If (early on 29 December 1980) Halt and his team were deceived by a lightship and four stars, we do not need to look for any more exceptional explanation for the report made on 26 December (27 December according to Halt). Convinced that an aircraft (or a 'UFO') had crashed, the patrolmen were prone to deception by conventional stimuli. These stimuli may have included the light from the lighthouse (illuminating the forest) and the lightship. However, the mention of red and blue lights indicates that the object was a star (it is reported that, initially, Halt had these colours reversed). Indeed a bright mirage of Spica would answer the description. Whatever the stimulus was, it is clear that on each occasion a distant and unidentified light was perceived to be (firstly) nearby in the forest and (latterly) at a great distance. This led to the conclusion that the object had, under intelligent control, fled from the observers. It was natural to assume that if the object had departed, it had previously been much closer, perhaps on the ground in the forest. A search of any forest floor will always find anomalous marks capable of a sinister interpretation by those looking for one.

Warren must have been a member of Halt's night expedition. Afterwards he was so tired that he fell asleep without undressing. His subsequent elaboration may derive from a dream.

Because Halt and his team could not identify the lights, they could find no explanation for the earlier and more sensational report (of a crash in the forest). They did not know about the fireball. Consequently it appeared that they endorsed the first report, and its status grew. Since they had seen 'UFOs', who could denigrate the report of a craft? Ever more sensational rumours were bound to circulate, until they reached what the RAF base commander described as 'two totally unscientific investigators'. Butler and Street, steeped in the UFO myth, were completely fooled, as later was Randles. She and Street even visited the USA to interview witnesses and contacts. But the credulity and ignorance of the civilian investigators were matched by those of the military investigators. It is disturbing that the defence of the West was (is?) in the hands of people who cannot distinguish lightships and stars and who appear to believe in alien visitors. It is particularly surprising that Air Force officers could not identify common astronomical objects, and that they were not familiar with the autokinetic phenomenon. They did not seem to know what readings to expect on their Geiger-counter (the fact that it clicked at all excited them) and Halt did not seem to know what kind of energy his Starscope could detect and inappropriately pointed it at a distant light. The obsessive official secrecy is also disturbing; the military had nothing to hide but their own ignorance. Neither the USAF nor the MoD knew what to make of Halt's report, and because they could not explain it they tried to conceal it. The experience gained by the USAF in investigating UFO reports over many years appears to have been wasted.

In a recent sensationalist book about the incident, Randles accepted that Halt's memo is wrong and that the fireball or UFO was first seen on 26 December (Randles 1991).

Table 10:1
A comparison of the characteristics of Orford Ness lighthouse and the Shipwash floating light (data from Trinity House).

light	Orford Ness	Shipwash
character	white flash every 5 s	three flashes 2·5 s apart every 20 s
output (cd)	5×10^6	5×10^5

11 The case of the flying airfield

UFO reports from professional pilots are always taken very seriously. However, it is unusual for one to be made public. It is even more unusual to be able to obtain a detailed report on such an incident from a national aviation authority. A report by the US Department of Transportation's Federal Aviation Administration (1987) on an incident over Alaska in 1986 is actually unique. The FAA's only concern was that there might have been a threat to air traffic; they were not concerned to explain the report.

The captain's tale

The aircraft, a Japan Air Lines Boeing 747 freighter (JAL 1628), was on a polar flight from Iceland at a height of 10·67 km. After crossing the Canadian border, it was instructed by Anchorage Air Route Traffic Control Center (AARTCC) to set course (215° true) for the Talkeetna VOR beacon (see figure 11:1). The time was 1709L (Yukon Standard Time) on 17 November 1986 (0209Z on 18 November).

As the aircraft swung left, Captain Kenju Terauchi saw two unidentified lights to port, apparently at his own flight level. At first he assumed that they were military aircraft from one of the nearby Air Force bases (Eilson or Elmendorf). However over the next few minutes the lights did not change in position and seemed to be matching his speed (972 km/h). Seven minutes after first seeing the lights, Terauchi was startled to see two strange bright objects apparently about 2 km ahead. He now assumed that the two 'craft' had fired retro-jets to decelerate until they were just ahead of him. There were two separate clusters of bright lights in a parallel array, each strip separated by a dark space. Occasionally a stream of lights like a charcoal fire ran across the centre of the clusters. The lights were like flames ejected by a multiple rocket exhaust, amber and white in colour. First Officer Takanori Tamefuji compared the lights to landing lights, the bright headlights of an approaching aircraft. Both captain and first officer observed that the

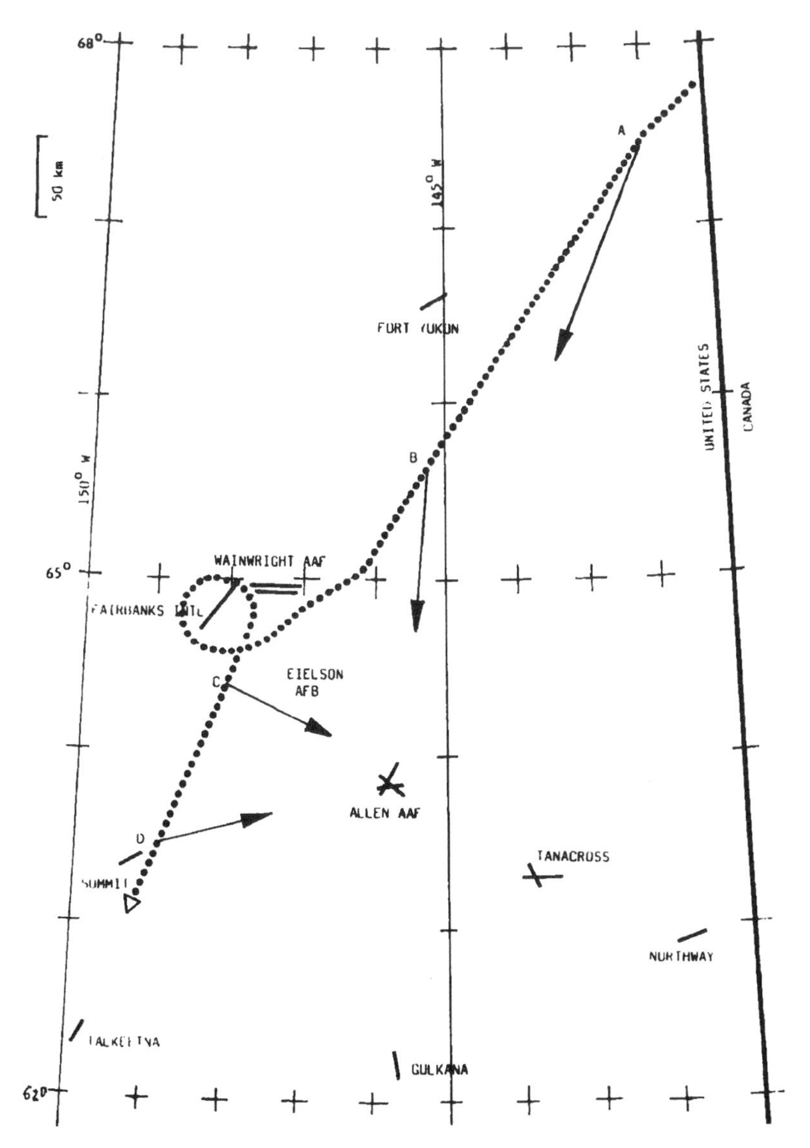

Fig. 11:1 Part of the track of JAL 1628 (dotted line) plotted on a map showing the surrounding airfields (runways not drawn to scale). The runway pattern is shown only where the longest runway exceeds 1219 m. The pointers indicate the direction of the unusual lights at various times.

lights, either side of a dark strip, moved together or rotated about it. After 2 minutes, during which the two clusters were one above the other, they changed to a side-by-side formation. Figure 11:2 shows Terauchi's own sketch of the clusters when side-by-side, while figure 11:3 shows one of the clusters in more detail (and the general arrangement when one above the other). The crew (it also included Flight Engineer Yoshio Tsukuda) became concerned and (at 1719L) they decided to report the lights to AARTCC. The FAA transcript shows Tamefuji to have asked AARTCC, 'do you have any traffic, ... seven o'clock above?'. Since the captain's report and sketches show the objects almost dead ahead, the word 'seven' must be a transcription error for 'eleven', a word that is difficult for the Japanese to pronounce correctly. By 'above' the first officer meant that the objects were between the 11 and 12 o'clock positions, perhaps at 11:30, as shown on figure 11:1 (from point A). However AARTCC knew of no other traffic in the vicinity and wondered what the crew were seeing.

The transcript of communications between JAL 1628 and AARTCC shows that the lights gradually moved left and aft, a fact well illustrated by Terauchi's own sketches (see figure 11:4). At 1725L (point B in figure 11:1) Tamefuji gave the bearing as '11 o'clock'. At 1744L (point C) it was '9 o'clock', and at 1748L (point D) it was '7, ... 8 o'clock' (see pointers on figure 11:1). Figure 11:3 appears to show that at some point the clusters rotated clockwise, and figure 11:4 indicates that they gradually reduced to two flat pale lights (figure 11:5). At 1730L Terauchi imagined that he saw a gigantic spaceship connecting the two pale lights (figure 11:5). This so alarmed him that he requested permission to take evasive action. He was first authorized to alter course, and was later requested to make a full right circle to see if he could shake off the 'spaceship'. During these course alterations, he was permitted to descend to 9·45 km. However the pale lights, and possibly the 'spaceship' (which only Terauchi reported), were still there when they completed the circle. Shortly afterwards, a passenger airliner, leaving Anchorage on a reciprocal course slightly east of JAL 1628, was asked to look out for the 'UFOs'. Looking west, its crew could see only the Japanese Boeing, but, as the aircraft passed each other, the Japanese crew reported that the lights disappeared (at about 1750L). By this time, JAL 1628 may have been at a height of only 7·62 km, having been given permission to descend to that flight level at 1742L.

The JAL crew attempted to locate the supposed spaceship(s) with their weather radar. They did so even though AARTCC could find no other traffic on their own radar. The crew set their radar at a range of 37 km, and aimed it horizontally. This produced a large target (a green strip) apparently about 13-15 km away in the direction of the lights. This image gradually moved left and aft until it disappeared at the limit of the radar (90°). About the same time AARTCC was receiving anomalous radar returns from the aircraft (a double image where there should have been only one).

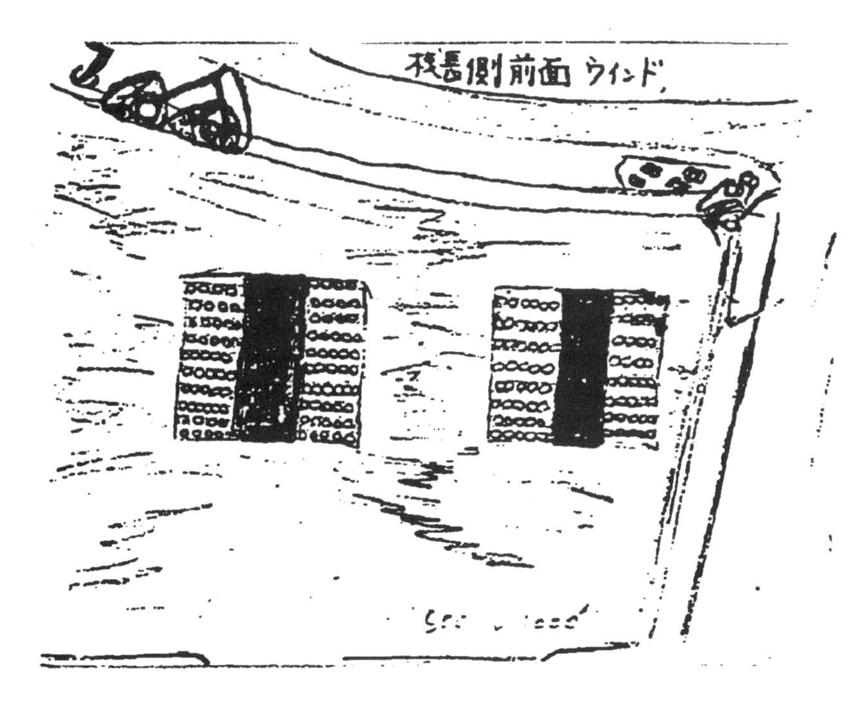

Fig. 11:2 Captain Terauchi's detailed sketch of the two clusters of lights he saw through the left cockpit window. Although he has blacked in the area between each set of lights, it cannot have been any darker than the surrounding gloom (which he did not blacken).

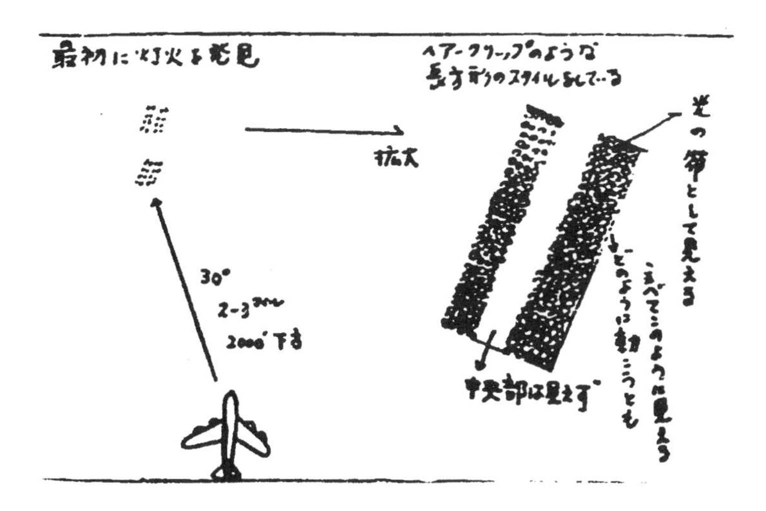

Fig. 11:3 Another sketch by Terauchi showing one of the clusters of lights in detail (besides the general arrangement, direction, distance and height, as he estimated them). Note that he has not blackened the space between the lights.

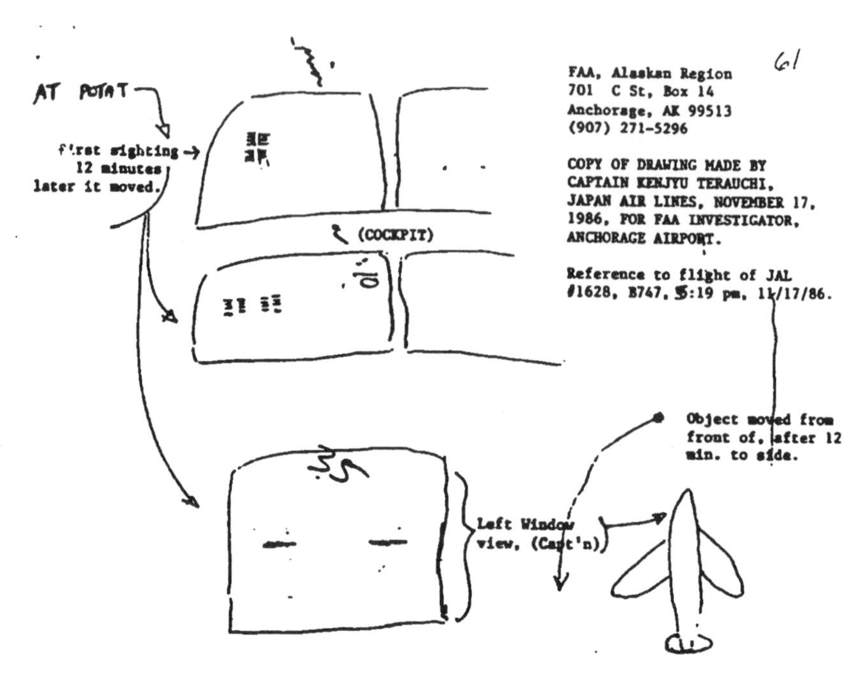

Fig. 11:4 Part of p. 61 of the FAA report, showing how the lights changed and gradually moved aft.

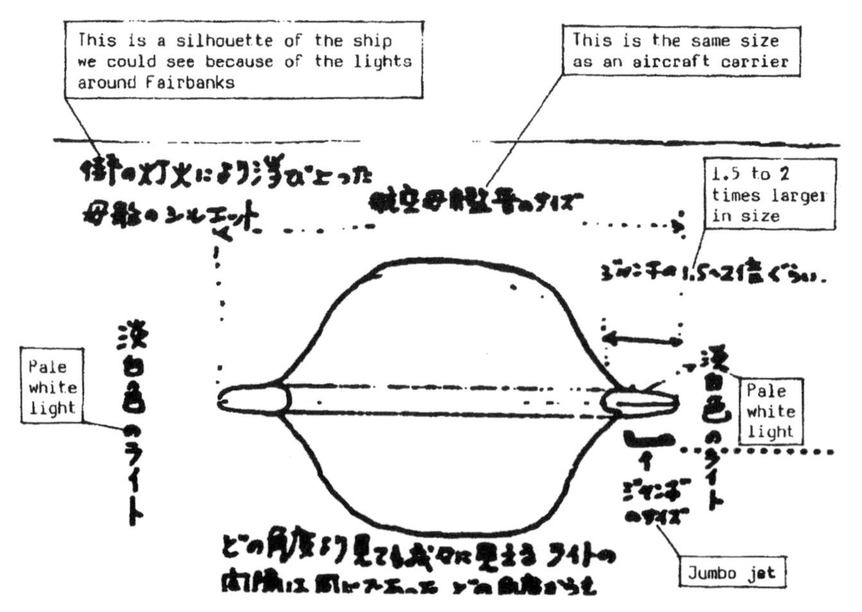

Fig. 11:5 Terauchi's sketch of the gigantic spaceship he claimed to have seen between the two pale lights. His estimate of size was based on the assumption that the craft was quite close. English translations from Maccabee (1987).

An inadequate explanation and review

In a review of the case, Klass (1987) concluded that, while one of the 'UFOs' was the planet Jupiter (then about 11° above the horizon in the south-east), the other (the 'flame-coloured lights') was 'bright moonlight reflected off turbulent clouds of ice crystals'. He did not adequately explain what the JAL crew reported, or indeed exactly what occurred.

The nearly-full Moon lay 12° or so above the horizon behind the aircraft (about the 7 o'clock position initially) and its light could not have been reflected backwards by ice crystals (if there were any). Nor could such a reflection have shown the structure reported by the JAL crew. Although the crew did not report seeing Jupiter, they did report seeing 'stars', one of which might have been the planet. When looking south-east, the crew might have mistaken Jupiter, but, since the unidentified lights themselves were always on the horizon, they could not have been either the Moon or Jupiter. Nor could Jupiter have disappeared, except behind thick cloud, and no such cloud was reported. The crew's report clearly shows that two objects remained in sight, although changing shape, throughout the incident. There was no question of losing them and later seeing a different object.

Klass's explanation was strongly criticized by Maccabee in a letter to *New Scientist*'s Ariadne (see her account in the issue of 8 October 1987).

What did the captain see?

The steady aft movement strongly suggests that the light source lay on the ground in Alaska. Indeed all four of the bearings point to an area centred on Allan Army Air Field (AAAF) at Delta Junction. This leads to the suggestion that the lights were the approach lights of AAAF's main runway. This runway (2280 m long) is aligned on a bearing of 212°, practically parallel to the course of JAL 1628. Initially it must have appeared almost head on. This hypothesis is reinforced by the reported shape and structure of the clusters of lights. They agree very closely with the general arrangement of approach lights, namely two sets of barrette lights marking the touchdown zone on the runway (see colour plate 11:1). As the flight continued, the line of the lights must have turned clockwise, becoming more and more slant, as shown in figure 11:3, until eventually the lights were viewed sideways as a strip. This hypothesis can even explain the occasional stream of light across the pattern, as aircraft using the runway.

When the lights were first reported, AAAF was about 450 km away over the horizon, and it should not have been visible to the crew of JAL 1628. Although the aircraft came within 120 km of AAAF, and the crew might have seen its lights, at no time did they report doing so. In any case, under normal conditions, the airfield would have been too small to be seen. The only way in which these lights could have been visible initially is via mirage; later lights were too large to be direct images. A mirage would also explain the sudden brightening of the image and its irregular movement, as if flying.

The mirage hypothesis

If what the crew saw was a superior mirage of the AAAF lights, then a temperature inversion must have existed somewhere between the two. Although the FAA report gives no comprehensive weather data, it does state that conditions were very calm and clear and that there was a temperature inversion at a height of 7·16 km. However it gives neither the location nor the extent of this inversion. Conditions were also such as to severely interfere with radio communications; Terauchi reported static during VHF transmissions with AARTCC and communications were broken or unintelligible several times. At one point, AARTCC instructed the first officer to change frequency. The inversion can have been responsible for these difficulties, in which case it lay ahead and in the direction of AAAF.

The inversion can also have been responsible for the anomalous image on the aircraft's radar and the double image on AARTCC's radar. A green image indicated a weak echo (strong echoes appeared in red), inconsistent with the detection of a nearby craft (Klass 1987). Klass suggested that the echo was from ice crystals. It is possible that the inversion layer contained charged particles. These would reflect radar signals and at the same time interfere with communication with Anchorage. If the aircraft's radar was set horizontally then only a sidelobe reflection could have detected the inversion 3·50 km below. The size and colour of the signal received does indicate a large weak reflector.

The FAA thought that the anomalous double return was caused by a problem with the aircraft's transponder. They described how an 'uncorrelated primary and beacon target' occurs when there is a slight mistiming of the transponder beacon. Some concluded that this was all there was to the incident. However there is no evidence that such a fault was discovered in the transponder, and it is more likely that the second return was caused by refraction through the inversion layer (along a path that was longer than the most direct one).

It should not be surprising therefore that both the mirages and the radar signals lay in the same direction. They can have had the same cause, the temperature inversion.

A mirage explains, not only the visibility of such a distant source, but the double images. Figure 11:3 indicates that the images were not reversed, but this may be the result of an error of memory. Two images side-by-side may have been caused by splitting of the image along the inversion layer. Variations in shape and arrangement of the mirages are likely to have been caused by the line of sight moving across the inversion. The 'gigantic spaceship' may have been imagined or it may have been a real image as light from AAAF was seen over the whole surface of a curved thermocline between the two pale images. It seems that the crew lost sight of the mirage when it fell so far aft as to be difficult or even impossible to see from the cockpit.

Attempts to confirm that the runway lights at AAAF were actually on at the time (and that the runway was in use) have met with no success. Enquiries to the Pentagon and Fort Greely have received no response. Naturally the mirage hypothesis fails if it is shown that the runway was not illuminated.

Criticism of the mirage hypothesis

In December 1988 I sent an article about this case to the editor of *The Skeptical Inquirer* in the USA. It took him nearly a year to respond, telling me that, while he thought it ought to be published, he had more UFO material than he could cope with. He offered to hold it on file for eventual publication, but warned that there was a large backlog. He commented that the case had 'long ago dropped out of the news' and that my analysis had to be considered 'speculative'.

Subsequently I received a letter from Klass, who, as a member of the journal's editorial board, regularly received a list of forthcoming articles in addition to those on the waiting list. Evidently my article was on the latest list and Klass had asked for and received a copy of the article. Klass declared that my hypothesis deserved consideration. However he wanted to consider whether there was only one trigger mechanism, as I proposed, or two, as he had proposed. During subsequent correspondence, he persisted with the idea that, while the mirage might have been the initial stimulus, the later sightings were of Jupiter. He tried to prove this by reference to the radar plots of the JAL and United aircraft in the last stages of the incident. Unfortunately these plots do not show the position of JAL 1628 at the time of the captain's observation of the azimuth of the object, and I have not been able to obtain the relevant plots from the FAA. Klass was also exercised over the fact that a copy of an FAA chart supplied to him contained sketch numbers which do not appear on the final report released to me. He thought that the numbers undermine my hypothesis. Correspondence revealed errors both on his part and on mine, although mine made no material difference. Even though Klass was not able to produce evidence that invalidated the mirage hypothesis, he would not accept that it explained it completely. At the time of writing it is not clear whether or not *The Skeptical Inquirer* is still considering my article.

12 Conclusions

I could go on explaining UFO reports. But there are so many that it would take a lifetime. Very many significant reports have not been mentioned, and it may be alleged that while some reports remain unexplained, I have not completely solved the UFO mystery. However, I am confident that the AMH (or in some cases the MH) can solve most of the unmentioned reports. It is not necessary to deal with every report; the cases discussed in this work are a sufficiently representative sample of all reports.

In case there is any doubt about this, consider a random sample of high-profile cases. Sixty-three reports described in *The UFO Casebook* (Brookesmith 1990) are listed in Table 12:1, together with my evaluation. Some of the cases have been discussed in previous chapters.

Table 12:1
The UFO reports described in *The UFO Casebook*, with evaluations:
('pam' = possible astronomical mirage; 'id' = insufficient data)

Reporter	Location	Date	Evaluation
Howard	Atlantic Villa	29.6.54	pam/id
Miserey	Vernon	23.8.54	pam/id
Zamora	Socorro	24.4.64	Canopus
Villa	Albuquerque	18.4.65	hoax
Fernandez	Uzès	19.11.74	hoax
Pratt	Conisburgh	28.3.66	hoax
Wilcox	Newark Valley	24.4.64	Pollux
Fogarty	New Zealand	31.12.78	Venus
Marano	Turin	30.11.73	pam/id
Contin	Turin	30.11.73	pam/id
Wildman	Ivinghoe	9.2.62	Saturn
Moreno	Trancas	21.10.63	Canopus
RAF	Bentwaters	13.8.56	pam/id
Dewilde	Quarouble	10.9.54	Mars
Tejada	Ibiza	11.11.79	Sirius
Alpert	Salem	16.7.52	pam/id
Hussein	Pyrenees	?.7.78	pam/id
Barauna	Ilha da Trindade	16.1.58	Jupiter

Padrón León	Gran Canaria	22.6.76	pam/id
Cellot	Lot-et-Garonne	14.11.71	Vega
Heflin	Santa Ana	3.8.65	hoax
Chase (RB-47)	Winnsboro	19.9.57	Fomalhaut
?	Oloron-Ste.-Marie	27.10.52	pam/id
?	Gaillac	27.10.52	pam/id
Salandin	Southend-on-Sea	14.10.54	pam/id
Valentich	Bass Strait	21.10.78	Canopus
Trent	McMinnville	11.5.50	hoax
'Brown'	Melbourne, AUS	?.4.66	hoax
? (B-57)	?	?	film flaw
Campagnac	Tananarive	?.8.54	pam/id
Wolff	Malagasy	?.5.67	pam/id
Pretzel	Córdoba, ARG	13.6.68	pam/id
Villegas	Mendoza	1.9.68	hoax
?	Bear Mountain	18.12.66	hoax
Fry	Merlin	?.5.64	hoax
Fry	Joshua Tree	?.5.65	hoax
Green	Langenhoe	14.9.65	Rigel
Maskey	Felixstowe	20.9.65	id
NASA	Gemini XII	12.11.66	space debris
Robinson	Lubbock	25.8.51	pam/id
Hickson	Pascagoula	11.10.73	pam/id
Greenhaw	Hartwell	11.10.73	hoax
Llopis	Gran Canaria	5.3.79	rocket launch?
?	Barajas	?.12.79	pam/id
?	Lakeville	23.1.67	id
Kudou	Tomakomai	?.7.73	pam/id
Rossi	Lucca	25.7.52	pam/id
Amano	Sayama City	3.10.78	pam/id
?	Tulsa	2.8.65	hoax
?	Fort Belvoir	?.9.57	smoke ring
Mayher	Miami	29.7.52	id
Villa Boas	Sao Francisco de Sales	5-15.10.57	pam/id
Machado	Rio de Janeiro	27.6.70	Rigel Kent
Rocha	Curitiba	10.1.58	pam/id
de Souza	Iguapé	31.10.63	pam/id
Masse	Valensole	1.7.65	pam/id
?	Puente de Herrera	15.8.70	pam/id
?	Sao Vicente	4.11.57	Hadar
de Souza	Pilar de Goiás	13.8.67	pam/id
de Freitas	Itatiánia	30.8.70	Jupiter
Cyrus	Noé	29.8.75	pam/id
Mrs W	Launceston, AUS	22.9.74	pam/id
Russell	London	15.12.66	hoax

Of these 63 cases, only 50 (79%) seem to be genuine reports; 13 appear to be hoaxes, mostly faked photographs. Of the 50 genuine reports, 43 (86%) appear to be caused by sight of an astronomical mirage, the astronomical source being identifiable in about one third of these cases. In 31 of the genuine cases (62%), the source could not be identified because of lack of adequate data, although in 29 of them (93·5%) an astronomical mirage was probably the cause. The missing data include dates, times, times zones and (most frequently) the azimuth of the object.

If this sample is representative of high-profile reports, we can draw the following conclusions.

- Most photographs are faked, and these fakes are easily identified.
- About 90 per cent of genuine high-profile reports are caused by sight of an astronomical mirage.
- The remaining 10 per cent have other mundane explanations.
- Given adequate data, all reports can be explained.
- No reports are caused by sight of extraterrestrial craft or the occupants.

Analysis of this sample indicates that, on the whole, UFO reports are caused by mirages, usually of astronomical objects.

Science and ufology

UFO reports pose a special problem for professional scientists. They are damned if they do, and damned if they do not. If they show interest, especially if they incline to the idea that UFOs might be alien craft, they risk their reputations; if they avoid the subject, they are accused of wearing blinkers and reminded of the story of the discovery of meteorites. The Science Studies Unit in the University of Edinburgh noted that the fact that few scientists have reported seeing a UFO can be interpreted in two ways. Either scientists, unlike those who do report UFOs, are good observers and UFOs do not exist, or those scientists who do see UFOs (an unknown number) fear ridicule if they report the sighting, and so say nothing. This fear reinforces the belief that 'scientists do not see UFOs', and so a vicious circle is created (Harvey 1978). If it were generally known that there is a perfectly rational and scientific explanation for even the most bizarre UFO reports, there would be no need to fear ridicule.

Some scientists have nothing to fear, either because they debunk the reports, or because their reputations are too high to be tarnished. Menzel was protected by both these conditions. Others interest themselves because they are, by nature, mavericks, or, as Klass has suggested, because they have a strong desire to believe in extraterrestrial visitations. There have always been scientists who espoused interests which most of their peers eschewed. McDonald, a meteorologist at the University of Arizona, was such a scientist. His suicide indicates an instability that may have been the cause and not the effect of his interest in UFOs. Ufology has attracted several eccentric scientists, those who had already adopted an unconventional view of the world. Another example is Rutledge (1981), an eccentric university physicist whose judgement was clouded by his enthusiasm for UFOs. Hynek, an astronomer called in by the USAF to examine reports, was initially unsympathetic. However he eventually succumbed to the view that science cannot explain many 'core' reports and that these reports represent a new 'unexplained' phenomenon. He made himself a maverick, believing that the Condon Report was designed to discredit UFOs, not to investigate them. It is particularly ironic that the solution to the mystery is one which he in particular should have been able to reach.

As I have shown, the solution involves both astronomy and meteorological optics (and sometimes other specialties). In this age of specialization, it is rare for scientists to know much outside their specialty. Consequently a problem, the solution to which involves a combination of specialities, will only rarely be solved by a specialist. There can also be the problem of suspicion. One scientist observed that the subject of his book straddles the diffuse border between psychology and physics, with the result that it can be mistrusted by both disciplines (Middleton 1958:2). Such problems offer an opportunity to amateur scientists, especially if they have an interest in several disciplines and are not burdened with academic duties. This may have been my advantage. But amateurs also have the advantage that they have no reputation to lose. They can go where professionals fear to tread. Because they can stand outside mainstream science, or on neglected borders, they can see connections that are invisible to those within it. This may explain how I have come to explain what professionals like Hynek and Menzel could not (although Menzel had glimpsed the answer).

Story, perhaps influenced by Murray (1975) whose views he reproduced, believed that science has its limits and that it can go only so far in explaining the UFO phenomenon at the present time. He thought that the phenomenon itself lies beyond the limits of science, in the province of the philosophy of science (Story 1981:23). These views mark Story as a non-scientist, and it is not surprising that he has not found the solution. There can be no limits to science.

The Condon Report concluded that the study of UFOs (*sic*) has not added to scientific knowledge and that further study, in anticipation of scientific advance, could not be justified (Gillmor 1969:1). Others have claimed that all the data collected on UFOs (*sic*) are largely useless to science (Randles and Warrington 1983). I have shown that both these conclusions are wrong; many genuine UFO reports contain useful data on a little-known phenomenon, the mirage.

In the USA, some university science departments have interested themselves in UFO reports (not always with satisfactory results). Nevertheless staff at the New Mexico Institute of Mining and Technology exhibited no interest in the sensational report from their own town (Socorro), and appear to have dismissed it as a hoax. In the UK, university science departments show very little interest. Although Edinburgh boasted two universities at the time, no one from either came to investigate the report from nearby Livingston. It is already known that an interest in science, especially physics and astronomy, can be induced in university or college students by offering courses on UFOs. These courses should include the AMH and use it to teach optics and human perception. Field exercises could include the study and explanation of local UFO reports.

Scientists have made the mistake of following the public in associating UFO reports with belief in alien spaceships. They have also erred in assuming that, because such spaceships do not exist, the reports must have no value. All scientists should be prepared to find the cause of a phenomenon, even if that phenomenon is merely a collection of unusual reports.

Some scientists have concluded that people who report UFOs are mentally disturbed. It has been proposed that 'the apparent impossibility of the reports suggests to common sense that the most likely explanation lies in a psychic disturbance' (Jung 1959:17). Jung was confused about UFO reports and only reluctantly wrote about them. A few reports will come from mentally disturbed people, but even they must draw on the UFO myth. More important, sane reporters will also draw on the myth to embroider their reports. Jung was partly right in suggesting that mythology could be projected onto the appearance of real objects. However appearances can be deceptive; what looks real may not be. Whether or not a report is 'impossible' depends very much on what the investigator considers to be possible and whether or not he is aware of all possibilities. In my experience, very few investigators (including scientists) allow for all possibilities.

Ufoists have made the mistake of attempting to create a science of 'ufology', claiming that they are studying a new phenomenon. However, just because scientists cannot explain every report does not mean that a UFO phenomenon exists (Oberg 1979). Indeed, I have demonstrated that even the most apparently intractable reports can be explained by existing science. Ufoists have also made the mistake of calling on scientists to study 'the UFO phenomenon' (Randles and Warrington 1985). Since there is no phenomenon (other than the UFO reports themselves), it cannot be studied by scientists or anyone else. Ufoists are pursuing an imaginary phenomenon.

If mirages explain UFO reports, then UFO reports offer substantial data on mirages and may provide the evidence necessary to allow a better understanding of the phenomenon. By ignoring UFO reports, scientists may have deprived themselves of valuable data.

Essentially ufoism is anti-science, believing, not only that human science cannot explain the phenomenon, but that this 'fact' demonstrates a fatal flaw in it. Ufoists also believe that aliens possess a better, different type of science, alternative science. These beliefs should be of concern to all scientists and those who support science, mankind's greatest achievement. Every effort should be made to expose ufoism and to explain UFO reports. The MH (and AMH) should enable this to be done.

The lessons of investigation

Most UFO reports are made by sober, serious people who have genuinely seen something mysterious in the sky. They do not deserve ridicule or scorn. They deserve to be heard with sympathy. Sometimes they are very upset and need counselling.

Because their reports may contain valuable scientific data, the reports should be recorded with care and accuracy and in an objective manner. This cannot be done by ufoists, or investigators who believe in the ETH; it can only be accomplished by sceptics, and then only by those without hubris. Some sceptics are as inflexible and dogmatic as ufoists. Sceptical investigators should conceal their scepticism unless it becomes clear that it is welcome, and no investigator should reveal his explanation to the reporter unless asked. Not all reporters want to be told that they have seen some natural phenomenon, which (in any case) they are unlikely to understand. However, in the Livingston Case, I remained on friendly terms with the witness, despite disagreement over what he saw. I believe that we each accepted that the other was sincere.

In order to allow astronomical checks, the data must include (apart from the exact date and time) the altitude and azimuth of the object. Failure to find a bright astronomical object in a position where it (or a mirage of it) could explain a report which exhibits all the characteristics of an astronomical object (or a mirage of it) can be caused by inaccurate data, particularly time and azimuth. These parameters should then be questioned.

Investigators should not take reports at face value and should be aware of the impact and influence of the UFO myth. Most people in the developed world are familiar with the myth. Unfortunately this interferes with their ability to report objectively. An unidentified object tends to be interpreted as a UFO (an alien craft). Investigators should consider the possibility that those aspects of a report which conform to the UFO myth are most suspect. They should also be fully aware of the limitations of human perception and make allowance for them. The reliability of a UFO report is often hard to assess. There may be a core of truth in most reports. Few witnesses have cause to expose themselves to the harassment and embarrassment that publicity brings. A reporter can expect little sympathy, understanding or financial gain. Probably many keep silent out of fear or ridicule, and it must be assumed that a witness who requests anonymity for fear of ridicule is telling the truth. The more publicity a witness seeks, the less likely it is that the report is true. Exotic or very strange reports, or those from remote areas, are not necessarily *ipso facto* unreliable; there is relatively little distortion if the report is written by the prime investigator and published in a reputable journal. Nevertheless, the investigator can misinterpret the evidence and present it in terms of his own beliefs. Newspaper accounts should be distrusted, initially.

With some exceptions (see below), statistical studies of reports are valueless. The UFO mystery cannot be solved by analysis of reports in bulk; so many different stimuli are involved that the results are not meaningful. The mystery can only be solved by investigation of individual reports, especially strange reports where data are plentiful. Such investigation shows that, in most cases, the cause was a mirage, usually an astronomical mirage. It certainly shows that there is a prosaic, if unusual, explanation and that there is no evidence to support the ETH. In general it can be claimed that UFO reports are caused by sight of known objects or phenomena seen under unusual circumstances. In particular, the core reports are caused by mirages. The MH (including the AMH) is shown to be a powerful hypothesis, capable of solving even the most difficult cases.

It is of concern that mirages, particularly astronomical mirages, are not generally recognized. Even Menzel was at first deceived. Certainly astronomers are not aware that planets and bright stars can be seen as mirages at low altitude. The failure of aircraft pilots and air force personnel to recognize mirages is of special concern. This failure may be the result of inadequate knowledge of meteorological optics. The training of pilots and air force personnel should include familiarization with mirages, especially astronomical ones. Their aircraft could be endangered by ignorance of such phenomena; indeed some losses already appear to have been caused by such ignorance. The training should also include an understanding of perception difficulties and phenomena. Military personnel should leave scientific investigations to scientists.

The phenomenon of orthoteny has a simple explanation. Statistical studies of ley lines (where similar claims are made) show that the number of *loci in quo* on a line are no greater than would occur by chance. In fact the location of the witness need not be anywhere near the stimulus. In the case of astronomical stimuli the precise location of the reporter is irrelevant. Menzel made extensive criticism of Michel and his orthoteny (Sagan and Page 1972:163).

If all UFO reports have rational, prosaic explanations there is no cause to believe stories of crashed saucers and frozen aliens (let alone the idea that world governments are negotiating with aliens). In fact it is not reasonable that aliens have been contacted. If other advanced technological civilizations exist in the Galaxy at this time (and I do not deny this possibility), the probability that they have found us is as small as the probability we have of finding them. The distances between us are probably too large for physical contact. Indeed, first contact is most likely to be made via radio. Menzel was certainly correct in concluding that UFO reports do not represent extraterrestrial activity in any form, and that no amount of investigation will bring evidence in support of the ETH (Sagan and Page 1972:144). As Duncan Lunan has observed, the behaviour of UFOs is not at all what we would expect of spacecraft; 'that it's gone on for so long strongly suggests that they're natural phenomena' (Lunan 1974:308).

Government investigation of UFO reports has not been thorough, and has often been undertaken with inadequate understanding of the possible causes and (perhaps) with the intent to explain the reports at any cost. It is known that the Condon Report was intended as a whitewash, to justify closure of Blue Book, and that Condon himself did not take the subject seriously. However, the Report itself was seriously flawed and failed to explain many of the case it examined. In general, government agencies do not have the skill or knowledge to explain UFO reports. But rather than admit this, they either offer ridiculous explanations or conceal information that would enable others to explain them. However, the secrecy involved gives the impression that something important is being concealed, fuelling the UFO myth. If references to UFOs in government documents are censored, that can only be out of a misplaced zeal and attempts to protect witnesses. Governments are victims of their own preoccupation with secrecy. While there remain official secrets, it will always be believed that UFOs are one of the most closely guarded secrets. The fact is that the world governments have no adequate explanation for some UFO reports (although they are aware of many explanations). But no government will admit its ignorance. Governments should not get involved in UFO reports. They should refer them to some scientific agency, or university, and declare that they have no evidence that aliens have reached Earth. A Freedom of Information Act should be passed in the UK and all existing UFO records should be declassified and released. The USAF's conclusions on UFOs are summarized in Appendix 4 (q.v.).

Evidently police forces are no better equipped than the military for the investigation of UFO reports. Since they are often the first to receive a report, more should be done to educate them in the causes of reports. In particular, police officers should be trained in basic astronomy and meteorology, especially mirages. If not all officers, then at least one officer in each area should have such knowledge. Investigation is a police specialty, and it takes little imagination to see it extended to investigation of UFO reports.

The fact that several reports were made as the result of power failures indicates that modern night illumination prevents sight of more astronomical mirages. It is already recognized that modern street lighting scatters light into the sky, so making appreciation of the night sky difficult for urbanites, and making serious astronomical work almost impossible. A more general understanding of astronomy is one antidote to ufoism, but this must be accompanied by a reduction in light scatter in urban areas. Street lighting should be modified (as in Tucson, Arizona) so that it puts the light where it is needed and prevents it shining upwards. This might also produce more reports of astronomical mirages, so increasing knowledge and understanding of them. A reduction in air pollution would also improve urban seeing.

The lessons of the Astronomical Mirage Hypothesis

The UFO myth began with a report stimulated by sight of mirages of several mountain peaks, and many reports have had similar causes. However, the myth has been reinforced by many reports caused by sight of astronomical mirages, a phenomenon barely recognized by science (although observed in detail by at least one astronomer). In fact it appears that the double, merged, astronomical mirage has been responsible for the definitive shape of the classical 'flying saucer' (two soup plates stuck together). This is the dominant form of the astronomical mirage. UFOs are generally reported as discoids because that is the shape people see. Mankind has not imagined a new form of interplanetary (even interstellar) travel; it has observed an astro-meteorological phenomenon. The persistence of reports of this shape is caused, not by the imposition of pre-existing ideas on anomalous stimuli, but by repeated observations of a real, natural phenomenon.

The AMH explains how UFOs can appear to make manoeuvres which defy the laws of inertia and travel faster than the speed of sound without making sonic booms. They are not solid objects, merely images of distant light sources. As such they can perform manoeuvres as easily as the beam of a torch. The problem of the discoid's unsuitable aerodynamic qualities is resolved; it is not an aircraft. It seems likely that the 'falling leaf' manoeuvre is caused by the mirage image crossing layers of varying refractive properties, so throwing the image from side to side.

It should not be surprising that some reports of a UFO are made at a time when radar shows an unknown target in the same general area. The MH explains both phenomena. A temperature inversion capable of producing a visible mirage is, at the same time, capable of producing a radar mirage. The inversion can reflect most electromagnetic radiation, that at radio wavelengths more easily than that at visible wavelengths. Consequently, anomalous radar images are likely to be present when anomalous visible images can be seen. The radar target is most likely to be the ground (reflected off the inversion), or some distant reflector that would not normally be detected. The Condon Report concluded that anomalous propagation effects are probably responsible for a large number of UFO reports in cases involving radar and visual sightings (Gillmor 1969:174). The fact that the distribution of UFO reports correlates roughly with the rural population indicates that the stimuli for the reports are real and objective. Moreover it indicates that they are something more easily visible, or only visible, to people in rural areas. The AMH can explain this correlation; astronomical bodies are more easily seen in rural than in urban areas. The AMH also explains Thayer's observation that a significant number of the reports considered by the Condon Report team were made as a result of observations during calm weather in which anomalous propagation effects should be prominent. The reports were not coincidental with these meteorological conditions; they were the result of them. The fact that most reports are made during the hours of darkness (peaking about 2100L) is simply explained by the AMH; astronomical objects are more easily seen at night, and after 2100L there are fewer people outdoors.

The 1897 'airship' reports from the USA are so similar to twentieth century UFO reports that they probably describe the same phenomenon. It was natural to associate anomalous aerial shapes and lights with the aerial craft of which so much had been heard. In fact Count Von Zeppelin's first successful flight did not take place until 1900. Evidently some 'airship' reports were stimulated by sight of astronomical mirages. Unfortunately insufficient data exist to test this hypothesis. However many 'airship' reports were made in the spring of 1897, when Venus was very prominent in the evening sky.

If most UFO reports are the result of seeing a natural phenomenon, something similar to UFOs must have been seen throughout history, indeed throughout prehistory. Astronomical mirages must have been seen by our ancestors. It seems likely that these strange sights were interpreted in terms of the prevailing belief system. In prehistory, they must have been seen as manifestations of the gods. In the Middle Ages they may have led to the belief in flying dragons (breathing fire), witches flying on their broomsticks, or genii on their magic carpets! There is cause to believe that some mirages have been interpreted in predominantly Roman Catholic countries, even in modern times, as appearances of the Virgin Mary. In some cases mirages may have been recorded as appearances of will-o'-the-wisp or ball lightning. In 1947, mirages may have been (at least partially) responsible for the Swedish 'ghost rockets'. It is evident that some of the unidentified objects reported to have been seen from Hessdalen in Norway since 1981 (Strand 1984) were astronomical, although not necessarily mirages. Many of the objects were merely the lights of aircraft. Although Project Hessdalen equipped itself with many types of instrument, it does not appear to have considered using an ephemeris (or an astronomical computer program).

The AMH forebodes the decline of UFO groups and associations, many of which encourage superstition and mysticism. There can be no point in continuing to search for an explanation for UFO reports. Adequate explanations now exist for all UFO reports and there is no evidence that alien intelligence is involved (the preferred hypothesis of most members of UFO organizations). Such organizations have no reason to exist if all UFO reports have 'an obvious natural explanation'. The discovery and successful application of the MH and the AMH has solved the UFO mystery.

Appendix 1: The Halt Memorandum; see chapter 10

Heading: 'Department of the Air Force'
Dated : '13 Jan 1981'
Reply to: 'CD'
Subject : 'Unexplained lights'
To : 'RAF/CC'

1. Early in the morning of 27 Dec 80 (approximately 0300L), two USAF security patrolmen saw unusual lights outside the back gate at RAF Woodbridge. Thinking that an aircraft might have crashed or been forced down, they called for permission to go outside the gate to investigate. The on-duty flight chief responded and allowed three patrolmen to proceed on foot. The individuals reported seeing a strange glowing object in the forest. The object was described as being metalic in appearance and triangular in shape, approximately two to three meters across the base and approximately two meters high. It illuminated the entire forest with a white light. The object itself had a pulsating red light on top and a bank(s) of blue lights underneath. The object was hovering or on legs. As the patrolmen approached the object, it maneuvered through the trees and disappeared. At this time the animals on a nearby farm went into a frenzy. The object was briefly sighted approximately an hour later near the back gate.

2. The next day, three depressions 1.5" [38 mm] deep and 7" [178 mm] diameter were found where the object had been sighted on the ground. The following night (29 Dec 80) the area was checked for radiation. Beta/gamma readings of 0.1 milliroentgens [*sic*, per hour?] were recorded with peak readings in the three depressions and near the centre of the triangle formed by the depressions. A nearby tree had moderate (.05-.07) readings on the side of the tree toward the depressions.

3. Later in the night a red sun-like light was seen through the trees. It moved about and pulsed. At one point it appeared to throw off glowing particles and then broke into five separate white objects and then disappeared. Immediately thereafter, three star-like objects were noticed in the sky, two objects to the north and one to the south, all of which were about 10° off the horizon. The objects moved rapidly in sharp angular movements and displayed red, green and blue lights. The objects to the north appeared to be elliptical through an 8-12 power lens. They then turned to full circles. The objects to the north remained in the sky for an hour or more. The object to the south was visible for two or three hours and beamed down a stream of light from time to time. Numerous individuals, including the undersigned, witnessed the activities in paragraphs 2 and 3.

[Signed]
CHARLES I HALT, Lt Col, USAF
Deputy Base Commander

Appendix 2: Transcript of Col. Halt's tape recording

(as made by Ian Ridpath, but annotated by the author); see chapter 10

Halt: 150 feet [45·7 m] or more from the initial, or I should say suspected impact point. Having a little difficulty. Can't get the Light-all to work. Seems to be some kind of mechanical problem. Gonna send back and get another Light-all. Meantime, we're gonna take some readings with a Geiger counter, and pace around the area a little bit, and wait for another Light-all to come back in. [Garbled security communication] OK, we're now approaching the area, within about 25-30 feet [8-9 m]. What kind of readings are we getting? Anything?

Voice: Just minor clicks.

Halt: Just minor clicks? Where are the impressions? Is that all bigger they are?

Voice: Well, there's one more well-defined over here.

Voice: Security control ...

Halt: We're still getting clicks.

Voice: Security-6. We're at east gate.

Halt: Do you want to read that on the scale?

Voice: Yes sir. We're now on the five-tenths scale, and we're reading about, er ... [garbled]

Halt: OK, we're still comfortably safe here.

Voice: Do you have a Light-all?
[Garbled security communication]

Halt: Still minor readings. Second pod [pad?] indentation ... this one's dead[?]. Let's go to the other one over here.

Voice: Yes, now I'm getting some residual.

Halt: I can read now. The meter's definitely giving a little pulse. I was gonna say, let's go to the center of the area next and see what kind of a reading we get out there. You're reading the clicks. I can't hear the clicks. That about the center Bruce? OK, let's go to the center.

Voice: Yes I'm getting ...

Halt: That's the best deflection of the needle I've seen yet. OK can you give me an estimation? We're on the point five scale; we're getting ...

Voice: At approximately 0125 hours ...

Voice: We're getting right at half a millirem.
[short burst of piano music]

Halt: ... best point. I haven't seen it go any higher. OK we'll go out toward ...

Voice: Now it's picking up ...

Halt: This is the number one indentation where we first got the strongest reading. It's similar to what we got in the center.

Voice: Right in the pod [garbled].

Voice: Looks like an area here possibly that could be a blast ... [garbled].

Voice: Just jumped up to seventh tenths ...

Halt: Seven tenths? Right there in the center?

Voice: Uh huh.

Halt: We found a small blast, what looks like a blasted or scruffed-up area here. We're getting very positive readings. Let's see, is that near the center?

Voice: Yes it is; this is what we'd assume would be the dead center ...

Voice: [garbled] ... more as you go along ...

Halt: Up to seven tenths, or seven units let's call it, on the point five scale. OK, why don't we do this? Why don't we make a sweep here, I've got the gloves on now let's make a sweep on around the whole area about ten foot [3 m] out, make a perimeter run around it, starting way back here at the corner, back at the same corner where we came in? Let's go right back here. I'm gonna have to depend upon you counting the clicks. OK let's ...

Voice: I'll tell you as we get...

Halt: Let's put the Light-all on it and let's sweep around it. Put it on the ground every once in a while.

Voice: Looks like an abrasion on the tree ...

Halt: OK we'll catch that on the way back. Let's go round. Hit it Ted [Conrad?].

Voice: We're getting interest right over here. It looks like an abrasion pointing into the center of the landing area ...
Halt: It is. It may be old though. There are some sap marks or something on it. Let's go on back around. Hey, this is an awkward thing to use isn't it?
Voice: [indistinct]
Halt: Are we getting anything further? I'm going to shut the recorder off until we find something ...
Voice: Picking up.
Halt: Picking up? What are we up to? We're up to 2, 3 units deflection. You're getting close to one pod [pad?].
Voice: Picking up something ... picking up.
Halt: OK, still not going above 3 or 4 units.
Voice: Picking up more though; more frequent.
Halt: Yes, you're staying up around 2 to 3 to 4 units now.
Voice: Each one of these trees that face into the blast that we assume is the landing site all have an abrasion facing in the same direction towards the center.
Halt: That's interesting. Let's go this way round the circle. Turn it back down here.
Voice: Picking up ...
Halt: Let's see that. You're right, abrasion. I've never seen a pine tree that's been damaged react that fast.
Voice: ... a bottle to put that in.
Halt: Got a sample bottle?
[confused talk]
Halt: Let's identify that as point no. 1 that stake there. So you all know where it is if we have to sketch it. You got that Sergeant Nevills [?]? Closest to the Woodbridge base, be point 1. Let's go clockwise from there.
Voice: Point 2 ...
Halt: So this tree is between point 2 and point 3.
[security communication]
Voice: ... two other personnel requesting arrival on a jeep at our location.
Voice: Tell them negative at this time. We'll tell them when they can come out here. We don't want them out here right now.
Halt: The sample ... you're going to mark this sample no. 1 ... have them cut it off and include some of that sap and all ... is between indentation 2 and 3 on a pine tree about 5 feet [1·5 m] away, about 3½ feet [1 m] off the ground. There's a round abrasion on a tree about 3½-4 inches [10 cm] in diameter. It looks like it might be old, but ... strange, there's a crystalline ... pine sap has come out that fast. You say there's other trees here that are damaged in a similar fashion?
Voice: Yes ... [garbled] toward the center of the landing site.
Halt: OK, then why don't you take a picture of that and remember your picture ... ain't gonna be writing this down. Oh, it's gonna be on the tape.
Voice: You got a tape measure with you?
Halt: This is the picture. Your first picture will be at the first tree, the one between mark 2 and 3. Meantime I'm going to look at a couple of these other trees over here.
Voice: We are getting some ...
Halt: You're getting readings on the tree you're taking samples from, on the side facing the suspected landing site.
Voice: Four clicks max.
Halt: Up to 4; interesting. That's right where you're taking the sample now. Four. That's the strongest point on the tree?
Voice: Yessir. If you come to the back, there's no clicks whatsoever.
Halt: No clicks at all on the back; it's all on the side facing the ... interesting. The indentations look like something twisted as it sat down on 'em. Looks like someone took something and sat it down and twisted it from side to side. Very strange. We're looking at the same tree we took the sample off with this, what d'you call it? Starscope. Getting a definite heat reflection off the tree, what, about 3 or 4 feet [1-1·2 m] off the ground?
Voice: Yes, where the spot is ...

Halt: Same place where the spot is we're getting a heat ...
Voice: And a spot on the tree directly behind us I picked up the same thing, and one off to your right.
Halt: Three trees in the area immediately adjacent to the site, within 10 feet [3 m] of the suspected landing site, we're picking up heat reflected off the trees.
Voice: [indistinct]
Halt: What's that again?
Voice: Shine the light on it again Bob.
Halt: What, are you having trouble ...?
Voice: [garbled] ... right on the spot, and then when you wanna...
Halt: OK, turn the light on.
Voice: ... you'll notice the white ...
Halt: Hey! You're right, there is a white streak on the tree.
Voice: Indicates a heat ...
Halt: Let me turn around and look at this tree over here now. Just a second. Watch, because you're right in front of the tree. I can see it. Give me a little side light so I can find the tree. OK. Oh!
[security communication]
Voice: Alpha 2, security.
Halt: Now I've lost the tree. OK, stop, stop. Light off. Hey, this is eerie!
Voice: Why don't you do the pod [pad?] spots?
Halt: This is strange. Here, does someone wanna look at the spots on the ground? Whoops! Watch you don't step ... [garbled]. OK, let's step back and not walk all over it. Come back here. Somebody put a beam on them. You've got to be back 10 or 15 feet [3-4·5 m]. You see it? OK, lights off.
[voice on tape]
Halt: What do you think about the spot? Like to see the first spot? OK, that's what we'll call spot no. 3. Let's go to the back corner and get spot no. 1. Spot no. 1, here's spot no. 1 right here. Spot no. 1 right here. You need some light? There it is right there. Focused?
Voice: Focused.
Halt: OK. Looking now at spot no. 1 through the Starlight Scope.
Voice: Picking up a slight increase in light as I go over it.
Halt: Slight increase in light at spot no. 1. Let's go look at spot no. 2. Spot no. 2 's right over here. Right here. See it? OK, get focused on it. Tell me when. OK, lights off. Let's see what we get on it.
Voice: Slight increase.
Halt: Just a slight increase?
Voice: Try the center.
Halt: The center spot ... it really isn't the center, it's slightly off center, it's right there.
Voice: Right here.
Halt: We're gonna get your reading on it right there.
Voice: OK.
Halt: Tell me when you're ready.
Voice: Ready.
Halt: OK. Lights out. It's the center spot we're looking at now, or almost the center.
Voice: Slight increase.
Halt: Slight increase there. This is slightly off center toward the 1-2 side. It's some type of abrasion or something on the ground where the pine needles are all pushed back and where we get a high radioactivity reading a deflection of 2 to 3 maybe 4, depending on the point of ...
Voice: You say there's a positive after-effect?
Voice: Yes there is definitely. That's on the center spot. There is an after-effect.
Voice: What does that mean?
Voice: It means that when the lights are turned off, once we are focused in and allow time for the eyes to adjust, we are getting an indication of a heat source coming out of that center spot, which will show up on the ...

Halt: Heat or some sort of energy. It's hardly heat at this stage of the game. Looking directly overhead one can see an opening in the trees plus some freshly broken pine branches on the ground. Looks like some of them came off about 15 or 20 feet [4·5-6 m] up. Some small branches, about an inch [2·5 cm] or less in diameter.

...

Halt: 0148. We're hearing very strange sounds out of the farmer's barnyard animals. They're very very active; making an awful lot of noise.

Voice: ... pigmentation.

Halt: You just saw a light?

Voice: ... [garbled]

Halt: Slow down. Where?

Voice: Right on this position. Here, straight ahead in between the trees. [**1**]There it is again. Watch, straight ahead off my flashlight sir. [**2**]There it is.
[5 s between **1** and **2**]

Halt: I see it too. What is it?

Voice: We don't know sir.

Halt: It's a strange small red light. Looks to be maybe a quarter to a half mile [400-800 m], maybe further out. I'm gonna switch off. The light is gone now. It was approximately 120° from our site. [**3**]Is it back again?
[15 s between **2** and **3**]

Voice: Yes sir.

Halt: Well douse flashlights then. Let's go back to the edge of the clearing so we can get a better look at it. See if you can get the Starscope on it. The light's still there and all the barnyard animals have gone quiet now. We're heading about 110, 120° from the site out through to the clearing now. Still getting a reading on the meter. About two clicks. Needle's jumped. 3 to 4 clicks, getting stronger.

Voice: Now it's stopped. [**4**]Now it's coming up. There we go. About approximately 4 foot [1·2 m] off the ground, at a compass bearing of 110°.

Halt: He's turned the meter off. Better say that again. About 4 feet [1·2 m] off the ground, about 110°; getting a reading of about 4 clicks?

Voice: Yes sir. [**5**]Now it's dying.
[20 s between **4** and **5**]

Halt: Now it's dying. I think it's something other than the ground. I think it's something that's ...

Voice: ...tree right over ...

Halt: We've just run into the first night-bird we've seen. We're about 150 or 200 yards [137-183 m] from the site. Everywhere else is just deathly calm. There is no doubt about it. There's some type of strange flashing red light ahead.

Voice: Sir, it's yellow.

Halt: I saw a yellow tinge in it too. Weird. It appears to be maybe moving a little bit this way? It's brighter than it has been. It's coming this way. It doubt about it. This is weird!

Voices: Two lights! One light to the right and one light to the left.

Halt: Keep your flashlights off. There's something very very strange. Keep the headset on; see if it gets any ...

Voice: ... notation that this is ... [indistinct] ... has been removed.

Halt: Pieces are falling off it again.

Voice: It just moved to the right.

Halt: Yeah!

Voice: Off to the right.

Halt: Strange. One again to the left [?]. Let's approach to the edge of the woods up there. You want to do without lights? Let's do it carefully; come on. OK, we're looking at the thing. We're probably about 2 to 300 yards [183-274 m] away. It looks like an eye winking at you. Still moving from side to side. And when you put the Starscope on it, it's like this thing has a hollow center, a dark center, like the pupil of an eye looking at you, winking. And it flashes so bright in the Starscope that it almost burns your eye.
[garbled security communication]

Halt: We've passed the farmer's house and across into the next field and now we have multiple sightings of up to 5 lights with a similar shape and all, but they seem to be steady now rather than pulsating or glow with a red flash. We've just crossed a creek and we're getting what kind of readings now? We're getting 3 good clicks on the meter and we're seeing strange lights in the sky.

Halt: 2:44. We're at the far side of the second farmer's field and made sighting again about 110°. This looks like it's clear off to the coast. It's right on the horizon. Moves about a bit and flashes from time to time. Still steady or red in color. Also after negative readings in the center of the field we're picking up slight readings; 4 or 5 clicks now, on the meter.

...

Halt: 3:05. We see strange strobe-like flashes to the, er ... well, they're sporadic, but there's definitely some kind of phenomenon. At about 10° ... horizon, directly north, we've got two strange objects, er, half-moon shape, dancing about with colored lights on 'em. That, er, guess to be about 5 to 10 miles [8-16 km] out, maybe less. The half-moons are now turning to full circles, as though there was an eclipse or something there, for a minute or two.

...

Halt: 0315. Now we've got an object about 10° directly south, 10° off the horizon. And the ones to the north are moving. One's moving away from us.

Voice: It's moving out fast!

Voice: This one on the right's heading away too!

Halt: They're both heading north. OK, here he comes from the south, he's coming towards us now. Now we're observing what appears to be a beam coming down to the ground. This is unreal!

...

Halt: 0330, and the objects are still in the sky although the one to the south looks like it's losing a little bit of altitude. We're going around and heading back toward the base. The object to the south is still beaming down lights to the ground.

Halt: 0400 hours. One object still hovering over Woodbridge base at about 5 to 10° off the horizon. Still moving erratic, and similar lights and beaming down as earlier.

[duration of recording: 17 min. 50 s]

Appendix 3: Testing the Astronomical Mirage Hypothesis

The AMH can only be tested by ascertaining whether or not a bright astronomical body was near the horizon in the appropriate direction (see paragraph below on azimuth) on the date, and at the time, in question. This can be done by consulting an ephemeris, but that can be tedious. It is much easier, and quicker, using one of the many astronomical programs written for home or personal computers. Ensure that the program gives the altitude and azimuth of the Sun, Moon, naked eye planets and the brightest stars as seen from any point on the surface of the Earth. It also needs to give detailed data for the bodies of the solar system. However the programs require some essential data, as follows:

1. The location of the witness

This needs to be input as longitude and latitude (sometimes in decimal notation). It is not a very critical parameter, but a good atlas is essential for reasonable accuracy.

2. Date and time

These are very critical parameters and must be accurate. Because most programs require time to be input as Universal Time (UT), identical with modern civil GMT, it is essential to know how local time relates to UT. In any case, it is safer to use UT than local time.

Charts of times zones are sometimes found in encyclopaedias, but a definitive 'Standard Time Zones Chart of the World' can be obtained from the (US) Defense Mapping Agency in Washington DC (their agent in the UK is Messrs. Kelvin Hughes Ltd). This chart gives, in great detail, the number of hours by which Standard Zone Time must be increased or decreased to obtain UT.

When translating local time to UT it may be necessary to alter the *date* of the report to reflect the date at Greenwich. Some countries have found it convenient to modify Standard Time for part of the year, particularly during summer, in order to prolong daylight hours in the evening. This is accomplished by adopting the Standard Time of the zone immediately to the eastward, which advances local time (usually) by one hour. This 'fast time' is called 'Daylight Time', 'Daylight Saving Time' or 'Summer Time'. Some countries, for example the Soviet Union (since 1930), France (since 1946), Spain and Mexico, maintain fast time throughout the year, in which case it becomes their Standard Time. Daylight Saving Time start and finish dates for various countries are shown on the 'World Time and Foreign Exchange Chart', published by Euromoney Publications Ltd (latest 1986). In some countries (for example, Eire) the departure from Standard Time occurs in winter and is called 'Winter Time'. Winter Time is Standard Time *minus* one hour.

Investigation of older reports requires knowledge of the historical use of both Standard Time and Daylight Saving Time. This can be quite difficult. GMT was introduced in the UK in 1880, but before 1925 it began at noon (not midnight). The term 'UT' was introduced in 1928 to avoid confusion with the pre-1925 GMT. However many countries continued to observe apparent solar time (usually as recorded at their capital city). For example, until 1916 Eire observed Dublin Mean Time (GMT-25min). Occasionally countries change their Standard Time Zone. New Zealand Mean Time was UT+11½hr from 31 October 1868 to 6 November 1927, but from the latter date until 4 March 1928 NZMT was UT+12½hr. In 1945, New Zealand adopted its then Summer Time (UT+12hr) as its Standard Time. In 1968 Eire defined its Standard Time as UT+1hr. In 1986 Alaska adopted Yukon Standard Time (UT-9hr) for the whole state except for the Aleutians), but in 1987 it reverted to Alaska Standard Time (UT-10hr). The change to or from Daylight Saving Time usually occurs at 0100L (when advancing) or 0200L (when retarding).

Summer Time was first introduced in the UK in 1916, and has been in force every year from then on. From 1940 to 1945 and from 1968 to 1971 it was kept the whole year round, and from 1941 to 1945 (and in 1947) Double Summer Time (UT+2hr) was in force. The dates on which the changes occurred varied from year to year, but can be found in a good almanac.

Eire introduced Summer Time (DMT+1hr) in 1916, but adopted UK Summer Time (with GMT) after the First World War. It was continuous throughout the Second World War. Winter Time (UT) was introduced in 1971.

In the USA, Daylight Saving Time was first introduced in 1918 (ceasing in 1919), and it was used again during the Second World War (from 1942 until 1945), when Standard Time was advanced by 1 hour. It was reintroduced, for summer use only, in 1967. Some states split by time zones exempted themselves. Most of the USA was put on year-round DST from 1974 to 1975.

Canada introduced DST in 1918, although it then lapsed until reintroduced in 1940. Throughout Canada the observation of DST varies greatly from state to state. DST was introduced in Australia in 1917, but not for long. In 1942 it was reintroduced in all states until 1944 (earlier in Western Australia). Tasmania adopted a one-hour shift in the summer of 1967, followed by New South Wales, Victoria and the Capital Territory in 1971. Later Queensland and South Australia followed. Later still, Queensland abandoned DST, and in 1975 Western Australia abandoned a scheme adopted the year before. A referendum in New South Wales retained the scheme.

New Zealand adopted (30 min. advanced) Summer Time from 1929 and it was continuous throughout 1941 and subsequent war years. New

Zealand Daylight Time (UT+13hr) was introduced in November 1974, but usually operates only from October to March.

In most of continental Europe DST has been a late development. It was employed in France from 1916 to 1939 (as UT+1hr), but introduced in both France and Italy in 1976 (as UT+2hr), with some other EU states following a year later. However it was not introduced in Denmark until 1980, and in West Germany, Austria and Switzerland, not until 1981. The EU has attempted to harmonize the DST periods throughout the Community (even if it cannot bring about a single time zone). It has succeed in getting twenty-two countries in central and western Europe (including most EU states) to agree that DST should run from the last Sunday in March to the last Sunday in September. However the UK and Eire are permitted to run it until the fourth Sunday in October.

Star checks

A rough check on star positions (and not just those of the first magnitude stars) can be made by referring to a rotating star chart (for example, 'Planisphere'). When rotated to the date and local (apparent solar) time, the chart shows the whole sky of stars as seen from the latitude for which it is marked. Charts are produced for several different latitudes, most in the northern hemisphere.

In particular such charts can show which bright stars are on the horizon at the time in question.

Azimuth

UFO reporters may sometimes gives an azimuth in terms of degrees magnetic. It can be impossible to relate this angle to true north if the local magnetic declination (deviation) is not known, the more so for countries other than one's own. For the precise declination one should consult a detailed chart of the period. For modern reports, an approximation can be obtained from figure A3:1, which shows the declination for the whole world in simplified form for the epoch 1990·0.

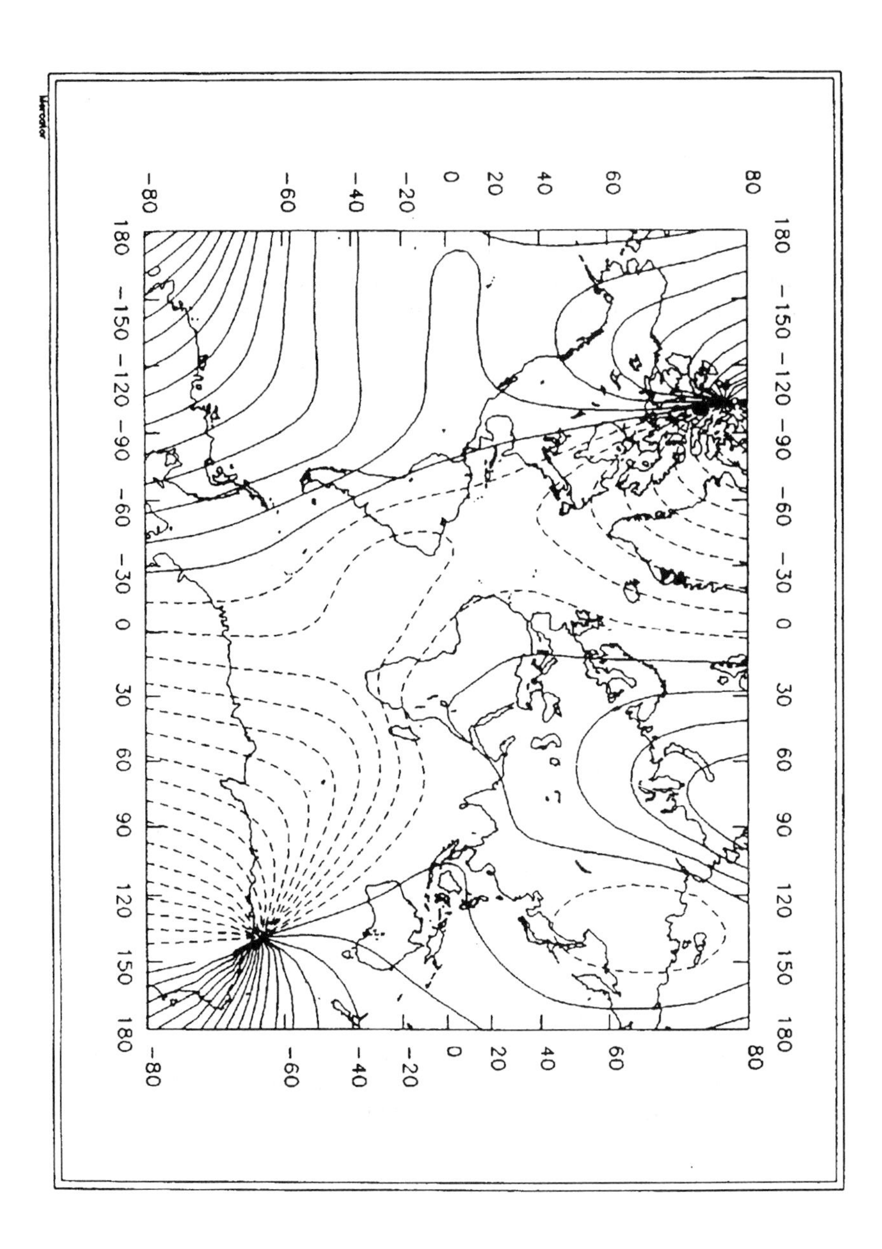

Fig. A3:1 Simplified world chart of magnetic declination for the epoch 1990·0. Solid lines indicate zero and positive declination; broken lines indicate negative declination. The contour interval is 10°. (British Geological Survey; NERC copyright reserved).

Appendix 4: The Conclusions of the USAF on UFOs

Fact Sheet

United States Air Force

Secretary of the Air Force, Office of Public Affairs, Washington, D.C. 20330-1000

87-34

Unidentified Flying Objects

History

The Air Force began investigating UFOs in 1948 under a program called Project Sign. Later the program's name was changed to Project Grudge, and in 1953 it became known as Project Blue Book. On Dec. 17, 1969, the secretary of the Air Force announced the termination of Project Blue Book.

The decision to discontinue UFO investigations was based on a number of factors, including reports and studies by the University of Colorado and the National Academy of Sciences, as well as past UFO studies and the Air Force's two decades of experience investigating UFO reports.

As a result of these investigations, studies, and experience, the conclusions of Project Blue Book were:

- No UFO reported, investigated and evaluated by the Air Force has ever given any indication of threat to our national security.
- There has been no evidence submitted to or discovered by the Air Force that sightings categorized as "unidentified" represent technological developments or principles beyond the range of present-day scientific knowledge.
- There has been no evidence indicating that sightings categorized as "unidentified" are extraterrestrial vehicles.

Between 1948 and 1969 the Air Force investigated 12,618 reported UFO sightings. Of these, 11,917 were found to have been caused by material objects such as balloons, satellites, and aircraft; immaterial objects such as lightning, reflections, and other natural phenomena; astronomical objects such as stars, planets, the sun, and the moon; weather conditions; and hoaxes. Only 701 reported sightings remain unexplained.

More Information Available

All documentation regarding the former Blue Book investigation was permanently transferred to the Modern Military Reference Branch, National Archives and Records Administration, 8th and Pennsylvania Ave., Washington, D.C. 20408, and is available for public review. A list of private organizations interested in aerial phenomena can be found in Gale's Encyclopedia of Associations, available in the reference section of most libraries.

Local Reproduction Authorized **October 1987**

Fact Sheet
United States Air Force

Public Affairs Division, Wright-Patterson AFB, Ohio 45433 (AC513) 257-4248

UFOs & PROJECT BLUE BOOK

On December 17, 1969, the Secretary of the Air Force announced the termination of Project Blue Book, the Air Force program for the investigation of UFOs.

From 1947 to 1969, a total of 12,618 sightings were reported to Project Blue Book. Of these, 701 remained "unidentified."

The project was headquartered at Wright-Patterson Air Force Base, whose personnel no longer receive, document or investigate UFO reports.

The decision to discontinue UFO investigations was based on an evaluation of a report prepared by the University of Colorado entitled, "Scientific Study of Unidentified Flying Objects"; a review of the University of Colorado's report by the National Academy of Sciences; past UFO studies and Air Force experience investigating UFO reports during the '40s, '50s, and '60s.

As a result of these investigations and studies and experience gained from investigating UFO reports since 1948, the conclusions of Project Blue Book are: (1) no UFO reported, investigated, and evaluated by the Air Force has ever given any indication of threat to our national security; (2) there has been no evidence submitted to or discovered by the Air Force that sightings categorized as "unidentified" represent technological developments or principles beyond the range of present-day scientific knowledge; and (3) there has been no evidence indicating that sightings categorized as "unidentified" are extraterrestrial vehicles.

With the termination of Project Blue Book, the Air Force regulation establishing and controlling the program for investigating and analyzing UFOs was rescinded. Documentation regarding the former Blue Book investigation has been permanently transferred to the Modern Military Branch, National Archives and Records Service, Eighth Street and Pennsylvania Avenue, N.W., Washington, D. C. 20408, and is available for public review and analysis.

News media inquiries regarding the Blue Book files at the National Archives may be made to the National Archives Public Affairs Office; telephone, (202) 523-3089. Other public inquiries about these records may be made to the Modern Military Branch; telephone, (202) 523-3340).

Since Project Blue Book was closed, nothing has happened to indicate that the Air Force ought to resume investigating UFOs. Because of the considerable cost to the Air Force in the past, and the tight funding of Air Force needs today, there is no likelihood the Air Force will become involved with UFO investigation again.

There are a number of universities and professional scientific organizations, such as the American Association for the Advancement of Science, which have considered UFO phenomena during periodic meetings and seminars. In addition, a list of private organizations interested in aerial phenomena may be found in Gale's Encyclopedia of Associations (edition 8, vol. 1, pp. 432-3). Such timely review of the situation by private groups ensures that sound evidence will not be overlooked by the scientific community.

A person calling the base to report a UFO is advised to contact a private or professional organization (as mentioned above) or to contact a local law enforcement agency if the caller feels his or public safety is endangered.

Periodically, it is erroneously stated that the remains of extraterrestrial visitors are or have been stored at Wright-Patterson AFB. There are not now, nor ever have been, any extraterrestrial visitors or equipment on Wright-Patterson Air Force Base.

(January 1985)

References

Allan, Christopher and Steuart Campbell (1986): Flying Saucer from Moore's? *Magonia*, 23:15-18.
Allingham, Cedric (1954): *Flying Saucer From Mars*. London, Muller.
Anon. (1968): The UFO Conspiracy. *Penthouse*, 3(2)17.
Arnold, Kenneth and Ray Palmer (1952): *The coming of the Saucers*. Boise (private).
Beaty, David (1991): *The Naked Pilot*. London, Methuen.
Bowen, Charles (1972): Hoaxer confesses after ten years. *Flying Saucer Review*, 18(6)2.
Boyce, Chris (1981): *Extraterrestrial Encounter*. London, NEL.
Brookesmith, Peter {ed}(1990): *The UFO Casebook*. London, Black Cat.
Brown, R Hanbury (1964): A Preliminary Measurement of the Angular Diameter of α Lyrae. *Nature*, 4924:1111.
Buckhout, Robert (1974): Eyewitness Testimony. *Sci. Am.*, 231(6)23.
Burt, Eugene H (1970): *UFOs and Diamagnetism*. New York, Exposition Press.
Butler, Brenda with Dot Street and Jenny Randles (1984): *Sky Crash: A Cosmic Conspiracy*. Sudbury, Spearman.
Callahan, Philip S and R W Mankin (1978): Insects as unidentified flying objects. *Applied Optics*, 17(21)3355.
Campbell, Steuart [Stuart](1981a): A Fantasy of the Fourth Kind. *UFO Insight*, 2(2)16.
---------(1981b): The Credibility of UFO Hypotheses. *The MUFON UFO J.*, 156:6.
---------(1981c): False report from Loch Ness. *Flying Saucer Review*, 26(6)19-23.
---------(1982a): *Close Encounter at Livingston* {ed. Charles F Lockwood and Leslie W Bayer}. Case History No. 1, BUFORA.
---------(1982b): Hypnotic Fantasies. *J. Transient Aerial Phenomena*, 2(3)52-55.
---------(1983a): The Birth of the UFO Myth: George Adamski. *The Probe Report*, 3(4)5-9.
---------(1983b): Lights of Fancy. ibid. 3(4)14-15.
---------(1985a): Poher's False Correlations. *J. Transient Aerial Phenomena*, 3(4)171.
---------(1985b): Throwing light on Rendlesham. *Magonia* 21:15-18.
---------(1985c): Investigation Report on 1980 Photograph At Pitlochry, Scotland. *Associate Newsletter* 6(1)1, Lima, CUFOS.
---------(1986a): Livingston: A New Hypothesis. *J. Transient Aerial Phenomena* (BUFORA), 4(3)80-87.
---------(1986b): Not coming through the glen. *BUFORA Bulletin*, 23:6.
---------(1987a): The Todmorden UFO explained. *J. Transient Aerial Phenomena*, 5(1)10.
---------(1987b): Mirage of a mountain? *J. Meteorology, UK*, 12(119)157.
---------(1987c): Mirage over Edinburgh. ibid., 12(123)308.
---------(1988a): Russian Accounts of Ball Lightning. ibid., 13(128)126.
---------(1988b): The Childerhose UFO: fact of fiction? *Brit. J. Photography*, (29 September), p 72.
---------(1989a): UFO: hoax or mirage? ibid., No. 6722 (15 June), pp 17-19.
---------(1989b): The 'miracle of the sun' at Fatima. *J. Meteorology, UK*, 14(142)333.
---------(1990a): Film of a UFO or Venus? *Brit. J. Photography*, No. 6767 (3 May), pp 24-25 and 29.
---------(1990b): Fear response in UFO reporters. *UFO Times*, 7:16, London, BUFORA.
---------(1991): Fireball by Day. *Brit. J. Photography*, No. 6814 (4 April), pp 22-23.
Chapman, Robert (1970): *Unidentified Flying Objects*. St. Albans, Granada.

Chibbett, Harold (1974): UFO in Nova Scotia. *BUFORA J.* 4(4)13.
Clarke, Arthur C (1975): *Report on Planet Three.* London, Corgi.
Crutwell, N E G (1959): Saucer men seen in flight: Amazing sighting from Papua. *Flying Saucer Review,* (Nov-Dec), p 7.
Devereux, Paul (1982): *Earth Lights.* Turnstone.
Dickeson, F and P (1981): The Motunau Photograph. *BUFORA J.,* 10(1)6.
Durham, Anthony and Keith Watkins (1967a): Visual perception of UFOs ... Part I. *Flying Saucer Review,* 13(3)27-29.
---------(1967b): Visual perception of UFOs ... Part II. ibid. , 13(4)24-26.
Edwards, Frank (1967): *Flying Saucers Here and Now!* New York, Lyle Stuart.
Emsley, H H (1952): *Visual Optics* (2 vols.).
Evans, Christopher (1973): *Cults of Unreason.* London, Harrap.
Evans, Hilary (ed.)(1987): *UFOs 1947-1987.* London, Fortean Tomes.
Falla, Geoffrey (1979): *Vehicle Interference Project.* London, BUFORA.
Fawcett, Lawrence and Barry J Greenwood (1984): *Clear Intent.* Englewood Cliffs, Prentice-Hall.
Federal Aviation Authority (1987): *JAL (Japan Air Lines) Flight 1628 Unidentified Traffic Sighting, November 17,1986 (Final Report.)* Anchorage, 3 May (DOT/FAA/AL-87/1)
Firestone, Kenneth Eugene and Ronald L Firestone {with William H Spaulding} (1982): Socorro-New Mexico-Revisited. *UFO Research Australia Newsletter,* Vol. 3, No. 4 (Jul-Aug), pp 15-22.
Flammonde, Paris (1976): *UFO Exist* (Book 1). New York, Putnam.
Fogarty, Quentin (1982): *Let's Hope They're Friendly.* London, Angus and Robertson.
Fontes, Olavo T (1960): UAO Sightings over Trindade. *The APRO Bulletin,* (Jan and March).
Fowler, Raymond E (1979): *UFOs: Interplanetary Visitors.* Hicksville, Bantam.
Fulton, Harold H (1969): New Zealand Farmer's Photograph. *Flying Saucer Review,* 15(4)32.
Gardner, Martin (1957): *Fads and Fallacies in the Name of Science.* New York, Dover Publications (2nd ed.).
Gilinsky, A S (1955): The effect of attitude upon the perception of size. *Am. J. Psychology,* 68, 173-92.
Gillmor, Daniel S {ed} (1969): *Scientific Study of Unidentified Flying Objects* (The Condon Report). London, Bantam Books (also published in London by Vision Press in 1970).
Good, Timothy (1991): *Alien Liaison.* London, Century.
Gregory, Richard L (1972): *Eye and Brain* (2nd ed.). London, Weidenfeld and Nicolson.
---------(1974): *Concepts and Mechanisms of Perception.* London.
Haines, Richard F {ed}(1979): *UFO Phenomena and the Behavioural Scientist.* London, Scarecrow Press.
---------(1980): *Observing UFOs,* Chicago. Nelson-Hall.
Hall, Richard H {ed}(1964): *The UFO Evidence.* NICAP.
Harvey, Bill (1978): Cranks and others. *New Scientist,* 16 March, p 741.
Hawking, Stephen (1993): *Black Holes and Baby Universes,* London, Bantam.
Hendry, Allan (1979): *The UFO Handbook.* London, Sphere.
Hume, David (1927): *Enquiries Concerning The Human Understanding and Concerning the Principles of Morals.* Oxford (original 1751).
Hynek, J Allen (1953): Unusual Aerial Phenomena. *J. Opt. Soc. Am.,* 43(4)311.
---------(1978): *The Hynek UFO Report.* London, Sphere.

---------and Julian Hennessey (1972): The Aldridge Case: PC. Leek's Photographs. *FSR Case Histories*, Supplement 9:1.
Imus, Henry A et al. (1951): Visual Illusions in Night Flying. *Am. J. Ophthal.*, 34:35.
Inglesby, Eric (1978): *UFO's and the Christian*. Regency Press.
Ireland, W (1979): *Unfamiliar Observations of lights in the night sky*, report no. 659. (Physics and Engineering Laboratory), DSIR, New Zealand. See also letter from Ireland and M K Andrews in *Applied Optics* 18(23)3889-90.
Jacobs, David M (1975): *The UFO Controversy in America*. Indiana University Press (AUPG).
Johnson, Frank (1980): *The Janos People*. London, Spearman.
Jones, Reginald Victor (1968): Natural Philosophy of Flying Saucers. In: *Physics Bull.*, 19 [also as an Appendix to Gillmor 1969].
---------(1978): *Most Secret War*. London, Hamish Hamilton.
Jung, Carl G (1959): *Flying Saucers: A Modern Myth of Things Seen in the Skies*. London, Routledge & Kegan Paul (translation by R F C Hull of *Ein moderner Mythus*, 1958).
Keatman, Martin and Andrew Collins (1979-1980): Physical Assault by Unidentified Flying Objects at Livingston. *Flying Saucer Review*, 25(6)2, 26(1)25 and 26(3)2.
Kinder, Gary (1987): *Light Years: An investigation into the Extraterrestrial Experiences of Eduard Meier*. Viking.
Klass, Philip J (1968): *UFOs-Identified*. New York, Random House.
---------(1974): *UFOs-Explained*. ibid.
---------(1977): *White Paper SOC-1* (3 March). private.
---------(1983): *UFOs: The Public Deceived*. Buffalo, Prometheus Books.
---------(1987): FAA Data Sheds New Light On JAL Pilot's UFO Report. *The Skeptical Inquirer*, Vol. XI No. 4, pp 322-326.
---------(1988): *UFO-Abductions: A Dangerous Game*. Buffalo, Prometheus Books.
Knight, David C (1980): *UFOs: A Pictorial History from Antiquity to the Present* (2nd ed.). New York, McGraw Hill.
Lehn, Waldemar H (1980): On the sighting of distant unidentified objects. *J. Atm. Terr. Physics.*, Vol. 42, pp 471-475.
---------and B A German (1981): Novaya Zemlya effect: analysis of an observation. *Applied Optics.*, 20(12)2043.
Leibowitz, H W and D A Owens (1975): Night Myopia and the Intermediate Dark Focus of Accommodation. *J. Opt. Soc. Am.*, 65(10)1121-1128.
Leslie, Desmond and George Adamski (1953): *Flying Saucers Have Landed*. London. Werner Laurie.
Liddel, Urner (1953): Phantasmagoria or Unusual Observations in the Atmosphere. *J. Opt. Soc. Am.*, 43(4)314.
Long, Greg (1987): Kenneth Arnold Revisited. *MUFON UFO J.*, (June), pp 3-7.
Lunan, Duncan (1974): *Man and the Stars*. London, Souvenir Press.
Maccabee, Bruce (1976): Midday Observations of Bright Lights in a Clear Sky. photocopied typescript report from Fund for UFO Research (summarized in a letter to *Physics Today*, 29:90).
---------(1979): New Zealand Film Report II. *MUFON UFO J.*, (June/July), pp 12-18. See also letters from Maccabee in *Applied Optics* 18(15)2527-8 and 19(11)1745-6.
---------(1987): The fantastic flight of JAL 1628. *International UFO Reporter*, Vol. 12, No. 2.
Malthaner, Hubert (1972): Mystery flying object rolls along a German road. *Flying Saucer Review*, 18(4)15.

Maney, Charles A (1965): Donald Menzel and the Newport News UFO: A Critical Report. *Fate,* (April), p 64.
McCampbell, James M (1976): *Ufology.* Millbrae, Celestial Arts.
McDonald, James (1971): UFO Encounter I. (Sample Case Selected by the UFO Subcommittee of the AIAA), *Astronautics & Aeronautics,* (July), p 66.
Meaden, G T (1993): Possible instance of incipient lightning affecting a motor car engine. *J. Meteorology U K* , 18(179)158 (see also fol. article).
Meinel, Aden and Marjorie Meinel (1983): *Sunsets, twilights, and evening stars.* Cambridge, CUP.
Menzel, Donald (1953): *Flying Saucers.* London, Putnam.
---------and Lyle G Boyd (1963): *The World of Flying Saucers.* New York, Doubleday.
---------and Ernest Taves (1977): *The UFO Enigma.* Garden City, Doubleday.
Michell, John {ed}(1979): *The House of Lords UFO Debate.* London and Bristol, Open Head Press and Pentacle Books.
Middleton, W E Knowles (1958): *Vision Through the Atmosphere.* Toronto.
Mills, A A (1980): Will-o'-the-wisp. *Chemistry in Britain,* 16:69.
Minnaert, M (1940): *Light and Colour in the Open Air.* London.
Mishara, Eric (1983): UFO update. *OMNI* 5(6)115.
Mrzyglod, Ian and Martin Shipp (1983): Rendlesham Revisited. *The Probe Report,* 3(4)16-20.
Murray, Bruce (1975): The limits of science. *Engineering and Science,* (April-May).
Myers, David G (1986): *Psychology.* New York, Worth Publishing.
Oberg, James (1979): The failure of the 'science' of ufology. *New Scientist,* (11 Oct), p 102.
Olsen, Thomas M {ed}(1966): *The Reference for Outstanding UFO Sighting Reports.* Riderwood, UFO Information Retrieval Center Inc.
Phillips, Ted (1972): Landing Report from Delphos. *FSR Case Histories,* 9:4.
Poher, Claude (1974): Time correlations between geomagnetic disturbances and eyewitness accounts of UFOs. *Flying Saucer Review,* 20(1)12.
Powers, William T (1966): The Landing at Socorro. In: *The Humanoids* (ed. Charles Bowen), Special Issue of *Flying Saucer Review* (Oct-Nov), London.
Randles, Jenny (1981): A Policeman's Lot. *Flying Saucer Review,* 27(2)3.
---------(1982a): The Rendlesham Forest Mystery. ibid, 7(6)4.
---------(1982b): Impact and After. *The Unexplained,* 9(106)2101-2105.
---------(1983a): Investigation Department Report. *BUFORA BULL.,* 10:5.
---------(1983b): *The Pennine UFO Mystery.* St. Albans, Granada.
---------(1991): *From Out of the Blue.* New Brunswick, Global Communications.
---------and Peter Warrington.(1983): The neglected science of UFOs. *New Scientist,* 10 February.
---------(1985): *Science and the UFOs.* Oxford, Blackwell.
Reed, Richard J (1958): Flying Saucers over Mount Ranier. *Weatherwise,* XI, 2, p 43.
Ridpath, Ian (1983): An explanation of the Woodbridge UFO. *Magonia,* 14:12.
---------(1985): A flashlight in the forest. *The Guardian* (5 Jan).
---------(1986): The Woodbridge UFO Incident. *The Skeptical Inquirer,* XI(1)77-81 (a slightly revised version of Ridpath 1985).
Ross, Helen E (1974): *Behaviour and Perception in Strange Environments.* London, George Allen and Unwin.
---------(1975): Mist, murk and visual perception. *New Scientist,* 66 (19 Jun), 658-660.

Roush, J Edward {Chairman}(1968): *Symposium on Unidentified Flying Objects.* Hearings before the Committee on Science and Astronautics, US House of Representatives, Ninetieth Congress, Second Session, July 29 (No. 7), Washington, US Gov. Printing Office.
Rutledge, Harley D (1981): *Project Identification.* Englewood Cliffs, Prentice-Hall.
Sagan, Carl and Thornton Page (1972): *UFOs A Scientific Debate.* London, Cornell UP.
Salisbury, Frank B (1967): The Scientist and the UFO. *BioScience,* (Jan), pp 15-24,
---------(1974): *The Utah UFO Display.* Old Greenwich, Devin-Adair.
Schuessler, John (1982): Blind terror in Texas. *The Unexplained,* 9(107)2121.
Sheaffer, Robert (1980): *The UFO Verdict.* Buffalo, Prometheus Books.
Sidgwick, J B (1979): *Amateur Astronomer's Handbook.* London, Pelham Books.
Simpson, David I (1976): Experimental UFO Hoaxing. *MUFOB* (March), p 3. Reprinted (1980) as Controlled UFO Hoax in *The Skeptical Inquirer* 4(3).
Smith, Willy (undated): *Mirages or UFOs.* (Five page article from UNICAT), private.
---------(1983): Trindade Revisited. *International UFO Reporter,* Vol. 8, No. 4 (Jul/Aug), pp 3-14.
Soltis, J F (1966): *Seeing, Knowing and Believing.* London, GAU.
Spanos, Nicholas P, Patricia A Cross, Kirby Dickson and Susan C Dubreuil (1993): Close Encounters: An Examination of UFO Experiences. *J. Abnormal Psychology,* Vol 102, No. 4, 624-632.
Stanford, Ray (1978): *Socorro Saucer.* Glasgow, Fontana.
Startup, Bill and Neil Illingworth (1980): *The Kaikoura UFOs.* London, Hodder and Stoughton.
Steiger, Brad (Eugene E Olsen) {ed}(1976): *Project Blue Book.* New York, Ballantine Books.
Story, Ronald D (ed)(1980): *The Encyclopedia of UFOs.* New York, Doubleday.
---------{with J Richard Greenwell}(1981): *UFOs and the Limits of Science.* NEL.
Strand, Erling (1984): *Project Hessdalen 1984: Final Technical Report Part One.* Duken, Project Hessdalen.
Street, Dot (1983): The Rendlesham Forest Mystery. *BUFORA BULL.,* 4, pp 20-21
Tacker, Lawrence J (1960): *Flying Saucers and the US Air Force.* London, D Van Nostrand.
Uman, Martin A (1971): *Understanding Lightning.* Oak Tree Press and Ward Lock Ltd.
Vinacke, W Edgar (1947): Illusions Experienced by Aircraft Pilots While Flying. *Aviation Medicine,* 18 (August),p 308.
Walker, S III (1968): Establishing Observer Creditability [*sic*]: A Proposed Method. *J. Astron. Sci.,* 15(2)92.
Watts, Alan (1964): An experiment on the effect of an external magnetic field on the ignition coil of a car. *BUFORA J. & Bull.,* 1(2)7-8.
Weale, Robert Alexander (1968): *From Sight to Light.* Edinburgh, Oliver & Boyd.
Weldon, John with Zola Levitt (1976): *UFOs: What On Earth Is Happening?* New York, Bantam.
Welfare, Simon and John Fairley (1980): *Arthur C Clarke's Mysterious World.* London, Collins.
Wickham, Anthony J (1968): *BUFORA Res. Bull.* Vol. 1, No 2 (27 July).
Wiersema, G S (1972): Landing on the Leusderheide. *Flying Saucer Review,* 18(6)10.

Index

(bold figures indicate main entry)

abduction(s), 13, 14, 16
abnormal psychology, 40-1
Adamski, George, 18-19
Air Ministry, 14, 46
aircraft, 14, 28, 30, **48**, 51, 53, 183
airship(s), 16-17, 68, 70, 186
Aldebaran, **88**
Allan Army Air Field, 173
Allingham, Cedric, 19
Alpha Centauri, **83**
Altair, **88**
altitude:
  defined, 21
  estimates of, 30
AMH (astronomical mirage hypothesis), 59, 177, 179, 181-3,
Antares, **89**
APRO, 8, 15
Arnold, Kenneth, 17-19, 98 ff.
astigmatism, 31, 156
astronomical mirage hypothesis--(see AMH)
astronomical objects (as sources of deception), **49**
ATIC, 11
atmospheric extinction, 51
autokinetic effect/illusion, 26
Avis, Christopher, 68-9
azimuth:
  defined, 21
  estimates of, 32, **205**

Baker, Richard, 96
ball lightning, **49**, 123, 187
balloon(s), 14, 29, 30, 40, 45, 75
Barauna, Almiro, 109-17
Bass Strait (Australia), 82
Beallsville (Ohio), 74
beliefs concerning UFOs, 12
Bennett, Michael, 79
Birch, Alex, 46
Blackburn, Lou, 90
Blue Book, 12
Boainai (Papua-New Guinea), 66
Brady, Brian, 138
brightness:
  astronomical, 21-2
  (estimates of), 30
British Air Intelligence, 39
British Scientific Intelligence (BSI), 43, 46
British UFO Research Association--(see BUFORA)
BUFORA, 18, 32
Butler, Brenda, 159-61
Byrnes, D Arthur, 121, 126, 130

Cabot Strait (Newfoundland), 66
Canopus, **82 ff,** 120
Capella, 53, 77, **87**
Cappoquin (Eire), 78-9
Carter, Jimmy, 88
Cash, Betty, 82-3
CAUS (Citizens Against UFO Secrecy), 160
Chactonbury Downs (Sussex), 74
Cheverly (Maryland), 94
Childerhose hoax, 46
Chiles/Whitted, 88
Churchill, Winston, 14
CIA, 96, 122-3, 128
Clarke, Arthur C, 9-10, 201
Colorado University, 10
colour (estimates of), 31
Condon, Edward U, 11, 186
Condon Report, 10, 20, 42, 77, 93, 96, 180, 184
Contact International, 15
contrail(s), 48, 77
corn circles, 49
Cowichan (British Colombia), 89
Cramp, Leonard, 46
Crockett, David, 135-40
Crowder, C N, 86
CSICOP, 127

definitions, 21
Delphos (Kansas), 80
Deneb, **94 ff,** 164
Devereux, Paul, 16
direction--(see azimuth)
Donnelly, Steve, 157-8
Drake, Frank D, 29, 31, 32, 33
Dutton, T R, 156

earth lights, 47
earthquake lights, 47
Edzell (Scotland), 73
Elsthorpe (NZ), 79
engine/light failures, **42-4**
epilepsy, 152-3

ETH, 11, 12
Extraterrestrial Hypothesis--(see ETH)

FAA (Federal Aviation Administration), 168
false association, **41**
Fargo (North Dakota), 75
Fatima, 50
Fawcett, Larry, 160
FBI, 14, 121
fear responses, 44, 83
films concerning UFOs, 13 ff
first magnitude stars, 54
Flying Saucer Review (FSR), 15, 36
Fogarty, Quentin, 132-6
Fomalhaut, **91 ff**
foo-fighters, 48
form:
  defined, 21
  estimates of, 30
Fortenberry, William, 70
Fox, Phillis, 34
Frazier, Kendrick, 127, 165
Freedom of Information Act, 14, 160, 165, 184
Freeport (Texas), 87

Gallup Poll, 40
ghost rockets, 37 ff, 187
Gibbs-Smith, Charles, 78-9
Gill, William, 66 ff
Glen Nevis, 89
Godfrey, Alan, 71-2
Godman AFB, 75
Good, Timothy, 19, 124
Gorman, George F, 75
Grant, Dennis, 135
Great Falls (Montana), 94
Greenwood, Barry, 160
Grinder, Opal, 129-30
Gromyko, Andrei, 16
Grossman, Wendy, 156
ground marks, 41, 147-8
Guard, Robert, 135-6
Guérin, Pierre, 36

Hall, Richard, 83, 129
hallucinations, 16, 24, 41, 152-3
Halt, Charles, I, 161 ff, 188, 189 ff
Haneda AFB, 76
Hannaford, Patricia, 151-3
Hartmann, William K, 96
Hector Airport, 75
HEH (Hollow Earth Hypothesis), 16, 18
Hessdalen (Norway), 187
hoax(es), 19, 35-6, 39, **45-7**, 178
hoax photographs, 46
Holder, Richard T, 121, 130
House of Lords debate, 12, 15
Huffman (Texas), 82
Hynek, J Allen, 14, 47, 53, 66, 75, 78, 100, 101, 118, 120, 122, 123, 125, 180
hyperventilation, 44
hypnosis, 13, 35, 42, 72
hypotheses, 11, 16, 24

illusions, 14, 23-30
Imperial College UFO Research Group, 25
induced movement, 26-7
International Flying Saucer Bureau, 14, 18
Ireland, W, 133, 134, 141

Japan Air Lines, 168
Jodrell Bank, 142
Johnson, David N, 107
Johnson, Ronald, 80
Jones, Reginald Victor, 37-9, 156-7
Jung, Carl, 16, 17, 20, 181
Jupiter, 50, 60, 67, **74-80,** 81, 89, 114-17, 134, 138, 173

Klass, Philip J, 46, 47, 65, 66, 70, 81, 83, 86, 87, 92, 93, 122-32, 136, 139, 165-6, 173-6, 179
Krauss, Max, 84-6

Landrum, Vickie, 82, 83
LaPaz, Lincoln, 123
Leet, William D, 80
Legare (the), 87
Lehn, Waldemar, 140, 142
lighthouse(s), 138, 161-3, 165-7
line of darkness, 53
Livingston, 143-6, 148, 154-5, 181-2
Llanerchymedd, 71
Loch Ness, 12, 41
Lunan, Duncan, 184

Mabin, David, 138

Maccabee, Bruce, 95, 132, 139-41, 173
magnification (in mirages), 57-8, 95, 115, 157
Maney, Charles A, 71
Mantell, Thomas, 74-5
Mars, 12, 19-20, 47, 50, 67-8, 70, **73-4,** 89
McDonald, James, 33, 62, 76-7, 82, 93, 105-6, 118, 179
Meier, Eduard, 45
memory (problems of), 33-4
men-in-black,. 14-15
Menzel, Donald, 49, 57, 58, 59, 61-4, 65, 67, 71, 75, 76, 88, 93, 96, 100, 105, 107, 113, 114, 123, 180, 183, 184
Mercury, 50, **66-8,** 71, 154, 156
MH (mirage hypothesis), 59, 177, 182, 183, 186, 187
MI5, 15
Michel, Aime, 17, 183
mirage(s), 48, 52, **54-9**
double, 96, 56-7
inferior, 54-5
quadruple, 57
superior, 55 ff
mirage hypothesis--(see MH)
MoD (UK Ministry of Defence), 40, 161, 165, 167
Moon, 7, 26, 27, 29, 49, 50, **65-6**
moon illusion, 29, 51
Moore, Patrick, 19, 132
Motunau (New Zealand), 90-1
movement (estimates of), 25
MUFON UFO Journal, 83
myth of UFOs--(see UFO myth)

Nash/Fortenberry, 70
Newhouse, Delbert C, 95-7
NICAP, 43, 118
Novaya Zemlya mirage, 55, 66, 140

observer credibility rating, 34
Orford Ness, 161, 163, 164, 165, 167
orthoteny, 17, 183

Palmer, Raymond A, 17-18
Pentagon, 162, 175
perception, 23-5, 29, 41, 182-3
physiological effects, 44
Pobiner, Bernard, 66
police, 45, 47, 71, 118, 129, 144, 147, 161, 184-5
Pollux, 87
psychological sources of deception, 40-1
psychosomatic symptoms, 44, 81, 83

Quick report, 73-4
Quintanella, Hector, 78, 123

Royal Australian Air Force, 67
Rackham, T W, 142
radar, 12, 20, 42, 81, 92, 134-6, 139-41, 160, 170, 174-5, 186,
RAF Woodbridge, 159, 162, 188
Raman brightening, 77, 117
Randles, Jenny, 83-4, 160, 166-7
Ranier, Mt., 98-9, 101, 103, 107
Rayleigh scattering, 51, 141
RB-47, 91
refraction (effects of), 32, 51-3, 59
reliability of UFO reports, 33, **34-6,** 182
Rendlesham (Suffolk), 159-62
Rigel, **86,** 93, 94

Saturn, 50, 63, 67, **80-1**, 164
sceptics, 10, 45, 47, 64, 113-14, 131, 160-1, 182
scintillation, 51, 53, 58, 62, 63, 141, 157
SCUFORI, 160
shape-- (see form)
shape constancy, 30
shape of UFOs, 20, 26, 55, 58, 185
Sheaffer, Robert, 92, 94, 139, 142
shimmer (in mirages), 59, 136, 138, 141
Shipwash lightship, 163-167
Simonton, Joe, 80
Sirius, 62, 65, **81-2,** 164
SIUFOP, 35, 36
size and distance (estimates of), 29-30
size constancy, 30
Skaneatales Lake (New York), 77
Skeptic, The, 156, 157
Skeptical Inquirer, The, 127, 142, 162, 165, 175, 176
Skyhook balloon, 75
Smith, Willy, 59, 60, 109, 117
Socorro, 118 ff, 181

Soesterberg (Netherlands), 87
South Hill (Virginia), 86
Spica, 63, **89-91**, 164
Stainton (Cumbria), 89
Stanford, Ray, 122, 129, 131
stars:
    brightest, 54
    magnitude of, 21-2
Startup, Bill, 132-5
Storrington (Sussex), 73
Story, Ronald D, 48, 118, 180
Street, Dot, 159-61
street lights, 47, 185
Sullivan, Walter, 10
swamp gas, 47

Tachikawa (Japan), 80
Tamefuji, Takanori, 169-70
Taylor, Robert David, 145 ff
Taylor, Philip, 83
Tectonic-Strain Theory, 16, 47, 48
temperature inversion, 46, 52, 55 ff, 186
Terauchi, Kenju, 168 ff
Thayer, Gordon D, 21, 92, 93, 186
thermocline, 55, 56, 57
Thompson, D C, 141
time span (estimates of), 32
Todmorden (Yorkshire), 71-2
Tombaugh, Clyde, 76
Tremonton (Utah), 95-7
Trindade (Ilha da), 109 ff

UFO myth, **12-20**, 24, 33, 34, 35, 41, 45, 64, 182, 184
UFO Report(s), 10, 11, 23 ff
    reliability of, 34, 35, 36
    statistical studies of, 20
UFOIN, 151
ufoism, 12, 182
ufoists, 13, 14, 19, 64, 181, 182
US Navy, 61, 65, 75, 95, 96
US Navy R5D, 65
USAF, 10, 14, 15, 18, 33, 35, 61, 62, 73, 81, 88, 93, 94, 96, 100, 118, 121, 159 ff, 167, 180,, 184, 188, 198-9
UTH (Ultraterrestrial Hypothesis), 16

Valentich, Frederick, 82
Vandenberg AFB, 72
Vega, 59, **84-6,** 93, 94, 97, 164
Venus, 42, 49, 50, 67-8, **68-73**, 75, 83-4, 88, 134, 136, 138, 140, 142, 154, 155, 156, 157, 186
Vero Beach (Florida), 83
Viezee, William, 53, 142
Virgin Mary, 186
visual acuity, 25

Warminster, 36
Warren, Larry, 160, 161, 166
will-o'-the-wisp, 47, 187
Wingfield, Jacqueline, 78
Winnsboro (Louisiana), 91
Wood, Peter, 89
Woodbourne (New Zealand), 132-4
Wright-Patterson AFB, 11, 121

Zamora, Lonnie, 118 ff